Giant Book of Optical Puzzles

  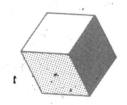 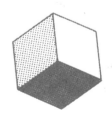

By Keith Kay, Charles H. Paraquin,
Michael A. DiSpezio, Katherine Joyce,
E. Richard Churchill, and Larry Evans

The Main Street Press

10   9   8   7   6   5   4   3   2

Published by Sterling Publishing Company, Inc.
387 Park Avenue South, New York, N.Y. 10016

Material in this collection was adapted from
Little Giant Book of Optical Illusions © Keith Kay
World's Best Optical Illusions © Charles H. Paraquin
Visual Thinking Puzzles © Michael A. DiSpezio
How to Make Optical Illusions © E. Richard Churchill
Astounding Optical Illusions © Katherine Joyce
Lateral Logic Mazes for the Serious Puzzler © Larry Evans
3-Dimensional Lateral Logic Mazes © Larry Evans

Illustrations on pages 118–135 by Nicholas Wade

Distributed in Canada by Sterling Publishing
c/o Canadian Manda Group, One Atlantic Avenue, Suite 105
Toronto, Ontario, Canada M6K 3E7
Distributed in Austrailia by Capricorn Link (Australia) Pty Ltd.
P.O. Box 6651, Baulkham Hills, Business Centre, NSW 2153, Australia

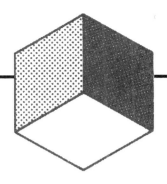

Table of Contents

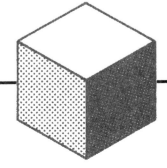

Optical Illusions

Optical illusions are pictures that play tricks on your eyes and baffle your perception. They are not the result of faulty vision or psychic suggestion. Depending on light, viewing angle, or the way the picture is drawn, we may see things that aren't there—and often don't see what's right under our nose. Why does it happen?

Sometimes the answer lies in the way our eyes work. When we use both eyes, we see an object from two slightly set-apart angles. Each one registers a different view. If we use only one eye, look what happens:

Close your left eye. Keep your right eye focused on the dog and move the book back and forth in front of you. At one point, the cat disappears completely. You have just found your blind spot. Everyone has one. It is the spot where the optic nerve cord leaves your eye, and there are no nerve cells to register an image. If you use both eyes as you look at the dog, you won't have a blind spot. The image from your left eye will make up for the blank in your right.

The shortcomings of our vision explain some types of optical illusions, but not all of them. Our eyes gather impressions, but it is the brain that interprets them. And the brain is always trying to make sense out of what it sees. So in spite of the fact that we know how perspective works, we go to the theatre or the movies and imagine that we're in a different world, tricked by a stage set and special effects. We watch magic acts and believe what reflecting mirrors show us. Illusion is everywhere—in art and architecture, in fashion and advertising, in the street and on television, even in the supermarket. If our eyes see something that the brain can't figure out, our minds "correct" the picture automatically.

Here is another illusion:

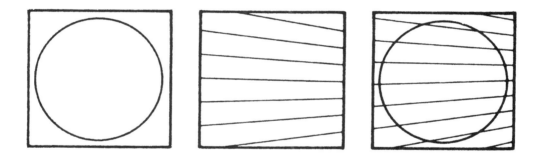

The box in the first picture contains an ordinary circle. The second box contains a field of slanted lines. Put them together and look what happens. The circle appears to become an oval and the box seems to be completely lop-sided. Test them with a ruler and compass. You'll see that they are exactly the same as they were before.

The human eye isn't as perfect as a camera lens, but that doesn't mean it is defective—just the opposite. Its adaptability is its strongpoint. In the semi-dark, for instance, our eyes function amazingly well. After about half an hour, our vision completely adjusts to the dark and its sensitivity increases 50,000 times! In the dark, we can see a burning candle from nearly 20 miles (32 kilometers) away!

Birds of prey (eagles and hawks) have much better vision than humans do in daylight. They see farther, but they suffer from night-blindness. Some other animals (owls, hedgehogs, cats) see well at night, but do not have very keen eyesight. So as human beings, we are lucky. We can see reasonably well during both day and night.

Humans are not the only ones who are tricked by optical illusions, either. Laboratory tests performed on fish and birds lead to the startling conclusion that these animals are fooled just about as often as we are, and sometimes in the same way!

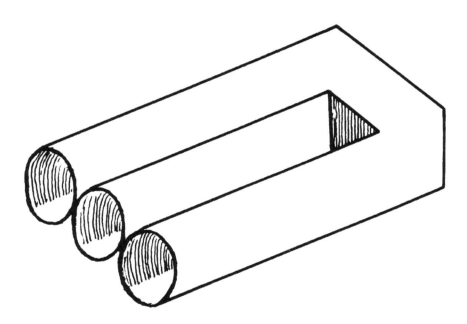

Deception? Illusion? Or just a careless artist?

Scientists have studied optical illusions for centuries, but they still don't agree about how or why all of them work. You'll see many different types of illusions in this book—geometric tricks, physiological tricks and psychological illusions—and you'll learn how many of them operate. But by no means are these *all* the optical illusions that are possible. The number of tricks you can play on your eyes is almost inexhaustible. These illusions are simply meant to amuse you, inspire you to explore this delightful scientific hobby yourself and perhaps even invent some new illusions of your own.

One suggestion: as you turn to each picture, look at it first with your naked eye. Don't check it out with a ruler or tracing paper until afterwards—when you can't believe your eyes!

A practical-looking construction. Can you build it?

Twin brothers: one of them has a bigger appetite. Which one?

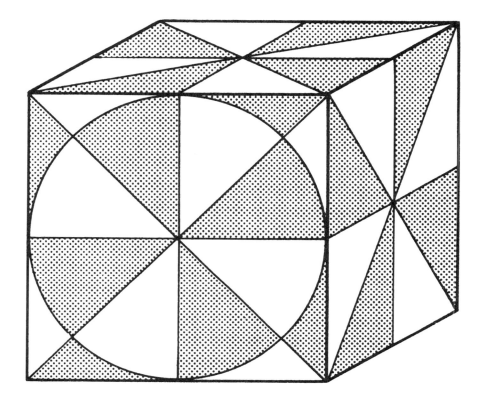

Is this cube higher and wider in the back than in the front?

Is this letter "E" toppling forward or sinking down?
Look at it steadily for half a minute.

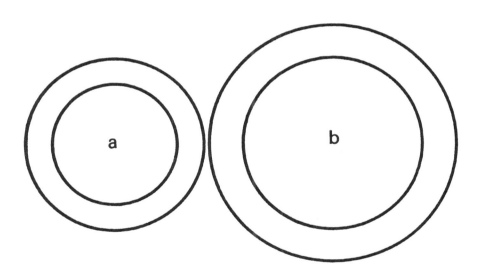

Is the outside circle of "a" smaller than
the inside circle of "b"?

Which of these movie-goers is the tallest?

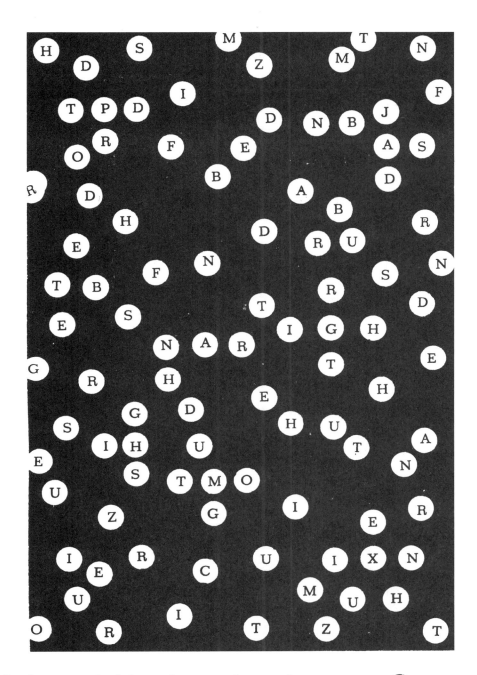

In this crowd of dots, there are five in the shape of a cross. Can you pick them out?

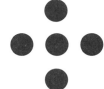

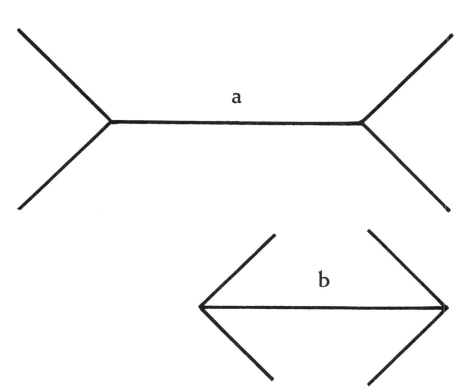

How much longer is line "a" than line "b"?

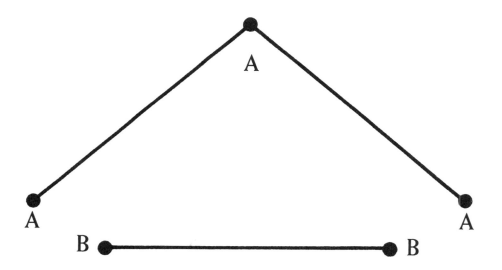

Are the two sides labeled "AA" each the same size as "BB"?

Look at the shapes at the bottom of this page. If anyone told you that you wouldn't be able to find them—even though you were looking right at them—would you believe it?

The drawings that follow show how difficult it can be to see familiar shapes and figures when they are in unfamiliar surroundings. Each shape is hidden once (same size) in its corresponding diagram. For example, shape number 1 is hidden in drawing number 1, and shape number 2 hidden in drawing number 2. Can you find them with your naked eye? Try this without using tracing paper—at first!

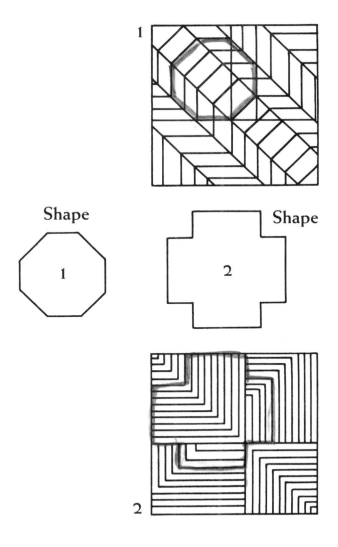

Shape

Shape

1

2

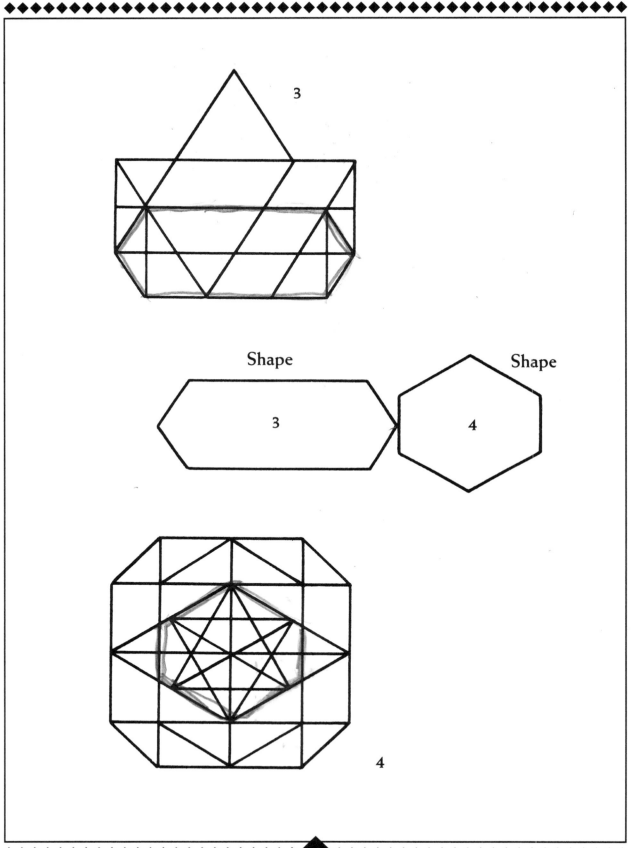

3

Shape

Shape

3

4

4

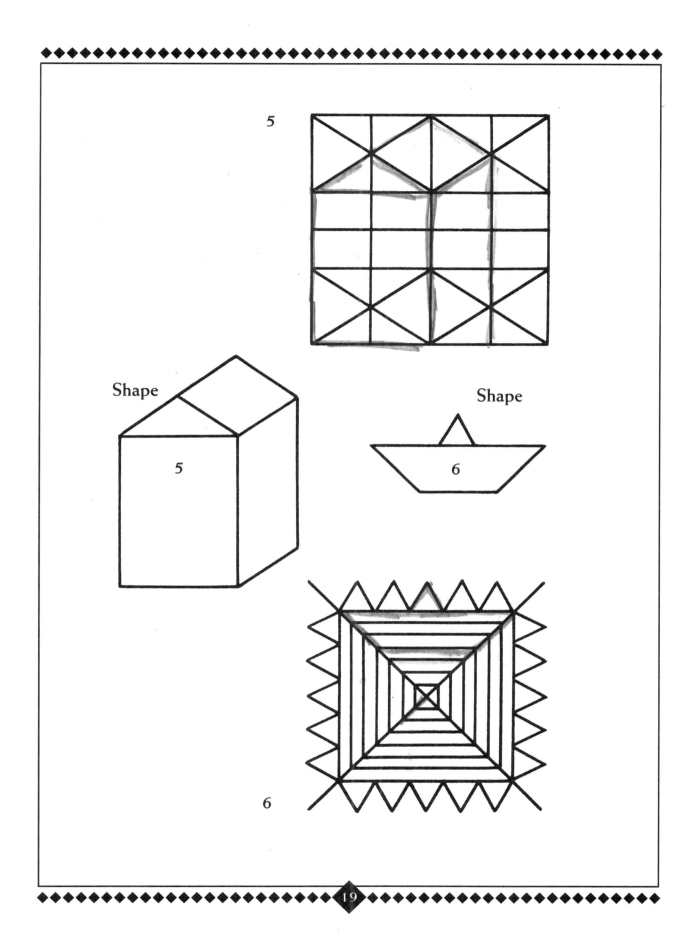

5

Shape

5

Shape

6

6

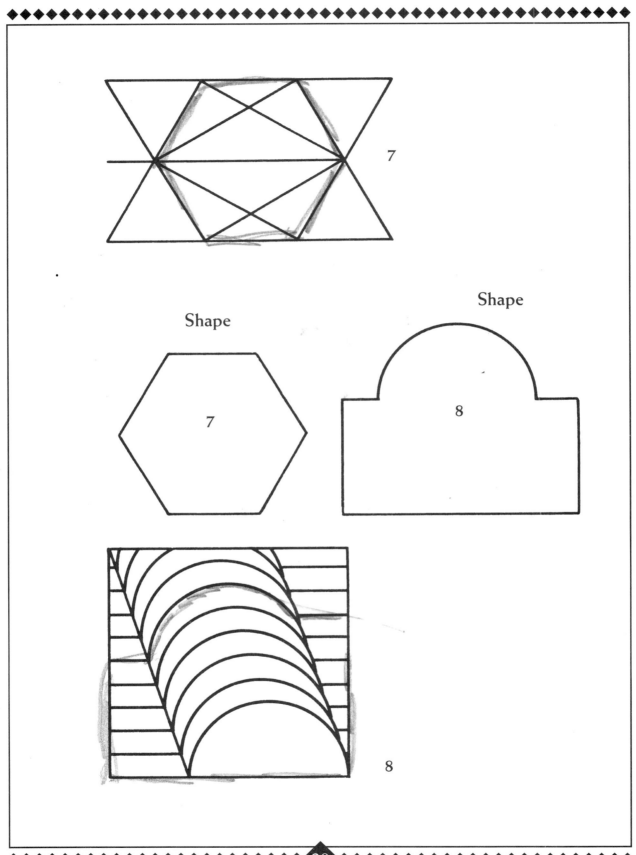

7

Shape

Shape

7

8

8

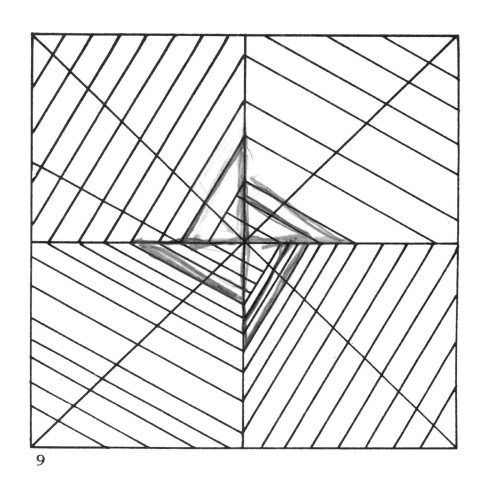

9

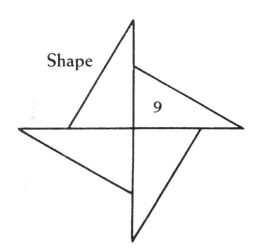

Shape

9

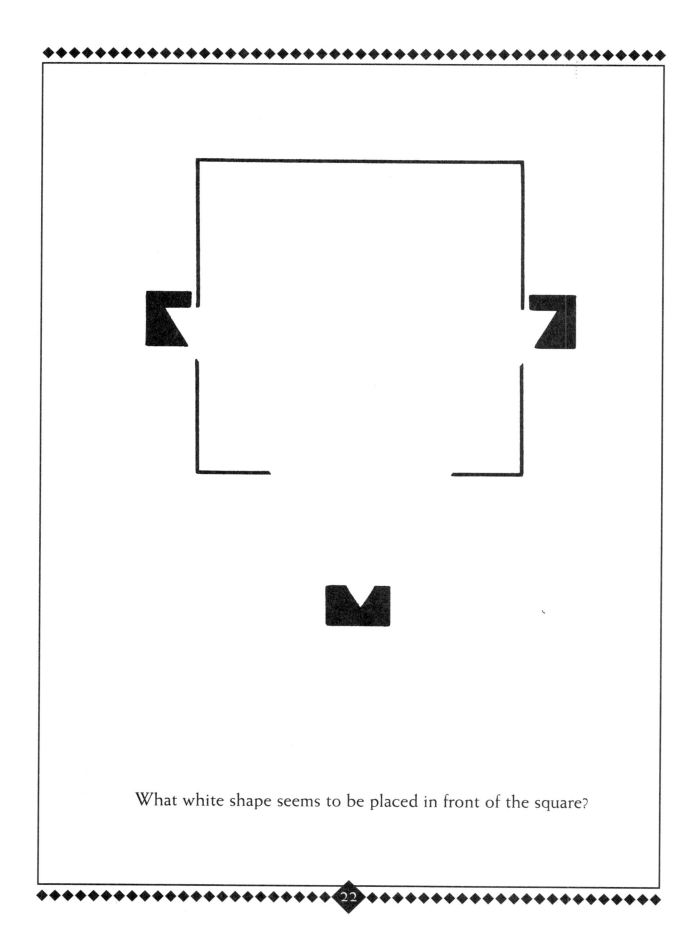

What white shape seems to be placed in front of the square?

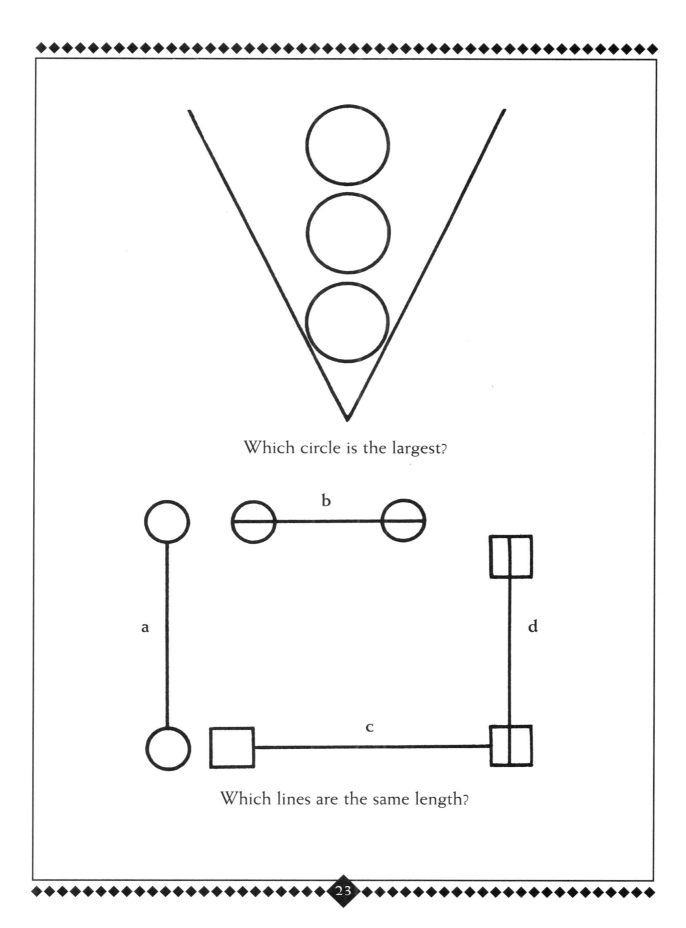

Which circle is the largest?

Which lines are the same length?

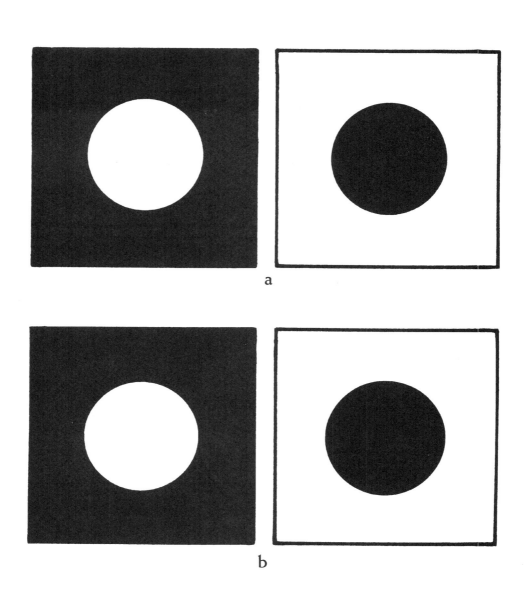

a

b

Which of the circles are the same size? Those in row "a"
or those in row "b"?

Which Easter egg fits into which egg cup?

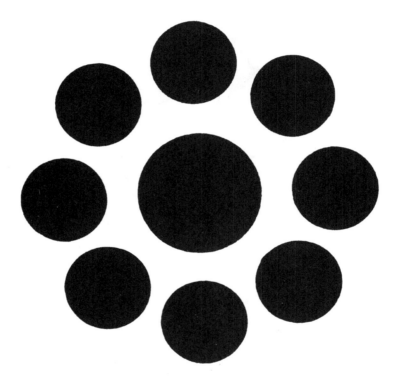

Which inner circle is larger—the one on the left?

Or the one on the right?

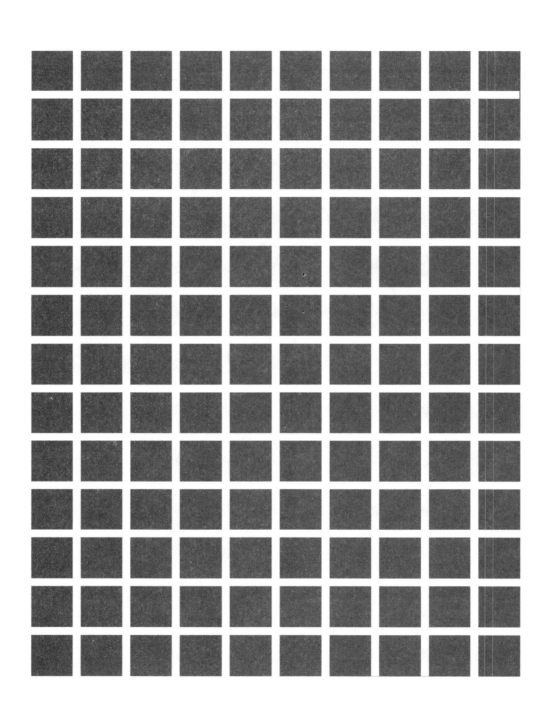

Which grey area is brighter?

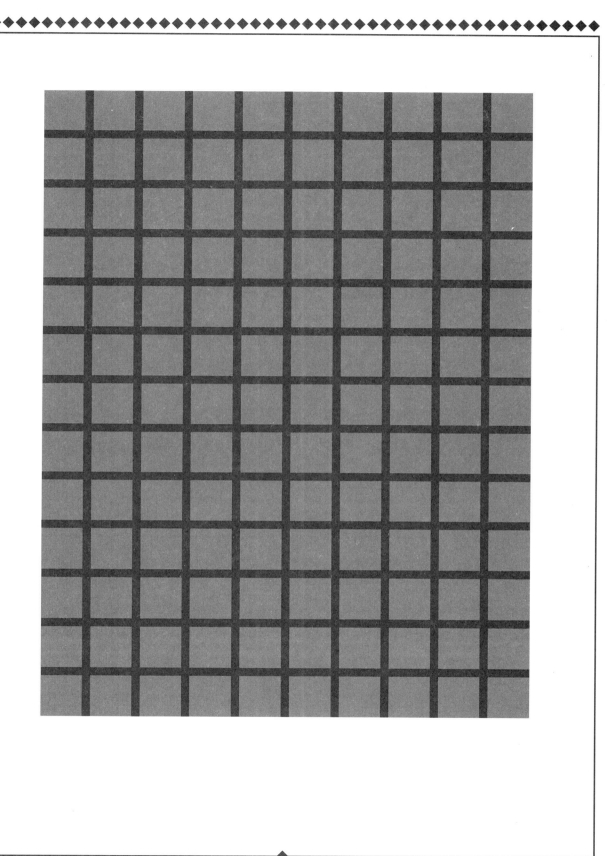

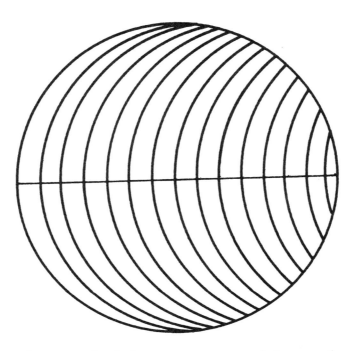

Can you find the exact center of this circle?

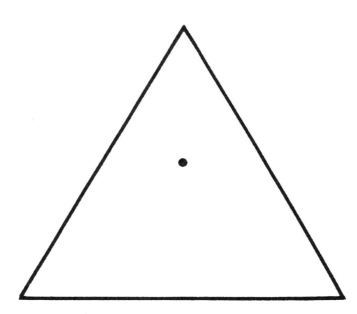

Is the dot midway between the point and the base of this triangle?
Or is it too high up?

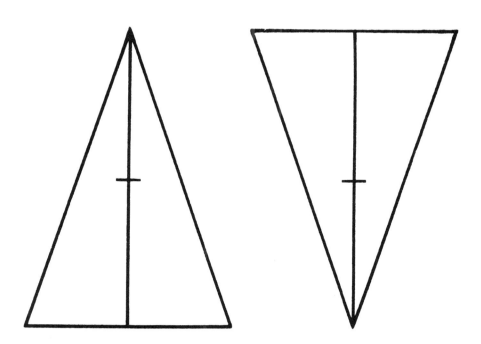

Are the cross-bars exactly in the middle of the center line
of these triangles?

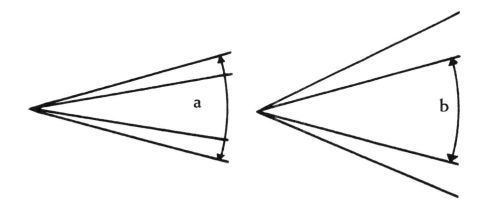

Is "a" larger than "b"?

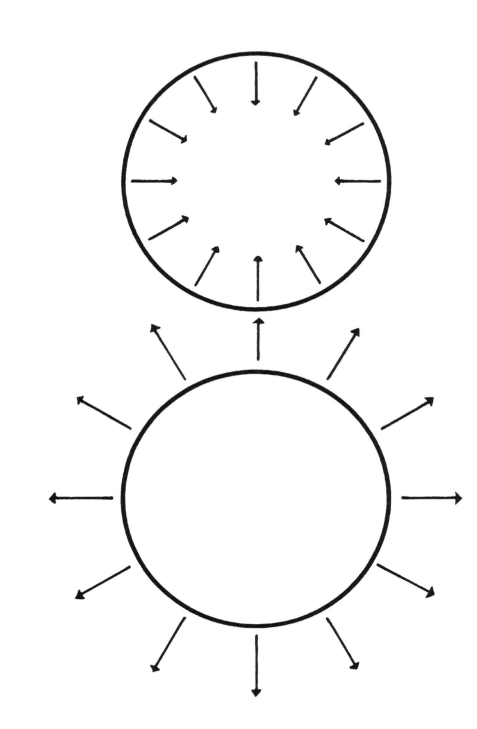

Which circle has the greater diameter?

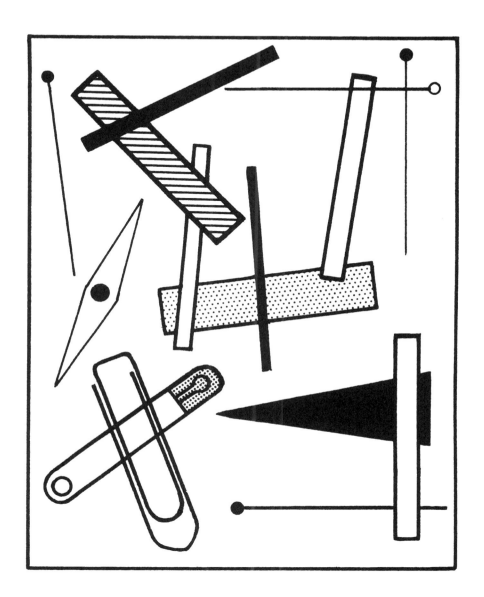

Which is the longest object in this picture?

Visual Thinking Puzzles

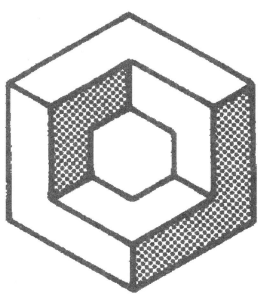

Wrap It Up

You don't need a crystal ball to see into the future. All you need is your brain.

   The shape below is formed from three smaller pieces. These pieces are connected by a tiny hinge at their point of attachment. Suppose you were able to rotate the pieces so the neighboring sides aligned flatly and squarely. Which one of the shapes below could this structure look alike?

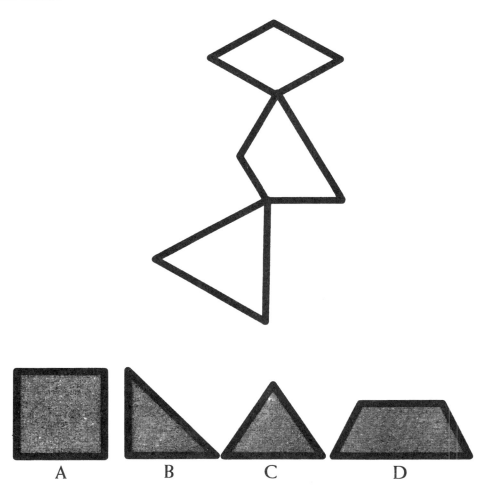

A   B   C   D

Pi Pieces

There are many skills we associate with visual thinking. Some of these skills may be much more difficult to master than others. For example, the ability to mentally rotate objects is often harder than we might imagine.

Try this: If you were to assemble these pieces into a circle, what would the figure formed by the inner lines look like?

Spacing Out

For a moment, let's leave the eye-brain puzzles and just "space out."

A shuttle astronaut leaves her craft to work on a disabled satellite. She lands on one corner of the satellite (which is a perfect cube) and realizes that she must walk across the satellite's surface to the opposite corner. To conserve oxygen, she must follow the shortest possible route. Is her planned route (identified by the dotted line) the shortest path between opposite corners?

Code Caper

What animal is represented in the code below?

Hint: From our earliest years, we learn to identify objects by the space they occupy. Artists, however, sometimes use the space that doesn't occupy something. It's called negative space and it's the fabric that surrounds things. Perhaps a little negative space might help you solve this puzzle?

Cut the Cube

Can you visualize 3-D space? If so, imagine a solid block of clay shaped into a perfect cube. Can you visualize it? Great. Now, let's change it with a modeling knife. How can a single cut produce the six-sided face shown here?

Link Latch

Your optic nerve links the eye and the brain. This "connecting wire" is not passive. As messages travel along its path, visual information is analyzed and sorted. By the time they arrive at the brain, the messages have already been partially processed and analyzed so that no time is wasted.

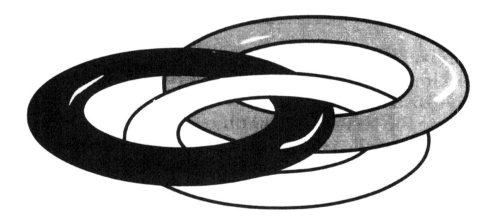

While digging through a box of links, a jeweler uncovers the three joined links shown above. She decides to separate the links. As she examines them, she finds a way to disconnect all three by opening just a single link. Can you?

Amaze in String

A pipe is located at the center of an odd loop of string.

Suppose the string is pulled by its two free ends. Will the string come free of the pipe or will it be caught by it?

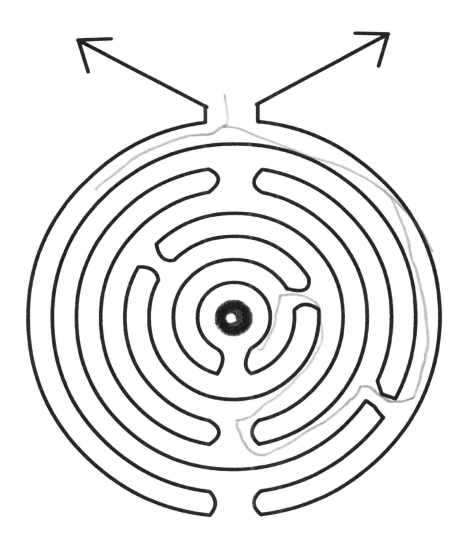

Superimposing Position

Suppose the values illustrated by the two graph forms below are added together. Which of the four choices will the combined final graph form look like?

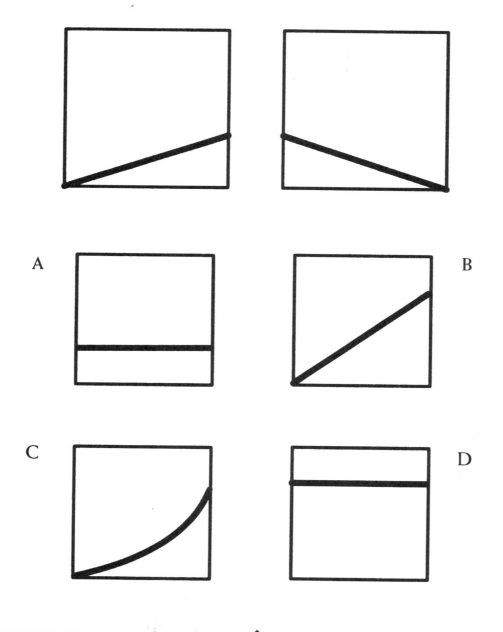

A

B

C

D

Faces Front

Suppose you can examine this five-block shape (although hidden, the fifth block is present in the middle of the shape) from any angle. How many different cube faces can you count?

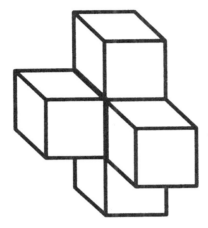

Suppose that hidden block (the fifth one) is evaporated. How many cube faces would now be exposed?

Now examine this nine-block shape from any angle. How many different cube faces can you count?

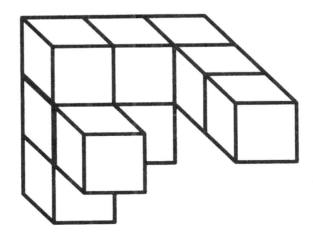

Impossible Profile

Even though you can't see the entire block structure below, you can make accurate statements about its appearance. If viewed from all directions, which one of the four profiles is impossible?

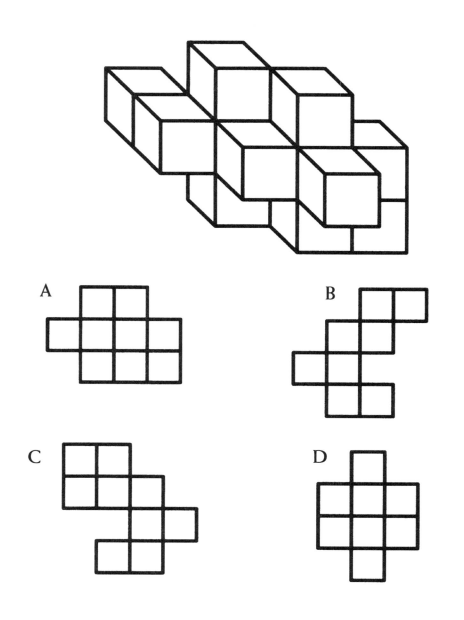

A

B

C

D

Pharaoh Folds

Which of the folding patterns below will produce a shape unlike the others?

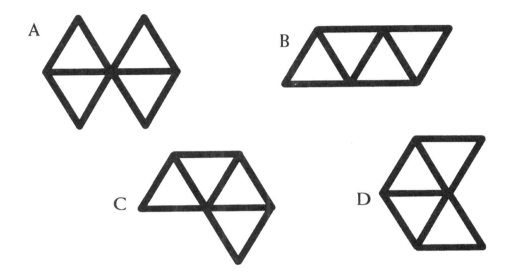

Brain Training

There are two parallel railroad tracks that connect the cities of Metropolis and Gotham City. Every hour, a train leaves from each city and travels to the other. The trip takes 3 hours in either direction. Suppose you are on board a train that is leaving Metropolis. Counting the inbound train that enters the Metropolis station as you pull out, what is the total number of inbound trains you will pass as you travel to Gotham City.

How Many Triangles?

How many equilateral triangles can you uncover
in the pattern below?

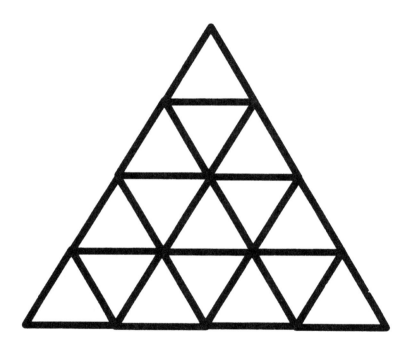

On the March

An army of neurotic ants lives in the jungle of some remote country. In their journey they've uncovered a trail formed by three overlapping circles.

Here's the challenge: The ants have to find a route that covers every part of this odd trail. The route can't cross over itself (nor can the ants back up and retrace any steps). Can you uncover their continuous route?

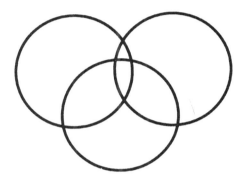

Here's route two with the same restrictions.

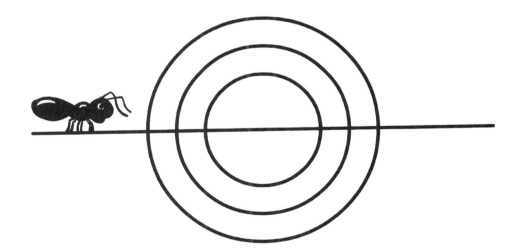

Stop and Think

How many different paths can lead you through the octagonal maze below. From start to finish, you can only move in the direction of the arrows.

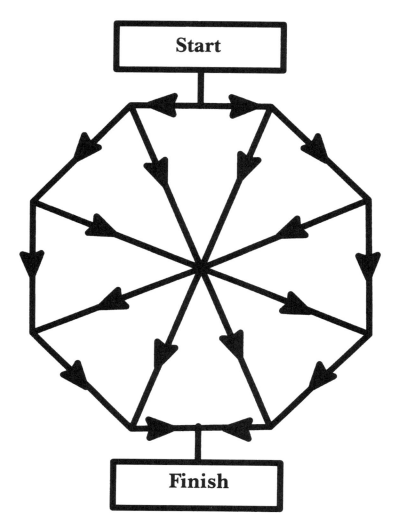

Hint: There is a way to do this puzzle without tracing out each path. Can you uncover the strategy?

Circular Code

What number belongs in the blank slice below?

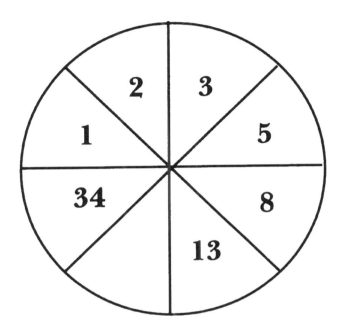

Shakes

Six people attended a gala for visual thinkers. If all guests shook hands with everyone else (no pair shook hands more than once), how many handshaking events were there?

Block Heads

Which pattern of blocks is unlike the others?

A

B

C

D

E

F

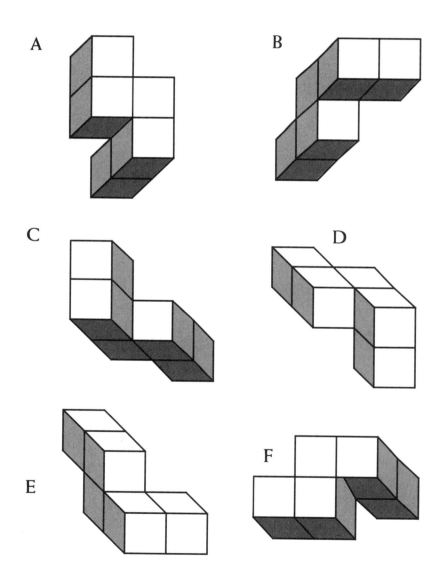

Puzzling Pages

A blast of wind has separated the pages of a local newspaper. From the page numbers shown below, can you determine how many pages were in the complete newspaper?

Controversial Cube

Which two cubes below can be constructed by folding this pattern? Let's assume that the pattern is the "outside" of the material.

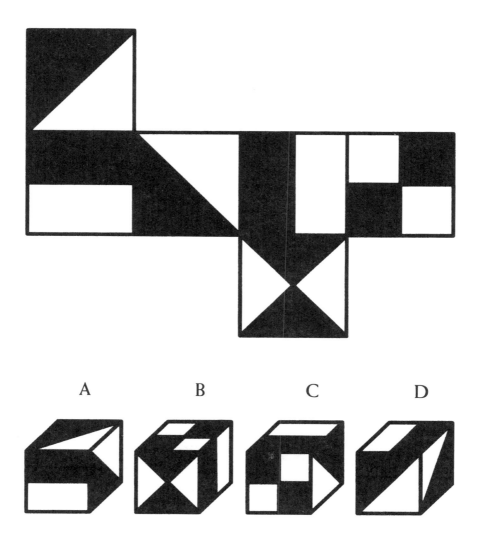

A   B   C   D

From Whence It Came?

Now let's reverse the thinking process. Can you identify the outer pattern from which the cube was folded?

A   B   C   D

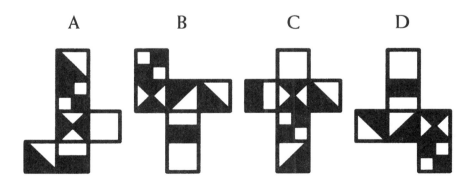

Sink Your Teeth

Both cog A and cog D have sixty teeth. Cog B has thirty teeth. Cog C has ten teeth. Suppose cog B makes twenty complete turns every minute. Which will spin faster, cog A or cog D?

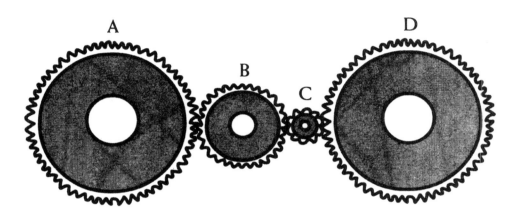

Hands-On/Minds-Off

Examine each of these hands carefully. Then decide which one of the nine is unlike all the others?

Going In Circles?

Are the belts and wheels arranged so that they will spin freely as this mouse races up the treadmill?

Roll With It

If you rolled this pattern into a cylinder, which one of the choices below will it look like?

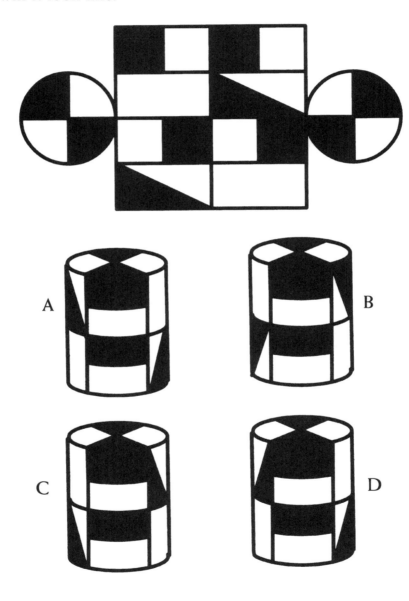

Dial Dilemma

The instruments in a cockpit are positioned so that a pilot can quickly glance at the indicators and know instantly if there is a problem. In the panel below, one dial does not fit the pattern. Can you locate it quickly?

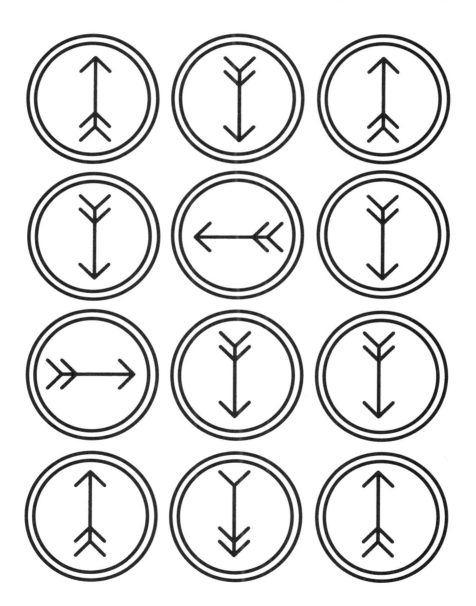

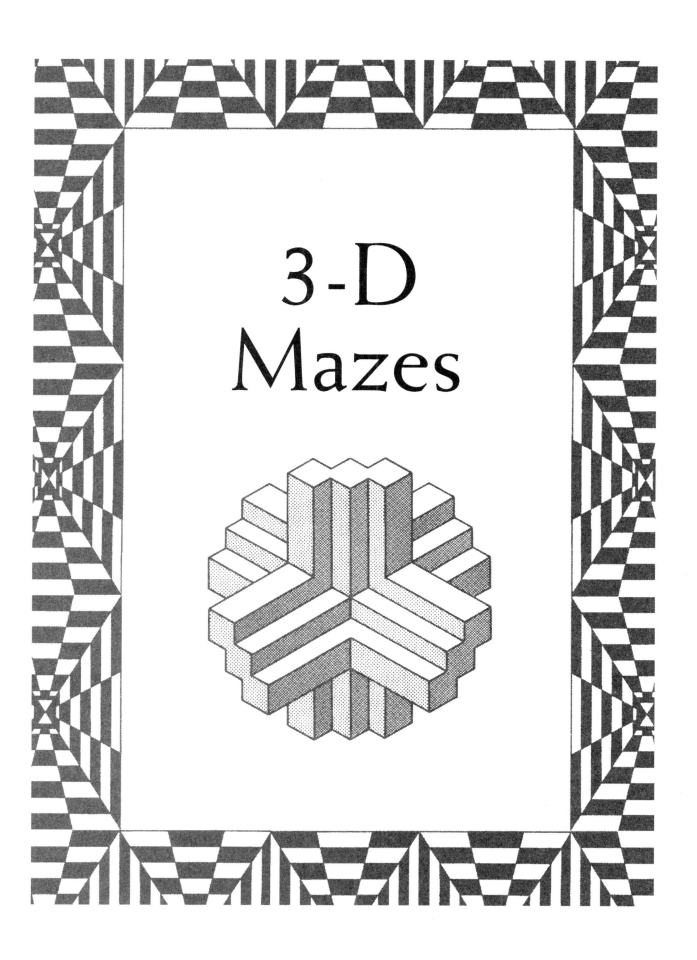

3-D
Mazes

The Barricades

Begin at the IN arrow and remove only TWO barricades to solve the maze.

Almost Straight Down

Enter the maze at any point at the top and follow the black path to the bottom exit. Many paths lead to the exit; however, you may travel upwards only ONCE.

In the Beginning

Begin with the triangle, visit every black circle only once, and then return to the triangle.

Doors and Stairs

Now that youv'e had a tiny hint of what a Lateral Logic Maze is, let's move on to the next plateau. The next six puzzles ask you to project yourself into the maze and deal with open and closed doors, stairways, upside-down rooms and walls without doors at all.

In the maze on page 64, you enter the building through the front door and proceed into each room in a logical fashion. The maze on page 65 takes you on a bit longer trip through a building, and on page 66 you have three stories of an office building. Be very careful when you climb the stairs on page 66 because you don't want to get lost.

Good luck on your travels in this section. We'll meet again when you reach Solid Geometry.

Walls Only

Begin at the IN arrow and enter each enclosed room only once, then exit. How many doors must you cut?

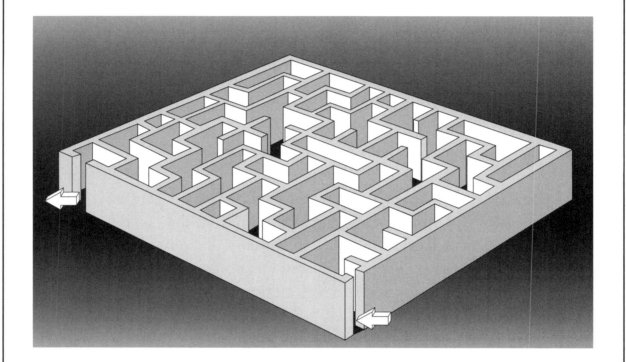

The House of Mystery

In this mystery-house maze, open only FIVE doors on your way from the IN arrow to the OUT arrow.

The Office Building

Enter the three-story office building at the main entrance and exit at the same place. You must visit all three floors using the stairs. You may only open TWO doors during your visit. Be sure to use the correct stairs!

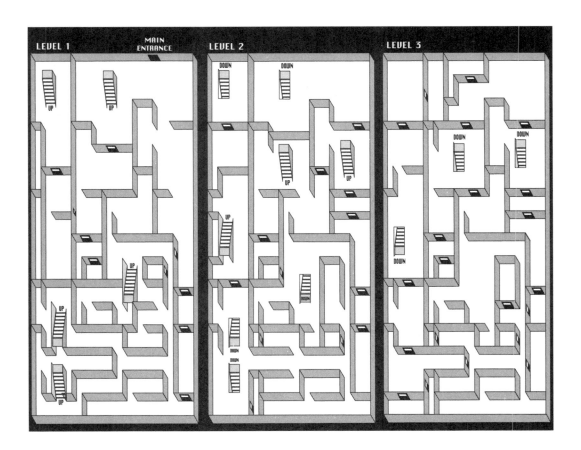

One to Win

Enter the maze and walk through ALL the open doors while opening only ONE closed door. You may pass through each opening only once.

Number Fun

Start with the number 3, in the center of this maze, and travel 3 spaces horizontally or vertically. Then move the number of spaces indicated on the NEW square. Work your way to any of the squares marked with a symbol. You may travel over each square as often as you like.

❄	8	6	5	7	7	2	4	6	2	❄
8	3	9	6	3	8	3	9	5	6	4
4	9	5	3	6	9	9	4	6	8	9
6	8	3	9	7	3	4	4	2	5	4
2	5	8	3	4	9	3	2	3	9	1
4	2	4	6	9	3	5	8	3	9	2
9	5	6	2	6	7	9	2	6	8	2
6	3	8	4	7	4	8	4	9	9	6
5	8	5	4	4	7	5	9	4	8	4
2	7	4	2	5	7	2	9	2	8	6
❄	4	9	4	4	2	7	5	3	1	❄

Win Sum–Lose Sum

Begin at 2 and move in any direction (including diagonally) to an adjacent square. Add the number in this square to that in the square you just left. The sum of those two numbers will be a number in an adjacent square (2+4=6, etc.). Move there. Repeat this process until you reach 100.

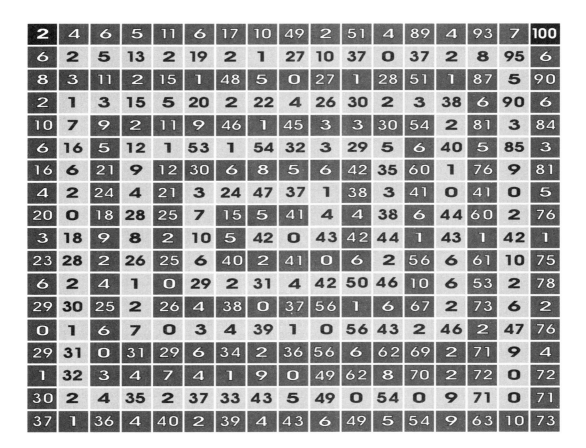

Geometry

Simple geometric shapes: hexagons, squares, triangles, and hex-nuts! Easy stuff for those geo-types. But these Lateral Logic Mazes add just a touch of madness to the proceedings. Maybe it's a hex or maybe it's a square. Or maybe someone's put a hex on a square. It's obviously a triangle, but where did the extra piece come from?

Don't be intimidated by a circle that has to become a square or things like that. Before you challenge each circle to a duel, try the maze as it is and see where it takes you. You might be surprised.

Once you overcome these puzzles, the rest of the book will be a breeze.

Hex or Square

The pieces below fit together as either a square or a hexagon. Make your decision and build one of the options. Now solve the maze as the path winds over and under itself.

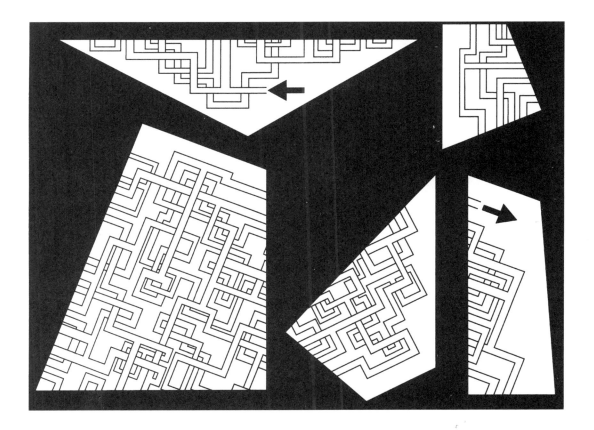

Square Circles

Begin with the S and work your way through the maze horizontally and vertically (NOT diagonally), alternating from square to circle. Try to reach the C. By the way, one circle should be a square. Change it to win.

Three Nuts

The path shown on the puzzle begins at the 1, and touches all the nuts only once. Find a path that begins at 2 and also touches all the nuts. Now find another that begins at 3. It's not as easy as it looks.

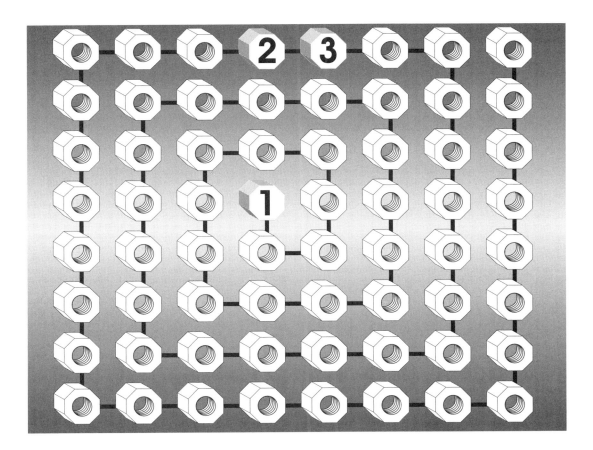

Visual
Trickery

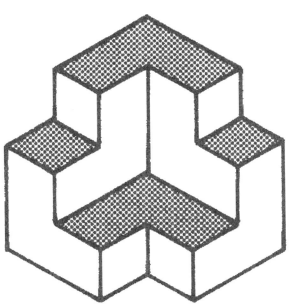

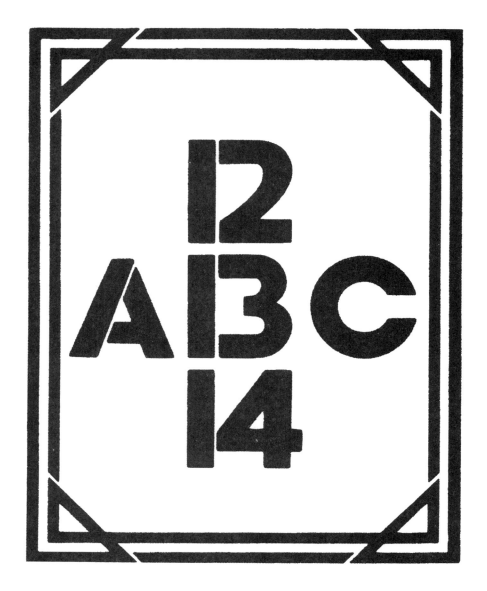

What do you see in the middle of the frame? Is it a letter "B" or
the number "13"?

Rotate the page in a circular motion. What happens?

Stare at this skull for about 30 seconds (try not to blink) — and then look at a sheet of white paper. What do you see?

What is mysterious about these donkeys?

Are these stacks of banknotes sloping downwards to the right, or are they pointing down to the left?

At first glance, we see a pig. But where is the farmer?

What are you looking at — the inside of a tunnel — or the
top of a mountain?

Stare at the center of the illustration. Then slowly bring the page
close to your face. What happens?

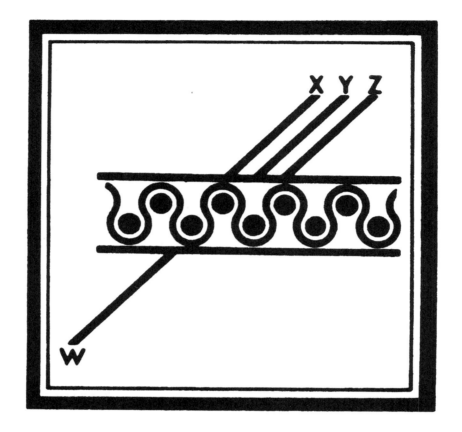

Which line connects with the letter "W"?

How many candles are there?

The famous magician Dunninger used this design as a logo. Do you notice something odd about his features?

Is there life after death?

Is the zebra white with black stripes or black with white stripes?

This is Garibaldi. Turn him upside down
and who does he become?

What do you see — black wine glasses or white vases?

Would you describe the back wheel of this cycle as a circle?

Can you spot the dog? What is he an example of?

Can you decipher the Mandarin's scroll?
Clue: It has to do with playing cards.

What's wrong with these fish?

Which way are the tubes facing?

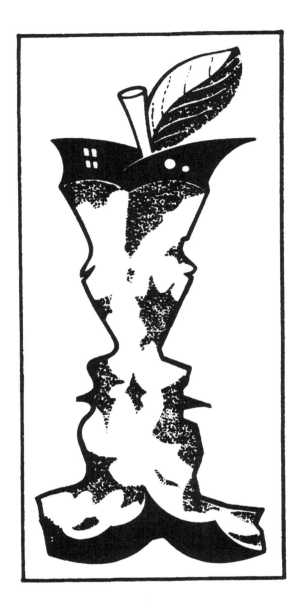

Do you notice anything unusual about this apple core?

This elephant is weird. Why?

Is this clown balancing on a white ball with a black pattern or on a
black ball with a white pattern?

Bring this page close to your face, and what happens?

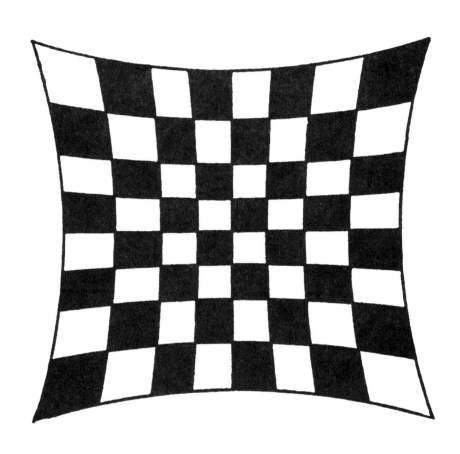

You can make this distorted checkerboard perfectly square
without touching it. How?

Tell this sad fellow a joke and make him smile. Come to think of it, there may be an easier way…

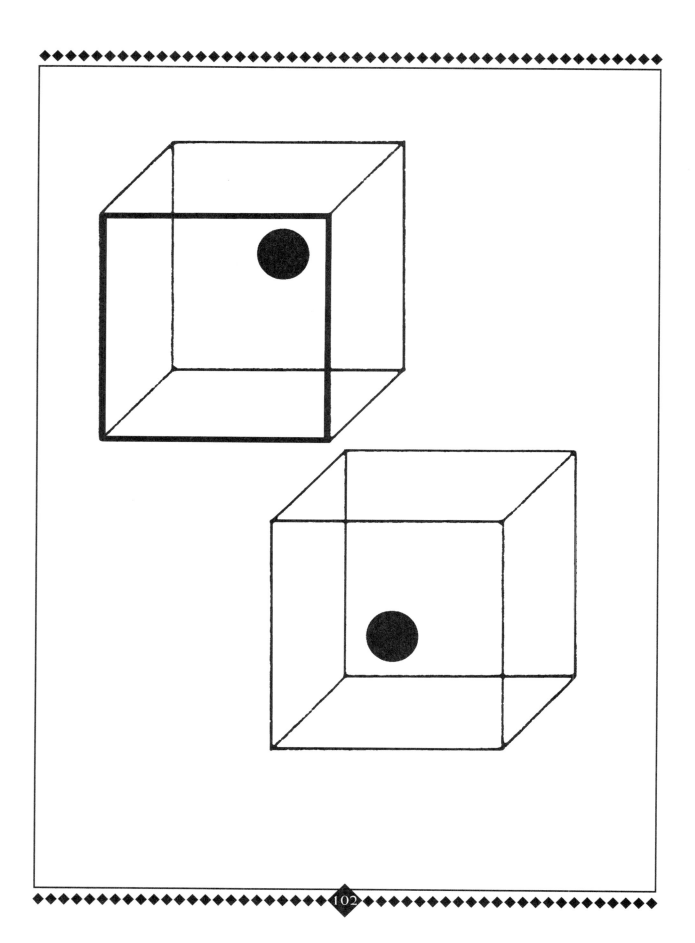

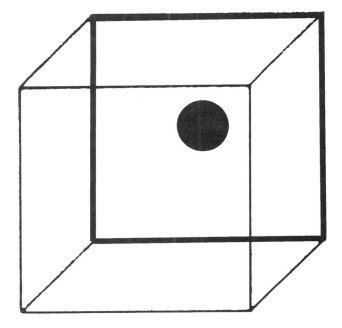

Do you see the area bounded by the darker lines as the outside of a transparent cube? Keep looking, and the bounded area will become the inner surface of a cube tilted a different way. Is the black spot on the front or rear face? Or is it inside the cube?

Rotate this page in a counterclockwise direction. What happens?

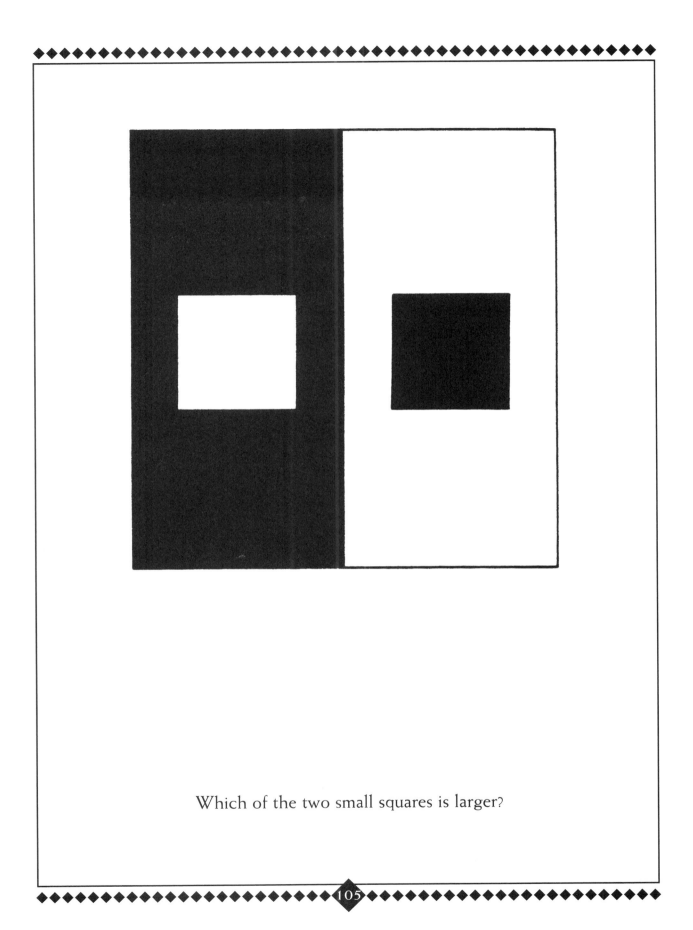

Which of the two small squares is larger?

Is Side "A" of this picture high or is Side "B"?

What do you see in this picture?

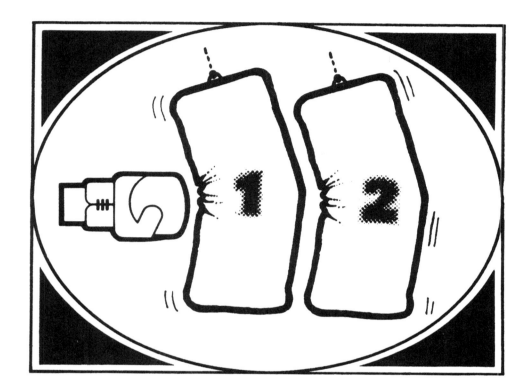

Which punching bag is bigger?

Is this a spiral?

What's the matter with these cubes?

What do you see in this picture—black arrows or white arrows?

Why do the fish in this illustration seem to swim in
one direction and then in the other?

Fishermen are always boasting about the size of the fish they have caught. This man has caught 2 fish. Which one is bigger?

This man is unhappy because his girlfriend has left him.
What does she look like?

What happens when you rotate this page in a circular motion?

Optical Illusion Designs

Shimmering Squares

The shimmering effect you see below is caused by optical distortion. This illusion is unusual because all the lines in it are sloped either forward at 45° or backward at 135°. To see why this helps make the illusion more interesting, try the following experiment.

Concentrate hard on one of the rows of lines that are sloped at 45°—like the bottom edge of a square. You'll find that all the squares formed by lines sloped at 45° appear steady, while the ones formed by lines sloping backwards at 135° look blurry and faint and seem to shimmer.

Then concentrate on a row of lines sloped at 135° and you'll see that all the squares formed with lines sloped at 45° will look blurry and faint and seem to shimmer.

This effect occurs because your eyes cannot focus on all of the illusion at once. The parts of the illusion that you do focus on will appear clear, while the parts of the illusion that are out of focus will look blurry.

All Square

This optical illusion is especially puzzling. If you study it closely, the ovals in the middle first seem to bulge out and then they seem to recede.

The reason why they change is that when your eyes scan the design from left to right, the position of the ovals suggests to your brain that the ovals are popping out. But then your eyes go back over the picture. With so many different ways to scan the illusion — and no clues to which way is "right" — you may see the ovals recede, or do any number of interesting tricks.

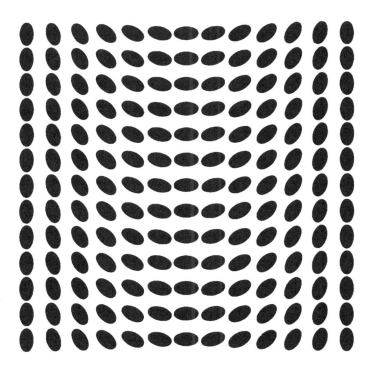

Making Waves

When you stare at this optical illusion for a while, the curved lines seem to form the crests and valleys of waves. They may even seem to move a little. If you stare some more, until your eyes get tired, you may also see phantom lines of color, especially in bright light, where the curved lines run parallel to each other — between the valleys and crests of the waves.

The restless motion of the waves in this illusion is caused by optical distortion.

Tricky Tiles

What makes this design vibrate? Right, it's optical distortion again! The repetition of the same design on each tile helps to make this illusion even more effective.

Jester

If you look at this circular checkerboard closely, it will seem to pulsate and shimmer. You may also see the black-and-white patches link up to form the petals of a flower.

The shimmering that you see is caused by optical distortion. But the petals formed by your brain are an example of another phenomenon called "good continuation." It happens because your brain is trying to make sense out of what it sees. It seeks out shapes or patterns that it recognizes. Sometimes it works so hard and so cleverly that it imagines an object that isn't really there. And then we have an optical illusion.

Networking

In this neat illusion, tiny white dots appear to join together to form phantom white crosses. This is another example of your brain trying to make sense of the visual information it is receiving — good continuation.

But there is another interesting phenomenon at work here. You can also see tiny grey dots in the center of the black crosses. Why? Special cells in your visual system respond strongly to small patches of light and dark. If a small light patch is surrounded by more light, these cells will not respond so strongly to the small patch of light in the middle. If a small dark patch is surrounded by more darkness, these cells will not respond so strongly to the small patch of dark in the middle.

So in the case of the black crosses, your visual system does not respond fully to the middle of them, and you see them as grey instead.

It doesn't have to be this way, though. You can force your eyes and brain not to "overlook" the mid point of the crosses. If you focus your eyes and attention fully upon one cross at a time, you will be able to see it as an ordinary black cross.

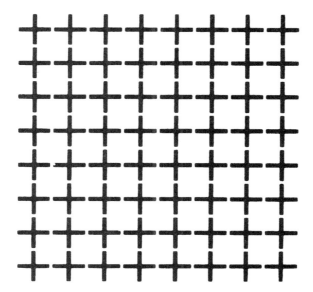

Zinnia

When you look at this illusion, you may see some grey or white spots at the points where the black lines meet. This is caused by your eyes' response to dark and light, as in "Networking."

And, if you go on studying this design, you may also see that these imaginary dots "link up" to form a series of circles that radiate out from the middle of the illusion. This is another example of good continuation.

Lattice

Here is an example of the role that contrast plays in your perceptions. Although there are only two colors used in this design — black and white — the tiny white dots in the middle, where the black lines intersect, seem brighter and whiter than the larger white squares. This is because the tiny white squares are more completely surrounded by the black lines than the larger white squares.

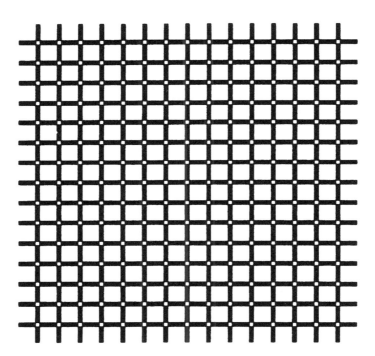

Square's Square

This illusion may remind you of "Shimmering Squares," in which lines drawn at different angles confuse the brain. The squares here that have been drawn on the background pattern may look as if they have been bent, but in actual fact they are perfectly straight!

This is an example of the "Zollner effect." It shows how straight lines appear to bend if they intersect with or are seen against a background of curved lines or lines drawn at different angles. This strange effect occurs because your eyes and brain work together to try to make the straight lines fit into the background pattern.

Spiral Square-Case

The squares in the foreground look as if they are bent, right? Well, they do look that way. But this is another example of the Zollner effect. If you hold a ruler up alongside them, you'll see that the lines in the square are just as straight as they can be. It's only the curves of the spiral background that make the square seem bent.

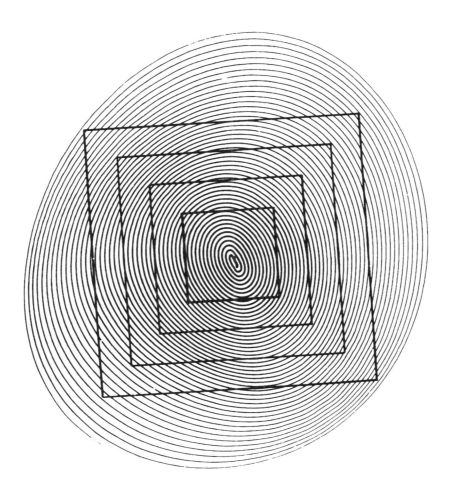

Squashed Circles

You can see all sorts of different effects when you look at this illusion.
You may see flickering spokes radiating out from the central circle —
turn the page from side to side to accentuate this effect. You can also
view the central and smallest circle in two ways: as the top of a cone
or as the end of a funnel.

The flickering spokes are a result of optical distortion.

Seasick Circle

If you watch this drawing while you turn the book around in a circle, you will be able to see a series of spirals moving up and down in three dimensions.

This is what's called a "stereokinetic effect." It's the result of a complex series of interactions between your eyes and your brain.

When this design rotates, the images sent to your brain are constantly changing. Because each circle is drawn with lines that vary in thickness, there is no stable point in the illusion for you to focus on. This is confusing to your brain, which likes to make orderly patterns out of what it sees. So your brain looks for another pattern and sees that some of the curved lines seem to link up to form a spiral. As the curves that form the spiral rotate and change position, each of your eyes simultaneously sends your brain a slightly different image. When your brain puts this all together, it decides that it must be seeing a spiral moving up and down.

The Temple

This illusion combines two effects. It is a reversing figure: one way to look at it is as a pyramid viewed from above, with the smallest square forming the top. The other is as a passageway leading towards a tiny square door. If you look steadily at this illusion, you will probably see it flash between these two images.

It is also an example of optical distortion, because of the way it seems to shimmer.

The Escalator

When you look closely at this optical illusion, you may get the impression that the horizontal panels are moving with a tiny jerking motion. The central panel may also seem unexpectedly bright. The reason that the "Escalator" appears to move is that, no matter how hard you try, you can't keep your eyes perfectly still, and as they move about, so do the images in the illusion.

Escalator Experiment

To fully appreciate this illusion, ask a teacher or librarian to photocopy this picture onto a plastic film to make a transparency. Place the transparency over the illusion and move it from side to side. You will experience the incredible "moiré effect" when the two patterns are superimposed.

You have undoubtedly observed the moiré effect before. It is in the patterns you see when two lace curtains overlap. They are produced where the thicker strands of the lace cross over each other to form a pattern.

You can also create a moiré effect using two combs. Hold them up to the light and slowly rotate one of the combs against the other. You will see a series of moiré fringes or bands appearing and disappearing.

Moiré Grating

This is one of the simplest types of moiré pattern, one formed by two identical gratings. The pattern you see is so strong that it is very difficult to see the path of each individual straight line. Try tracing the path of any straight black line with your finger and you'll see.

The Eternal Staircase

Can you figure out which corner of the staircase is the highest? Probably not. Because this is not a real staircase — it's an "impossible figure." The drawing works because your brain recognizes it as three-dimensional. And a good deal of it is a realistic depiction. The first time you glance at it, the steps in "The Eternal Staircase" look quite

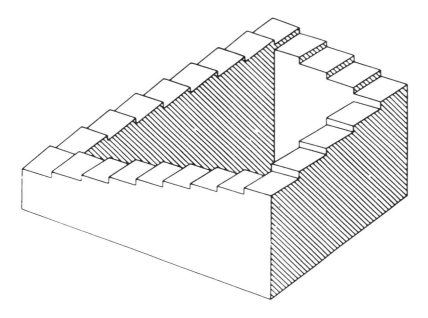

logical. It is only when you look at the drawing closely that you see that the entire structure is impossible.

"The Eternal Staircase" was first created by Lionel S. Penrose, a geneticist, and his son Roger. It later became known through the work of Maurits Escher, an artist who worked in the early part of the 20th century. Escher used many impossible figures such as this in his art, creating extremely odd paintings.

The Impossible Triangle

Even if you were an expert carpenter, you'd never be able to construct this figure. Each of the three joints in the triangle is drawn with great accuracy. But the rods connecting them are not!

The fascinating thing about these illusions is that your brain is so convinced they are drawings of three-dimensional figures, that it is almost impossible to see them as the flat outline drawings they are.

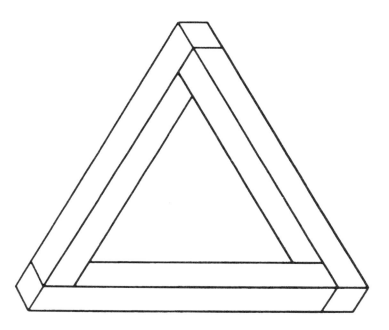

Chrysanthemum

When you look at this design, you get the impression that it is not flat, but three-dimensional. Some parts of the illusion appear higher and some lower, which gives the impression of depth. However, if you look at the curved lines that define the bumps and hollows of the flower, you will find a curious situation. Look at the curve that defines the outer edge of the flower, for instance, and follow it right around in a circle. You will see that in some places the curved lines seem to define a hump — and at others a hollow. This object could not exist in three dimensions. "Chryanthemum" is another example of an impossible figure.

It also shimmers—so it is also a case of optical distortion.

More
Mazes

Blow Out

This is a basic 3-dimensional maze. The pipes are channel tubes that float in perspective over and under each other. Enter the maze at the WHITE ball and crawl through the tubes to the BLACK ball. There is more than one solution, but if you can't find any, a solution can be found in the back of the book, on page 250.

Structure Impossible

Work your way through the construction from globe to globe. On your way, try to travel through each BLACK cube only once. You may not retrace your path but you MAY return to the starting cube as often as you like.

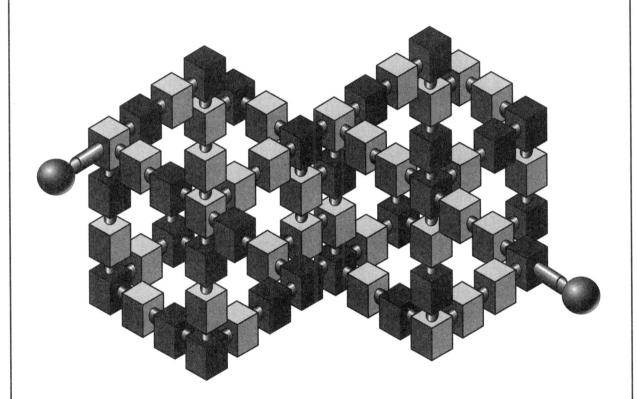

The Warehouse

Enter the warehouse and walk to the back exit. You may open only FIVE doors on your journey.

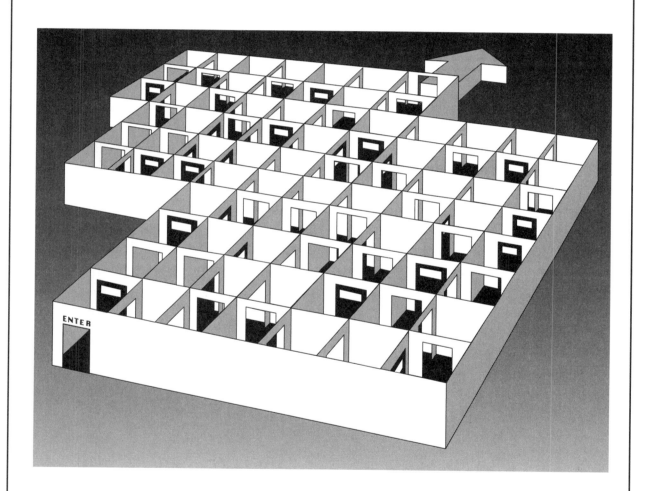

The Cubic Hotel

Your room is the BLACK cubicle in the east wing of the hotel. To save money, the developers have eliminated the hallways from this hostelry. Enter the correct entry door and find the way to your room.

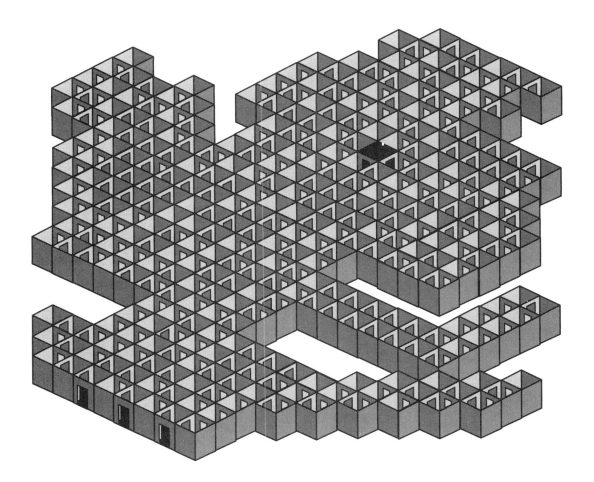

Cube Madness

The nine cubes in this puzzle have 15 sides showing. Some of the sides are in the correct place and some are not. To solve this maze, rearrange the incorrect sides and then travel from arrow to arrow as the path winds over and under itself.

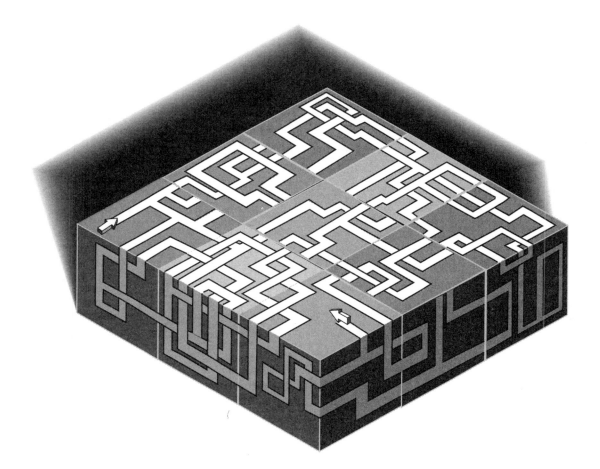

Round and Round

If you start from the central globe, only one of the four mazes leads to an OUT arrow. Using just your eyes, can you discover the correct maze?

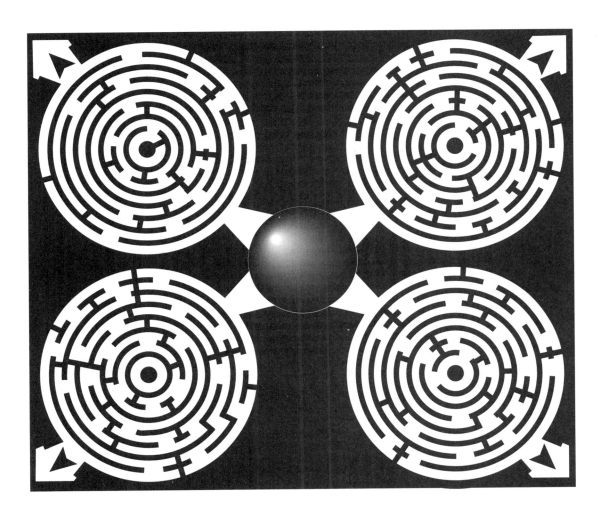

Pipe Down

Enter at the WHITE ball and travel through the pipes, touching ALL the balls once. You may not retrace your steps as you return to the WHITE ball. You may add TWO connecting pipes to solve this puzzle if you need them.

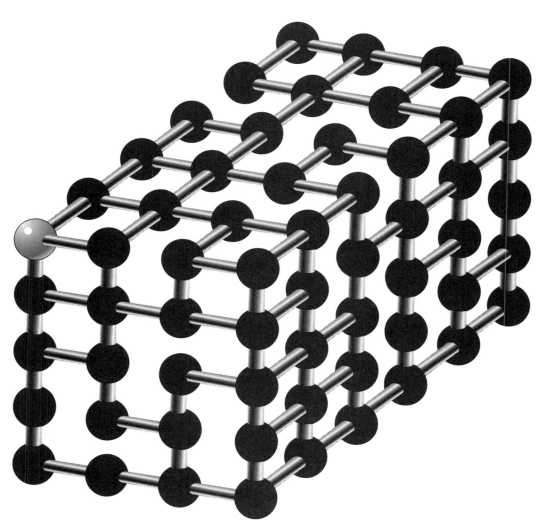

Ball, Pyramid & Cube

From the IN arrow find a path that touches all the objects only once before exiting. You must alternate between objects (ball—pyramid—cube, or ball—cube—pyramid) as you travel along your route. You must maintain the same sequence you began with throughout your journey.

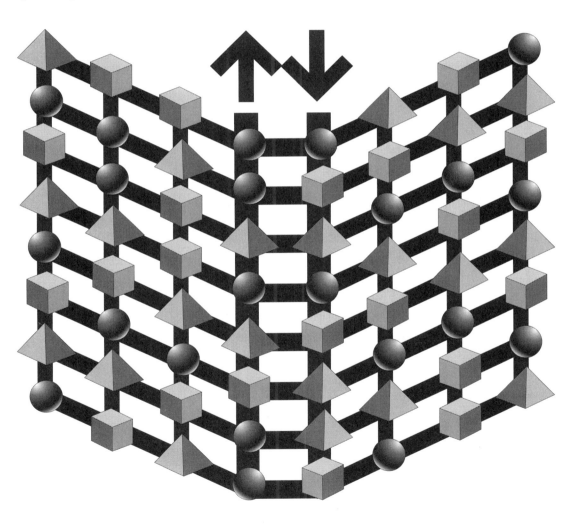

In and Out

Starting at the BLACK pyramid, crawl through the pipes, touching all the solid objects in sequence (pyramid—ball—cube or pyramid—cube—ball). Then exit at the BLACK pyramid. You may not retrace your steps or touch any object more than once. You must also maintain the sequence you began with.

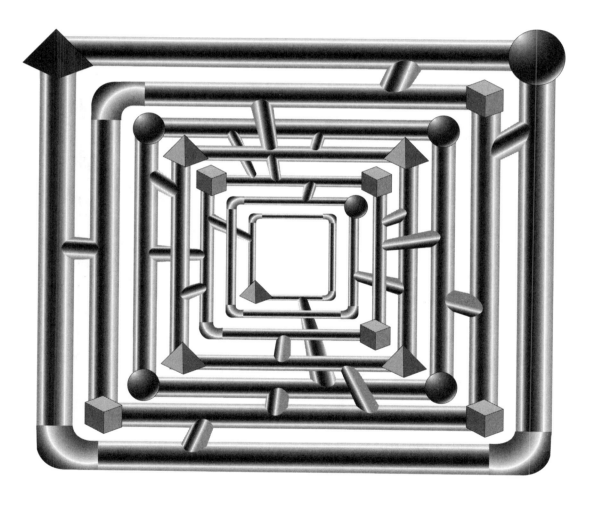

Ending Well

Follow the arrows and touch every space except the center. Be careful, however. Two arrows are facing in the WRONG direction.

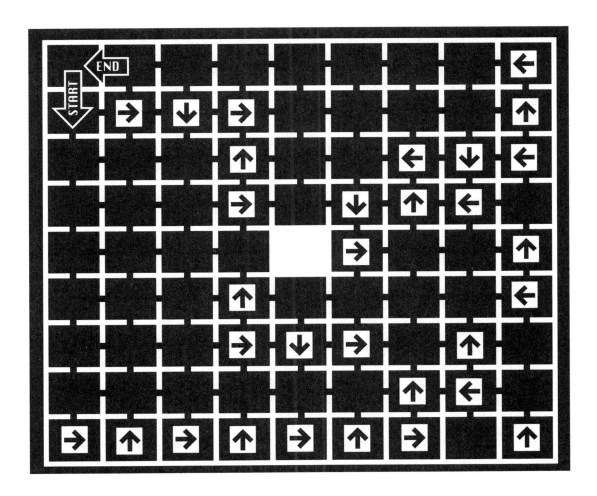

Clear Logic

Follow the path from the IN arrow to the OUT arrow. The path is etched on clear glass so you can follow it around the solid shape. The path flows over and under itself.

Jump Ball

Voyage into the maze by starting at the BLACK ball. When you reach a GRAY ball, jump to any other GRAY ball and continue through the pipes to the next GRAY ball. Jump again and continue the process until you touch all the GRAY balls; then exit at the WHITE ball. You may not retrace your path or touch any GRAY balls more than once.

The Black and White Ball

Enter the maze at any ball and travel to an opposite (WHITE to BLACK or BLACK to WHITE) ball. Then jump from the ball you have just reached to a ball of opposite value. Continue through the pipes, repeating the first sequence until you have touched all eight balls. Then exit at the OUT arrow. You may retrace your path as often as you like. There are many solutions to this maze, and you can find one solution on page 251.

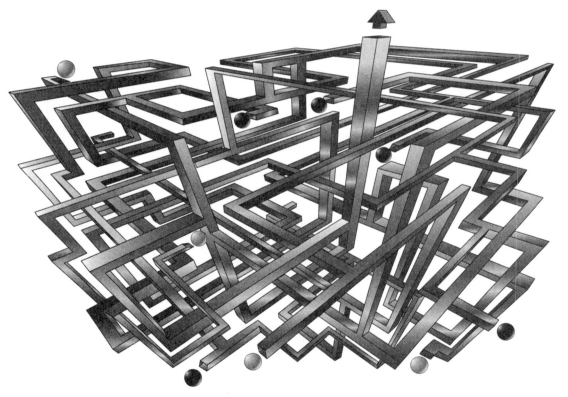

Way Out

Find the IN arrow and enter the maze on a search for fourteen balls. When you reach a ball, you must jump to another ball of opposite value (BLACK to WHITE or WHITE to BLACK), then enter the pipe and repeat the process. You must touch ALL the balls in the prior sequence before exiting at the OUT arrow. You may not travel over any path or touch any ball more than once.

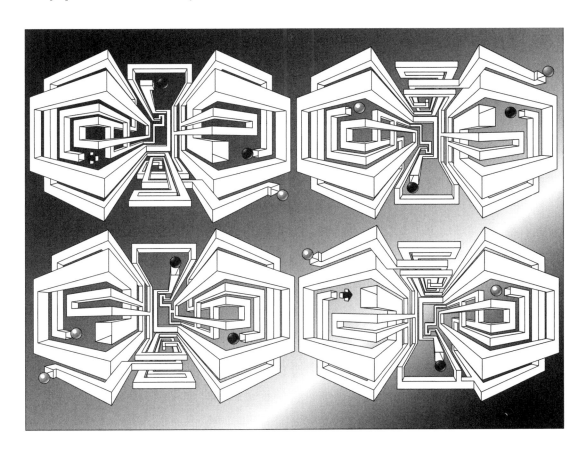

Movers,
Floaters,
and
Spotters

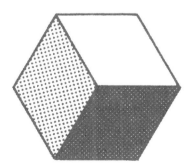

An optical illusion is something that looks different from what it really is. Some optical illusions, like the ones in this book, look different because they seem to move.

Some optical illusions appear because we have two eyes, while others are the result of our brain remembering one thing while our eyes are seeing another. Still other illusions happen because we think we see one thing when we actually see something else.

Here are a few optical illusions that result from seeing things with two eyes.

The Floating Finger

Hold your hands in front of your face at eye level, about 15 inches away from your eyes. Illus. 1 shows how. Keep the tips of your index fingers about 1 inch apart.

Illus. 1

Focus on a wall several feet behind your fingers. Almost at once you will see something strange. Between the tips of your fingers is a tiny, disembodied finger floating in space. Strangest of all is the fact that this little finger has two tips, one at either end.

Slowly move your hands closer to your face. Keep the tips of your fingers the same distance apart. The nearer your hands come to your face the longer the little floating finger becomes.

Pull your hands away from your face and the little two-ended finger gets shorter and shorter. Illus. 2 shows this illusion.

Illus. 2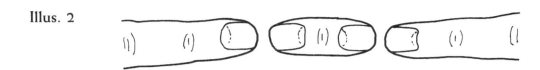

Now, focus your eyes on your fingers instead of the wall. Just like that, the floating finger vanishes.

When your fingers move closer to your face the space between them enters a "blind spot" (you'll find out more about these on page 160). Rather than go blind, your brain knows what should be there and fills the spot with what your eyes *do* see. In this case, your eyes see the ends of your fingers and your brain uses this sight to fill the blind spot. That's why you see the floating finger even though it's not there, and why it disappears when you look at your actual fingers.

The Jumping Finger

Hold up the index finger of either hand and shut one eye. Move your index finger until it points directly at some object or is directly under some object. The illustration below shows how.

Close one eye and don't move your finger. Did your finger jump? Try closing your other eye. It jumped back again!

Of course your finger did not move (at least it's not supposed to). So what happened? Because your eyes are several inches apart, each one actually sees a slightly different picture. Your brain puts the two pictures together to tell how far an object is.

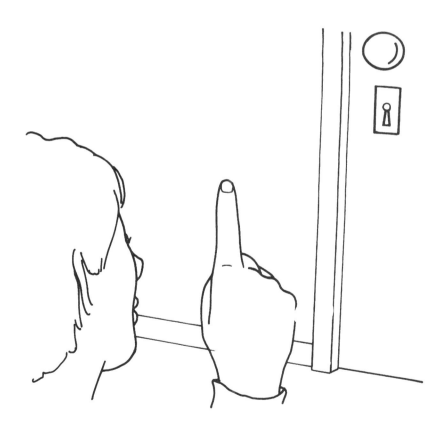

The Bouncing Ring

Open up both your eyes and form your thumb and forefinger into a ring like the one shown below.

Hold this ring out at arm's length. Move it around until you find something across the room which fits nicely into the ring. Focus your eyes on the object inside the ring.

Close one eye. Is the object still inside the ring? Depending on which eye you closed, the ring may stay still or bounce back.

Without moving your ring, close your open eye and open your closed eye. Now what do you see inside your ring?

With one eye open the object lines up inside the ring, but with your other eye open the object bounces away. Why?

When you see things with both eyes one eye has more control than the other. The eye that has more control is sometimes called the "dominant eye." When you close your dominant eye, the picture changes.

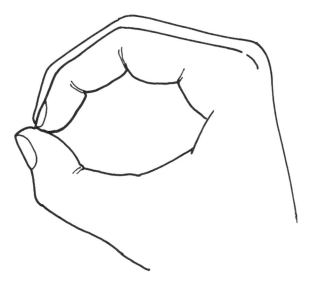

Growing New Fingers

While you're holding hands and fingers up, here's another moving illusion. Hold your index finger at arm's length, and keep both eyes open. Look at some object across the room that is in line with your extended finger. The illustration below shows how.

Focus on the object across the room and now you've got an extra finger. Now focus on your finger. You see *two* objects instead of one!

Obviously, you did not grow an extra finger, nor did the object across the room suddenly double. What you did was see two different pictures with each eye.

Blind Spots

Do we always see — all the time — unless our eyes are closed or we are in a dark place? Maybe, maybe not.

Hold the illustration at the bottom of this page about 15 inches in front of your face. Close your left eye, and look directly at the airplane with your right (open) eye.

Slowly move the book closer to you, looking *directly* at the airplane with your right eye. Move the book closer and farther until something strange happens. Suddenly the rocket will disappear!

No, it didn't leap off the page, or move somewhere else. What happened was it got lost in your blind spot. Don't worry, everyone has one in each eye, so you're not going blind.

Now close your right eye and open your left. With the left eye stare directly at the rocket, and move the illustration closer and farther until suddenly the airplane disappears. The plane moved into the blind spot in your left eye.

Viewing the illustration with only one eye at a time you get a chance to locate your blind spot. When you are looking at things with both eyes this tiny blind spot causes no problem. What one eye does not see the other does.

Hole in Your Hand

Do you have a hole in the palm of your hand? No? Don't be too sure.

Roll a sheet of notebook paper into a hollow tube about 1 inch across. Hold the tube to keep it from unrolling or use a strip of cellophane tape to fasten the loose edge down. This is up to you.

Hold the tube up to one eye as shown below. Keep your other eye open.

Don't poke yourself in the eye with the tube.

Locate something across the room that is small enough to be seen through the hollow tube. The object should be 12 to 15 feet away. Keep both eyes open, and look at the object through the tube.

Now bring your other hand up in front of the eye not looking through the paper tube. (The illustration below shows how to do this.) Suddenly you develop a round hole in the palm of your hand! And you're looking at the object through that round hole!

Naturally, this is just an optical illusion. This is one more time when seeing with both eyes makes you think things are not as they actually are.

Now is as good a time as any to mention the fact that you will get lots more fun out of this book when you share the illusions with others. See how each moving optical illusion works. Then share it with friends and family.

The Traveling Rectangle

Sometimes your brain remembers an image even after you no longer see it. This is another optical illusion that moves from place to place.

Stare directly at the black rectangle in the illustration below. Count to 30 as you stare. Try to blink as little as possible. but don't worry if a blink or two slips in. It won't spoil anything.

After staring for a count of 30, look up from the page. Now stare right at a dark wall or some other dark surface. Keep staring. What appears?

You know the rectangle didn't move off the page, but there it is! Even stranger than the fact that the rectangle moved to the wall is the fact that the one on the wall is light or even white instead of black like the one in the book!

This is called *afterimage*. Afterimage is responsible for many moving optical illusions. Some of them trick us into thinking we see colors that are different from those we really see. But more about that later.

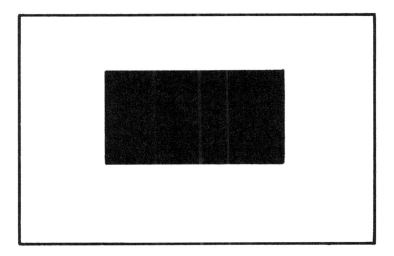

Lines and Lines

Take a quick look the illustration below. As you can see there are two slanting lines that meet two parallel lines.

So what is so special about this? The special thing is that your eyes and mind have created an optical illusion.

Let's see if a little moving around will clear up the illusion. Take a piece of paper with a straight edge. Place the straight edge along the two slanted lines.

This is one of those times when just a little movement does an amazing thing to an optical illusion.

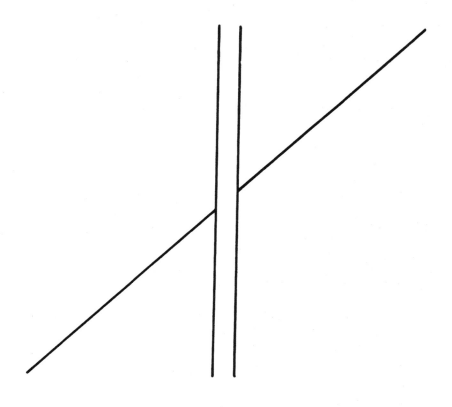

Three Arrows

For this illusion you need a glass that you can see through.

First, fill the glass part-way with water: then look at these three arrows. Copy these arrows onto a sheet of notebook paper. Place the arrows low on the page so that you can easily slip the paper behind the filled part of the glass.

Hold the paper with the arrows a few inches behind the water glass. Look through the glass of water at the arrows. Move the paper back and forth until the arrows come into focus.

The arrows get longer and shorter, because the curved water acts like a magnifying glass.

But what else do you see? Check the arrows you drew. The outside arrows point to the right, and the inside one points to the left. Now look through the water again.

Of course, the arrows didn't reverse themselves. They look this way because you're looking through the water rather than the air. The water does the same thing to the arrows that a convex lens does. A convex lens is the type with the bulged-out sides, and it reverses whatever you're looking at. The illustration below shows how the light enters the glass of water, and how it reaches your eye.

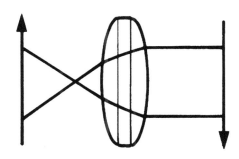

The Broken Pencil

While you have the water glass handy, find a pencil. Holding the pencil vertically, dip the point into the water.

Move either your head or the glass so that your eyes are directly in line with the surface of the water. The illustration below shows what you'll see. Once again, the "convex" water has bent the light, and the pencil in it.

Tip the pencil a little from side to side. Lift it up in the water just a bit.

Many years ago a state had a law that was based on this sort of optical illusion. The law said that a person who saw a crime committed on the other side of a glass window could not be a witness, because glass was convex and poorly made in those days. The glass created the illusion.

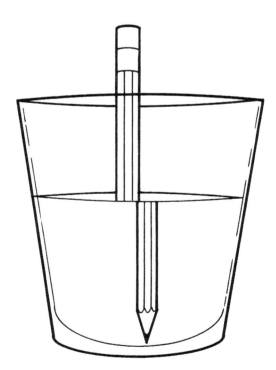

Two-Faced

Look at this illustration.
Now turn the page upside down and look at the drawing again.
See how much can change with just a little movement?

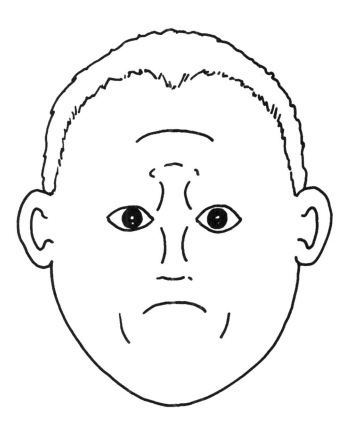

See-Throughs

The Pinwheel

There is nothing new about a pinwheel: these toys have been around for hundreds of years. However, there is something about this toy which you may never have realized.

First, let's make a pinwheel. You'll need a piece of square notebook or typing paper. To make a rectangular piece of paper square, fold the bottom corner up as shown in the illustration below on the left. Cut away the shaded part of the paper. Unfold the paper and you have a perfect square.

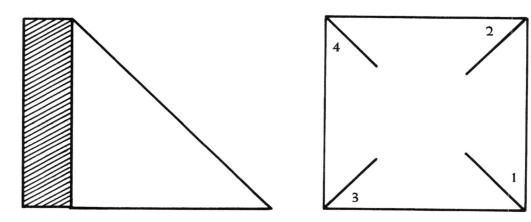

Make four cuts in this square piece of paper along the four dark lines as shown in the illustration above on the right. Each of these lines runs exactly halfway to the center.

The four lines in this same illustration each have a number. Begin with point 1 and bend (don't fold) it down to the middle of the paper. Push a pin through a point about 1/4 inch from the tip of the point.

Now bend point 2 over to the middle so that it is under point 1. Push the pin through it as well.

Do the same for points 3 and 4 and you have just about finished making your pinwheel.

It is a good idea to put a tiny dot of glue on the bottom of each point before adding the next point. This will keep the pinwheel's points together and make it spin better. If you don't have glue handy a little piece of transparent tape works just as well. Be sure to glue or tape the last point to the main part of the pinwheel.

Mount your pinwheel on a long pencil with an eraser. Just push the point of the pin into the eraser and the pencil becomes the handle of the pinwheel.

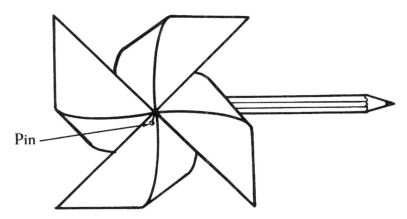

Pin

Hold the pinwheel in front of you so that the curved parts of the blades face forward. As you begin to walk, the wheel should spin, and the faster you walk, the faster it spins.

Now look at something in front of the pinwheel as it spins. You can look right through the spinning pinwheel blades and see perfectly.

Examine your pinwheel, and you can easily see there is just as much paper as there is open space. Yet when the pinwheel spins rapidly you can see perfectly through its blades. The solid part almost vanishes.

Once again, afterimage is the culprit. Your eyes are focused on the object behind the pinwheel, so you actually only see the pinwheel in fleeting glimpses. Since your mind is also focused on the object instead of the pinwheel, it holds onto this image as long as possible. By the time it fades, your eyes see the object between the pinwheel parts again.

The Spinning Disc

Make a disc about 6 inches across out of the side of a cereal box or some other stiff material. If you don't have a compass, just draw around a dish or the lid from a small pan.

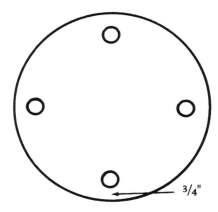

Now cut four round holes in the disc as in the illustration above. Each of these holes should be about the size of a nickel. Make the outside edge of each little hole about 3/4 inch from the outer edge of the disc.

Now make two very small holes as shown in the illustration below. Each of these holes must be exactly 1/2 inch from the center of the disc.

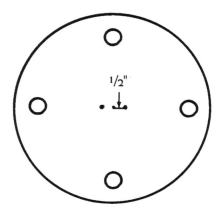

If you used a compass to draw your disc it is easy to find the center, but if not, trace around the disc on a sheet of paper. Cut out the paper circle which is the same size as your disc. Fold the circle in the middle

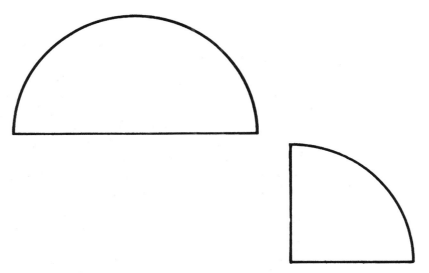

and crease the fold, so that it looks like the illustration above on the left. Fold it double again so that it looks like the illustration on the right. Place the curve of this folded paper over the outside of your disc, and the point of the paper is the center of the disc.

Cut a piece of string about 4 feet long. Run both ends through the holes near the center of the disc, and tie the loose ends together so that your disc looks like the illustration below.

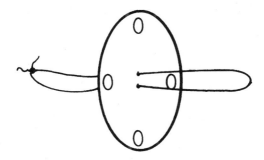

Slip two or three fingers into the loop at each end of the string. Spin the disc so that it makes a number of twists in the string. Be sure the disc remains at right angles to the string. The illustration below shows your disc ready to go.

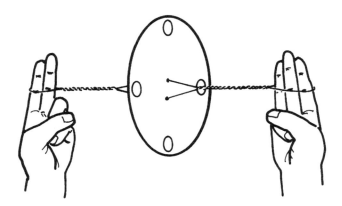

Pull your hands apart so that the disc spins as the string unwinds. Let its momentum start winding the string in the other direction. As this happens, allow your hands to begin to come together so that the string can wind up.

As the disc begins to slow, pull your hands apart and it will spin in the opposite direction. With practice, you can keep the disc spinning by moving your hands back and forth.

Now, look at the flat side of the spinning disc, and — surprise! Instead of seeing the four small holes flash past, there's a completely hollow ring. You can actually see through it as it spins.

If you have trouble keeping the disc at right angles, make one of thicker material, or, make two discs about 2 inches across, and glue one to each side of your disc around the center. Either way, all it takes is a bit of practice.

Narrow View

Moving optical illusions can take many forms. It's amazing to find out just what tricks our eyes can play on us.

Take a sheet of notebook or typing paper, and cut a narrow piece out of the middle of the paper so that it looks like the illustration below. The hole should be about 2 inches long and 1/4 inch wide.

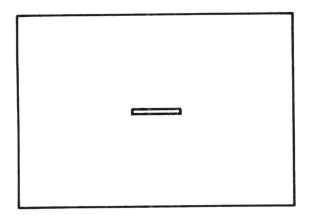

Lay the paper flat on any of the illustrations in this book. Be sure the narrow hole is over the middle of the picture. What do you see? Obviously, not much. Now begin moving the paper rapidly back and forth so that the opening slides up and down over the picture.

It takes only a few moves of the paper for you to realize that something strange is happening. You can actually see the entire picture, and the faster you move the paper, the clearer the picture becomes.

If you feel like experimenting, try this with another sheet of paper. This time make the narrow cut even narrower — less than 1/4 inch across. Keep the length 2 inches.

Can you still move the paper rapidly enough to see the picture? How small can you make the cut and still be able to see a picture under the sheet of paper?

See Through Grid

While you're looking through things, try a grid. This moving illusion has been around for many years. Your grandparents may have done it when they were children.

Start with a small piece of tracing paper. Tissue paper works well; even very thin typing paper works. Just check it by placing it over this page to make sure you can still see the print through the paper.

To make the grid, rule off a square about 2 inches in each direction of your see-through paper. Don't cut out the square because you need to have a little margin on at least one side to hold on to.

Draw parallel lines up and down every $\frac{1}{8}$ inch until you fill the square. Then draw another set of parallel lines across the square. These lines should also be $\frac{1}{8}$ inch apart. Your grid should now look like this:

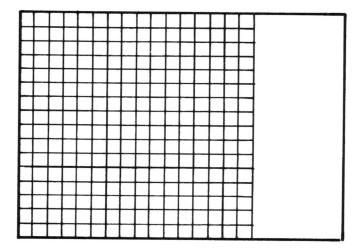

Now draw parallel diagonal lines every ⅛ inch from right to left across the square. Finish up the grid with a final series of parallel diagonal lines from left to right. The final grid is shown below.

Place the finished grid over this page. When you try to read what the page says through the grid, it is almost impossible.

Take hold of the edge of the grid paper where you left some margin around the grid. Begin moving the grid rapidly back and forth over the print you want to read.

What happens to the lines on the grid? What happens to the print on the page beneath the grid?

Afterimage strikes again. Remember, there *is* space between the lines. Once you focus on the page under the grid your brain will try to help you see the page as clearly as possible. When the grid moves, your eyes will focus on the page and your brain ignores the lines that move back and forth. So, when your eyes see the grid , your brain still holds the afterimage, and as it fades, your eyes see the object again.

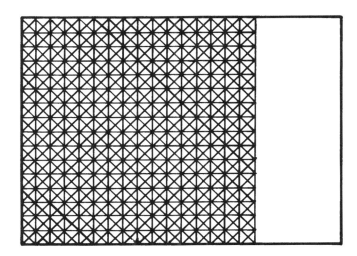

Seen Under Glass

Place a small, flat object on the table or on the countertop. A coin works fine: so does a paper clip or even a small piece of paper.

On top of this object, set a glass. Be sure that this is a clear glass that you can see through. Look through the glass from the top and the sides. Of course, you see the object beneath the glass.

Now fill the glass with water. Get it as full as you can without spilling. Set it on top of the object. Look through the glass full of water. You'll see the object under the glass again. So, where is the illusion?

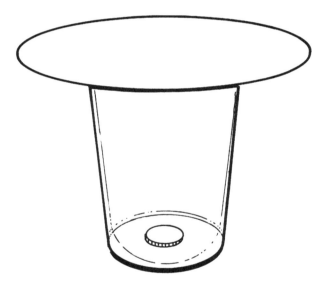

Place a saucer or a plastic lid from a butter tub on top of the glass, as shown above. Look through the side of the glass.

Remember that when light rays pass through water they are bent or turned at a different angle. When the saucer is on top of the glass the light rays which bend towards the top of the glass hit the saucer, shutting them in. The light rays from the coin can't be seen, so it seems to have vanished.

Strange Motion

Cut a circle 5 inches or so across from the side of a cereal carton. Any stiff material works fine but cereal cartons are usually pretty easy to find.

Make the cut shown below.

Be careful when you poke the point of your scissors through the cardboard. You want a hole in the cardboard, not your finger.

The little cut should be 1 inch long, 1/8 inch wide, and about 1/2 inch from the outside of the cardboard disc.

Next find the exact center of the disc and make a small hole there. If you forgot how to find the circle's center, look back at page 173. It works every time.

Push a pencil through the center so that it looks like the illustration below.

Hold the pencil between your hands. Keep both hands flat and press them together firmly against the pencil.

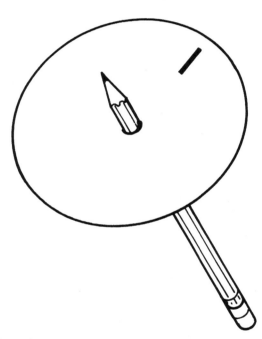

Move your hands rapidly up and down, so that the pencil spins back and forth between your hands. When the pencil spins, the disc will spin as well.

If the disc slips on the pencil use several pieces of tape to fasten it to the main part of the pencil.

Start a record turntable without a record on it. Place a piece of paper or cardboard on one side of the turntable, as shown here.

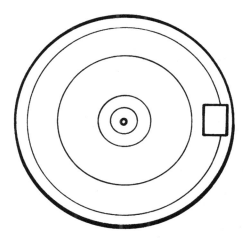

As the turntable turns, spin the disc between your hands. Look directly at the turntable through the narrow little slit in the disc. What's happening to the paper on the turntable? Is it actually jumping back and forth? It can't be.

Try spinning your disc faster or slower to see how this affects the way the paper on the turntable seems to act.

Do you have fluorescent lights around you? These are the ones which have the long tubes. Lots of classrooms have them.

Look at a fluorescent light through your spinning disc. If you get the speed just right you can get the light to blink on and off like a flashing strobe light you would see at a concert or disco.

Spots and
Colors

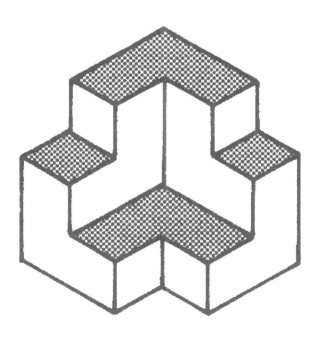

The Case of the Moving Spots

Look at this illustration. Everywhere white lines meet, you should see something interesting.

Obviously those grey dots are not part of the picture. Therefore, they have to be an optical illusion. Now, let's make them move.

Stare directly at one of the grey dots. What happens to it? Where does it go?

Try another of the grey dots. Look directly at it. Does it also vanish?

Floaters

Make a tiny hole in a piece of paper or a white file card. This is called a pinhole. If the hole you make is a little larger than a pinhole, that is just fine.

Now hold the tiny hole up to your eye. Stare at a light through the hole. *Don't stare at the sun.* A shaded lamp should be bright enough. The illustration below shows how to manage this.

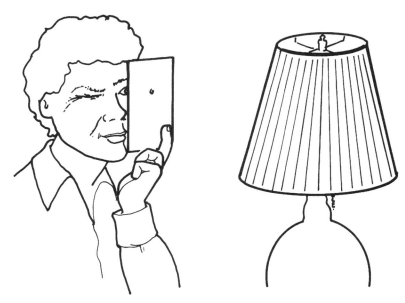

Close the eye not looking through the pinhole, and focus on the hole itself; you will begin to see slow-moving little circles or rings.

After a minute check your other eye. The same sorts of hollow little circles should appear.

These slowly moving little fellows are called floaters. They actually move inside your eyeball. These tiny floaters are normal and do not mean anything is wrong with your eyes. From time to time little cells inside the eye come free and float in the liquid which fills your eyeball. That's why they're called floaters.

Most people have another kind of floater inside their eyes. The way to check for these is to look down at the floor for a few seconds; then quickly raise your head and look at a light-colored wall. You may see one or more tiny little dark-colored objects which seem to be between you and the wall.

Don't worry if you can't see any floaters. Older people are more likely to have them than children, and some young people don't seem to have them at all. Remember, though, when you glance up and suddenly see a few little moving spots out in space the funny little dark spots really are inside your eye.

I don't think I'm supposed to see that!

Colorful Illusion

Begin by making a bright orange triangle on a white piece of paper. A triangle about 1 inch high is a good size.

Now make a card with a pinhole and, holding the orange triangle out in front of you, peer through the hole in the card as shown here.

What happens to the brightness of the orange triangle? Did the color fade or is it just an illusion?

Try this one. On a white piece of paper make a solid red square, about 1 inch across. Stare directly at it for about thirty seconds; then look away and focus on a white piece of paper or a white wall. Within a few seconds a square will appear. But it won't be red!

Now color a green circle on a piece of white paper. It's okay to use the paper with the red square, but fold the red square over out of sight. Stare at it intently for half a minute; then look at a sheet of clean white paper. What color is it?

Do the same thing with the orange triangle you made before. Stare at it; see what color the orange triangle becomes when you look away.

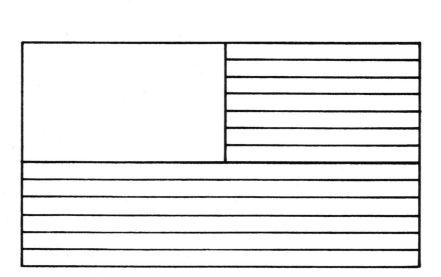

The illustration above should be familiar to you. Make the outline of the flag about 6½ inches high x 10 inches. The smaller rectangle at the upper left should be about 5 inches wide and 3½ inches high. Each of the 13 bands should be exactly ½ inch wide.

Color the small rectangle orange; then color the top band green and the second band black, alternating the bands, green and black, all the way to the bottom. You will end up with the bottom band colored green. There should be seven green bands and six black bands. Make your colors good and dark. Somehow it doesn't look right, does it?

Now, stare intently at the finished picture for about thirty seconds; then look away at a sheet of white paper or a white wall. It should look a little more familiar now. If you want, add some black dots to the orange field. Alternate five rows of six dots with four rows of five dots. If you begin and end with a row of six dots, you've done it perfectly.

This is a project you will probably want to put up on your wall or bulletin board. Place a sheet of white paper beside it so that others can see the illusion move from the original to the plain white page.

Spinning Colors

About 150 years ago some German scientists discovered a way to make black and white drawings look colorized. They discovered a disc that is still a great illusion today.

The first disc you will make is shown here.

Make this disc as large as you wish, but 3½ inches across is a good size. Use any stiff white material (a 4 x 5-inch file card is perfect).

If you don't have stiff white cardboard, make your circle on white paper, color it, and cut it out. Glue or tape it to any stiff material (like a cereal box).

A soft-tipped marker is excellent for coloring, but a black crayon will also do the job.

Color half the disc solid black; then put in the two sets of curved black lines. A compass or the edge of a round object can help with these curved lines.

Try to space the curves evenly. Draw them in pencil first; then go over the pencil lines with marker or crayon. If the spaces between the lines are not exactly the same the project will still work, so don't panic. Once the disc is colored it is time to see whether those German scientists knew what they were talking about.

First we need to spin the disc. There are three ways to do this.

One is to stick a straight pin through the center of the disc, making sure the head of the pin is at the front (so the disc won't spin off). Hold the pointed end of the pin tightly, and use your other hand to do the spinning.

A second way to spin is to push the point of a pencil through the disc's center. Hold the pencil between your palms and rub your hands back and forth. This spins the disc quickly in one direction, then back in the other. A straight-sided pencil works better than a round one. A couple of pieces of tape to attach the back of the disc to the sides of the pencil should also help.

The third way is to use the string spinner. If you forgot how to make one of these, look back at page 172. If you have any trouble keeping the spinner upright, just use a couple of pieces of tape on the back of the spinner so that the tape sticks to the strings as they go through the spinner. The illustration below shows how to do this.

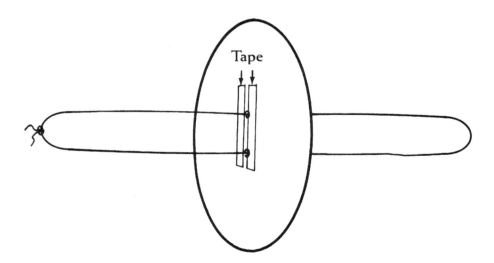

Give your disc a good spin. Watch what happens to the black and white design. If you don't see the colors at first, don't give up. Spin it some more, and take a good look.

You should see brown and blue appear. When the disc turns one way, the brown is towards the outside of the disc. When it spins the other way, blue is outside. Check it for yourself.

The illustration below shows another black and white disc which will turn to different colors when it spins. Make it the same way you made the previous disc.

When this disc spins, you should be able to spot the colors of blue, green, and brown. Just like the first disc, the colors change positions when you reverse the direction of the spin.

Color Wheel

You have probably seen a color wheel in the art room at school. It shows colors in special order. It's also an interesting spinning optical illusion.

Make a disc 3½ inches across. This time make it exact, because 3½ inches across is lots easier to divide into 21 equal parts. That's right, 21.

Use a ruler to measure along the outside of the disc and place a dot every ½ inch. If all goes well you will finish with 21 equal spaces. If the last space is a tiny bit larger or smaller than the others, it won't ruin the project.

The illustration on the facing page shows the disc with all those lines in place. It also tells what color to use in coloring each section of the disc.

Color each section of the disc according to this key: W=white, R=red, O=orange, Y=yellow, G=green, B=blue, and V=violet (purple). Colored pencils are easier to use than crayons, but crayons will do the job if you have a steady hand.

Once the disc is colored, give it a spin. As it moves faster and faster, you will see it change color. If you can get the disk to spin fast enough you will see only a white disc. More likely you will see a very light tan or even a light grey.

When the disc stops, there are all those colors, still in place. The light color was just another optical illusion.

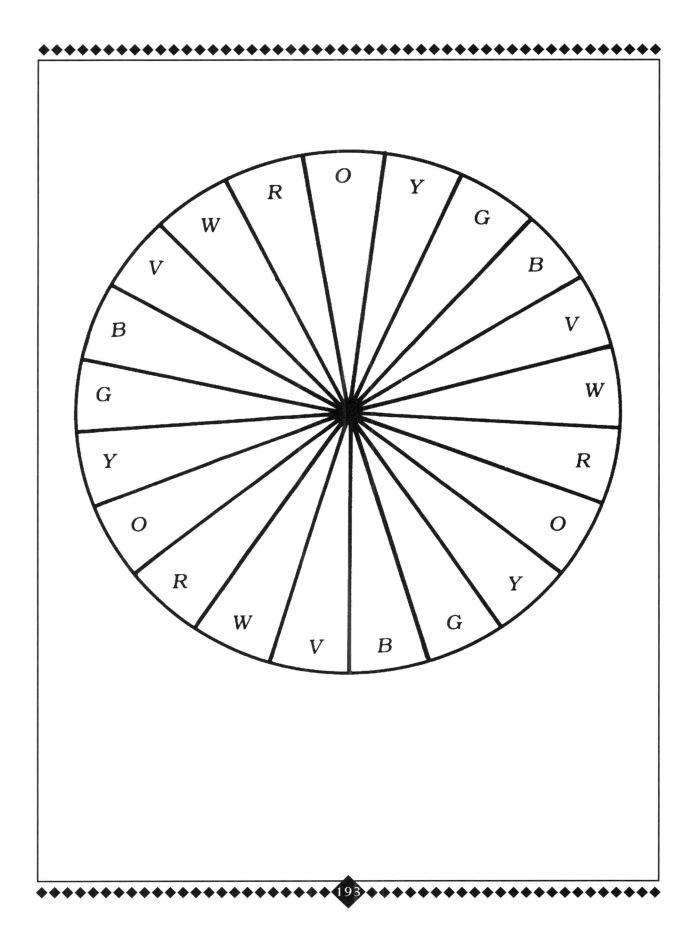

More Visual Trickery

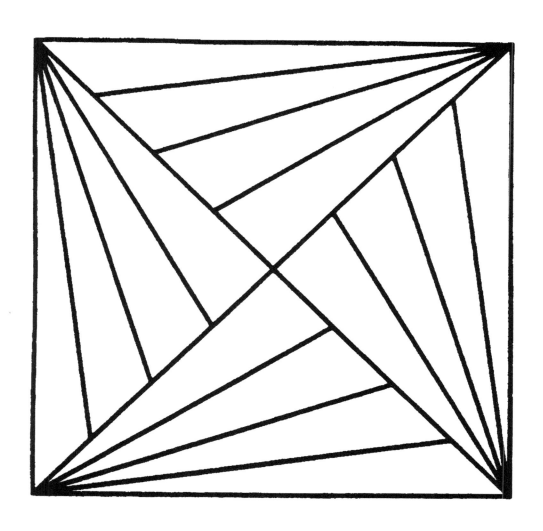

How many triangles can you find in this design?

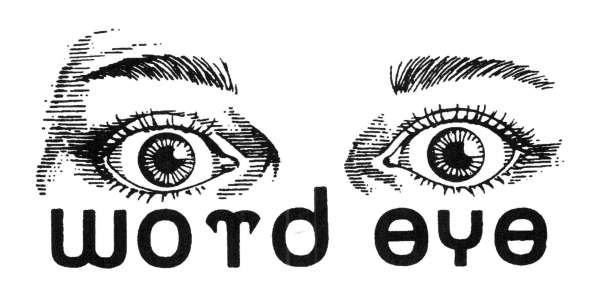

Look at the reflection of this picture in a mirror. You will see a word that is connected with your eyes. What is it?

a. Which lizard is longer?

b. The heart is closer to which end of the line?

Is the middle square bulging out?

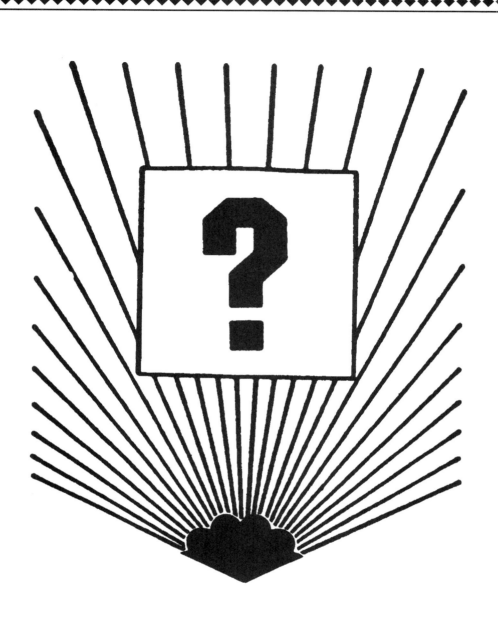

How about this square? Is it narrower on top?

What is unusual about this picture?

This student was very bright. Years later he became a professor. What do you think he looks like now?

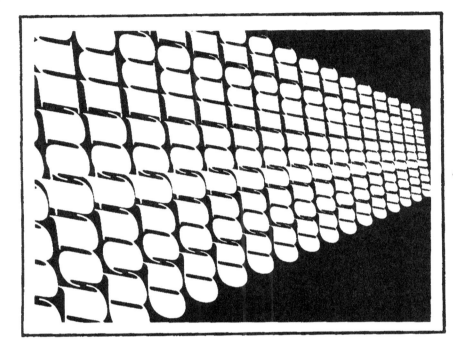

Is this a series of abstract shapes—or a message?

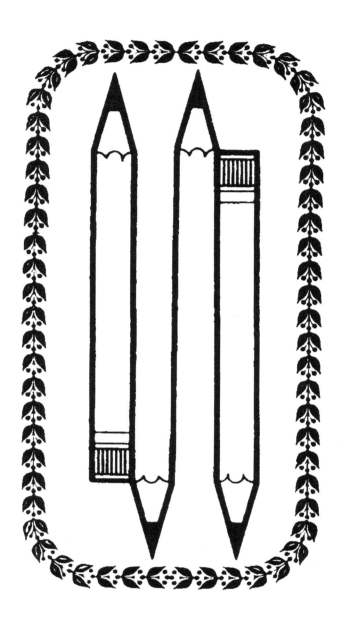

Can you use these disappearing pencils for writing secret messages?

This girl is enjoying the Magic Show, but where is the magician?

Which of these flowers has the larger center?

What's wrong with this picture?

Can you find this baby's mother?

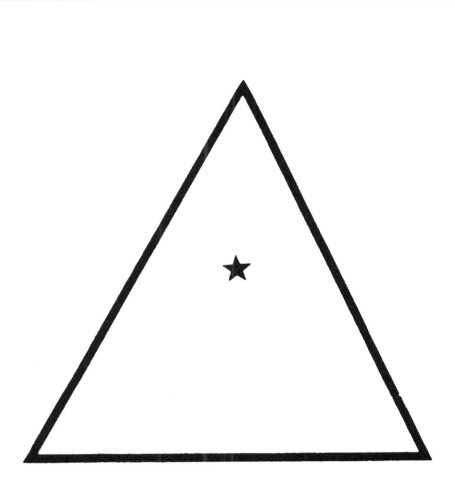

Is the star midway between the point and the base of the triangle?
Or is it too high up?

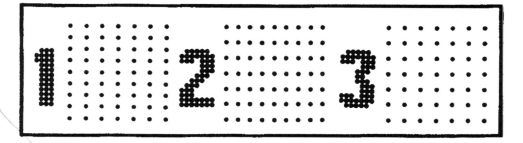

The dots in #1 seem to be arranged in vertical lines.
The dots in #2 seem to be arranged in horizontal lines.
How do you see the dots in #3?

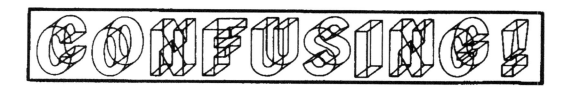

The transparent type face used to form the word CONFUSION is called "Bombere." What is unusual about it?

a. What's special about these ducks?

b. What is this word? The dots are missing from the I's.

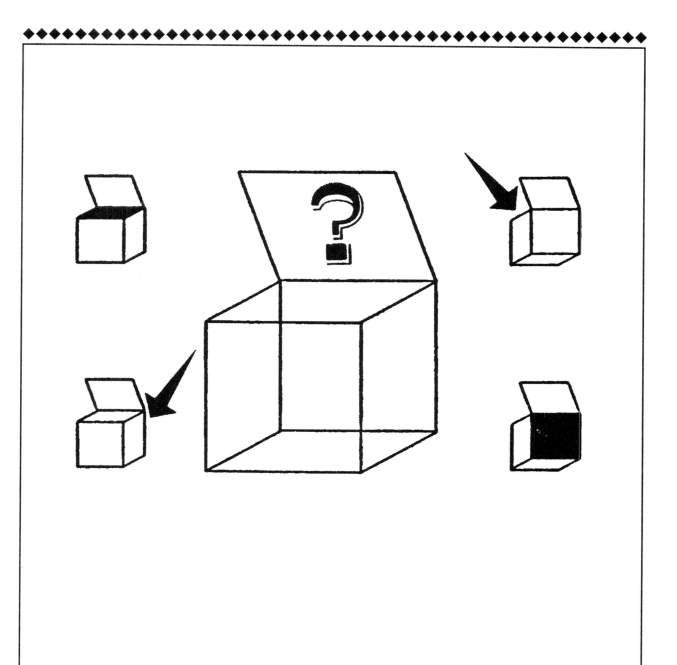

Which way should this box open?

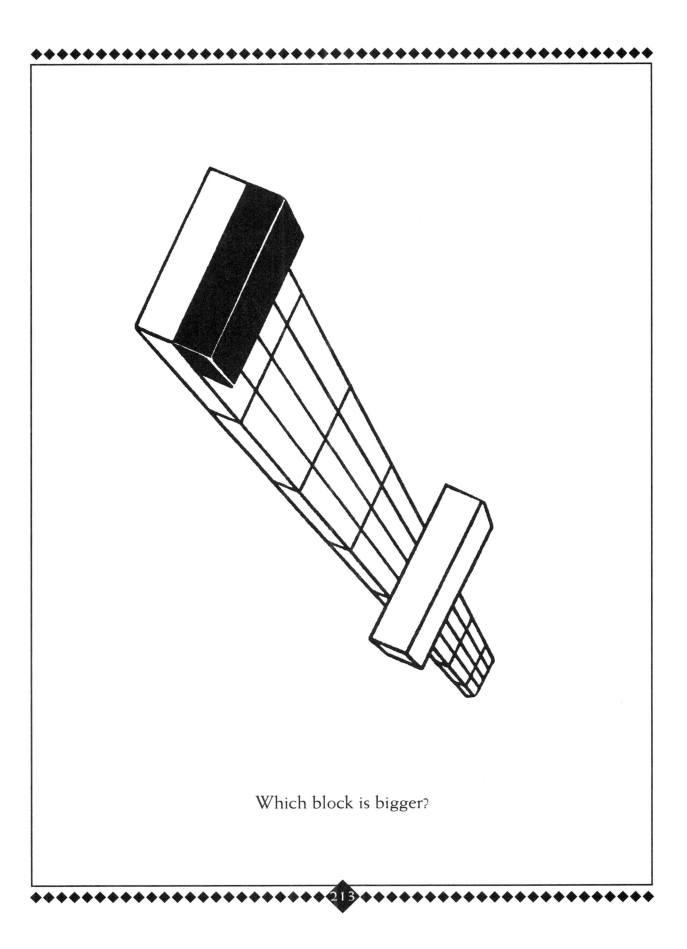

Which block is bigger?

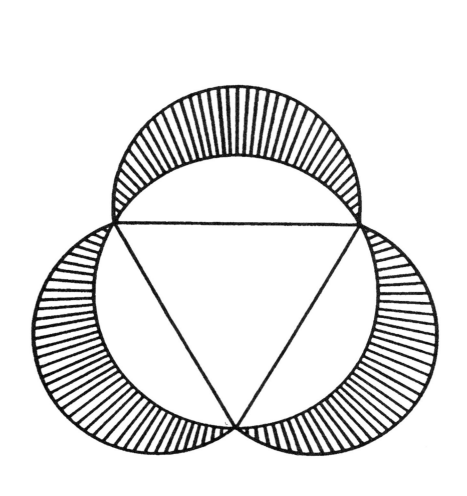

Is the white circle perfect, or is it crimped at the points
of the triangle?

This picture conceals the faces of two men. Can you find them?

Do you think the sides of the cloister arches are disjointed?
Or do they join up?

We read this sign as THE CAT, but the middle letters of each word
are identical. Yet we see them as H in THE and A in CAT.
Why is this?

What is the matter with the hoop that Geoffrey is holding?

What is this picture?

Is the square sagging at the right?

Which way are the letters facing? Are they pointing down
to the right or up to the left?

The patient is worried because his dentist is telling him that a tooth has to be pulled. How can he keep it from hurting?

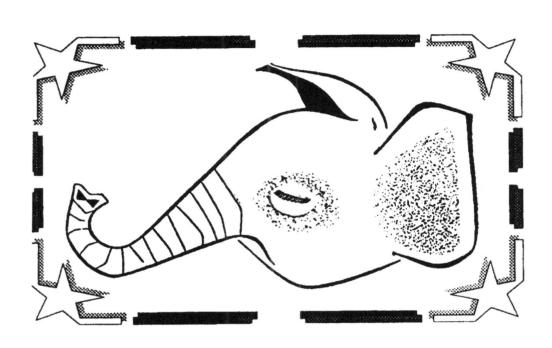

Jumbo the elephant is sad. Can you think of a way to cheer him up?

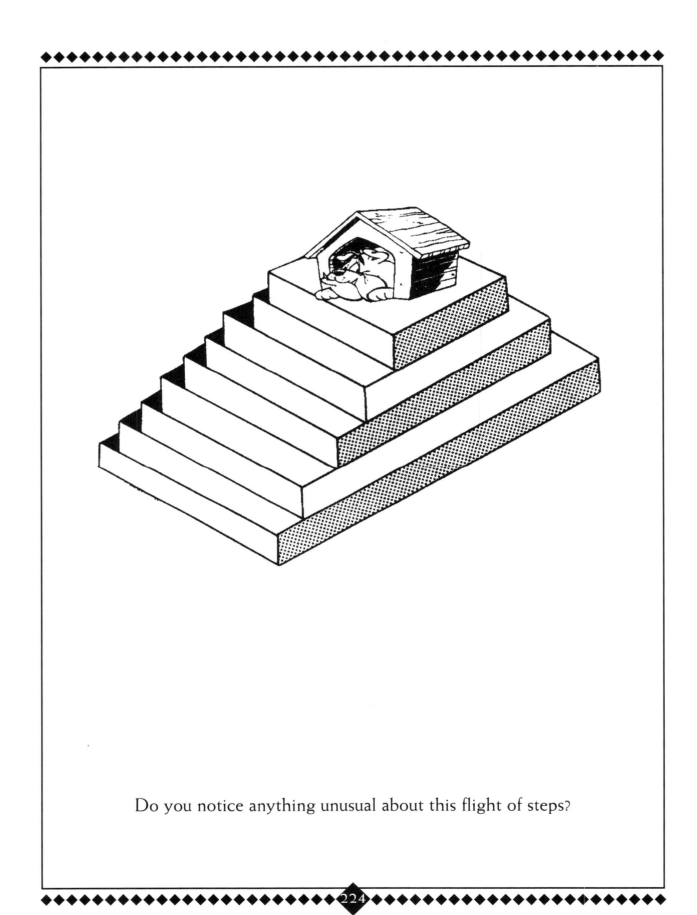

Do you notice anything unusual about this flight of steps?

This fellow helps Santa Claus. But where is Santa hiding?

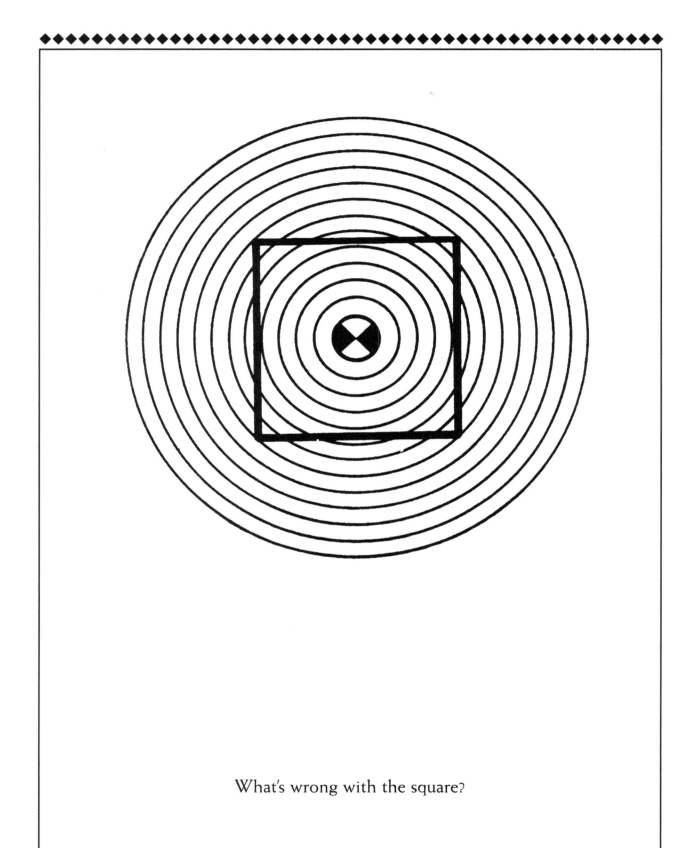

What's wrong with the square?

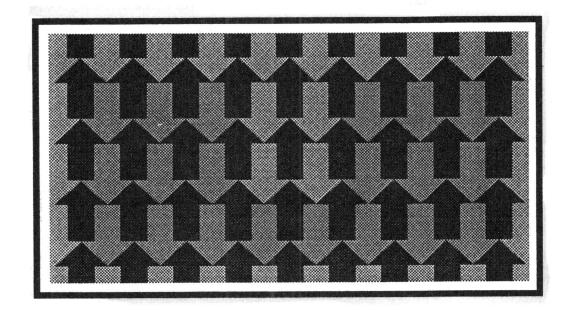

Which is it — dark arrows pointing upwards or light arrows
pointing downwards?

This soldier is looking for his horse. Any idea where it is?

BED	GREEN	DICE	RAIN
PEACE	EXCEDE	LION	DECK
BOX	CIRCLE	CODE	CHAIR
SWAN	CHICK	SMALL	CHOKED
DIXIE	DAISY	HOOD	CAT

Using a mirror, turn this page upside down and look at the reflection of the letters. It's odd that all the words in the black panels can be read easily — but not those in the white panels. How and why do you think this happens?

What is special about this diagram?

Are these balls the same size?

Meet Barnacle Bill, the old sailor. What did he look like when
he was young?

Rotate the page in a circular motion. What happens?

Which set of faces is larger?

Is this a block with a piece cut out? Or a block with a piece stuck on?

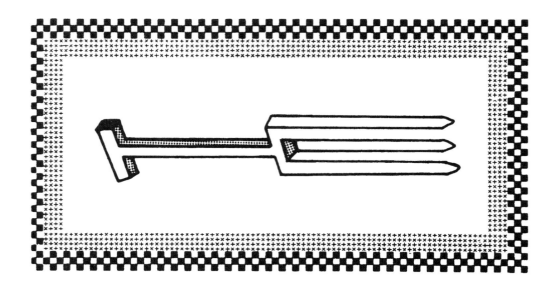

How many prongs are there on this fork? Do you see two or three?

What is this picture?

This sketch is based on "Death and the Bourgeois," which was drawn in the 18th century by Mathaus Merian the Elder. How do you think the painting got its name?

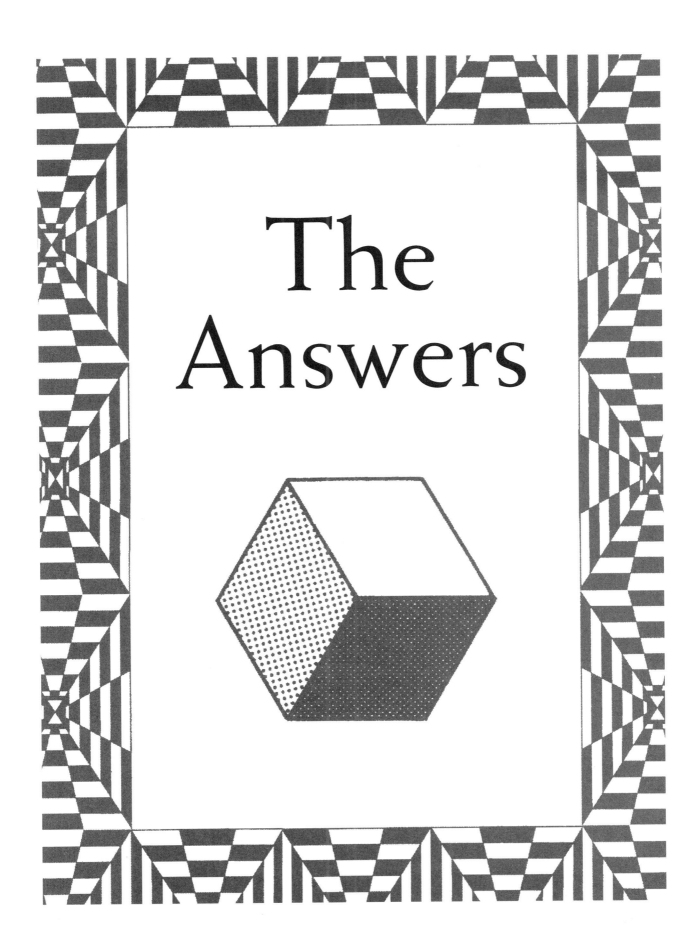

Page 8: Illusion. This is an impossible creation.

Page 10: Never. This is a trick drawing.

Page 11: There is no way to tell. The twin with the horizontal stripes seems to be fatter, but he really isn't. Our eyes follow the lines in his suit, so the twin on the right seems broader and shorter than his brother.

Page 12: No, but it seems higher and wider in the back because of the way it has been drawn. We expect the back of it to be further away and to look smaller. Since it is the same size, we automatically assume it is bigger in the back.

Page 13, top: Both are possible. It depends on how you look at it.

Page 13, bottom: No. But it seems to be, because "b" is in a larger area.

Page 14: They are all the same height. The man at the right looks tallest. We expect things to look smaller when they are farther away. The man at the right is farthest away and we would expect him to look the smallest. Since he doesn't, we assume he's really larger than the others.

Page 15: The dot-shaped cross is just to the right of the center of the diagram. It spells out "R-I-G-H-T." It may take you a while to find it, because the other dots distract your attention.

Page 16, top: They are the same length. Our eyes follow the lines. The "a" line seems to expand because of the "wings" on the ends. Line "b" is cut off by its arrowheads, so it looks shorter.

Page 16, bottom: Exactly. They seem longer in relation to their surroundings.

Pages 17–21:

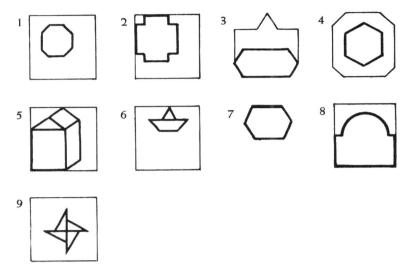

Page 22: A triangle with equal sides.

Page 23, top: They are all the same size.

Page 23, bottom: Line "a" equals "b" and "c" equals "d." Line "a" seems longer than "b" because we unconsciously add the circles on the end of the line to it's length. The same is true of line "c" with its open square.

Page 24: In "a" — both are the same size, but the white one seems larger. When bright light falls on the retina of our eyes (where the nerve cells are), more nerve fibres react than had actually been hit by the light. This causes a "spreading effect," and the light object seems larger than it actually is. In "b," the black circle is actually larger, although both seem to be the same size.

Page 25: Each egg fits into all the egg cups.

Pages 26 and 27: The inner circles are the same size. The one on the right looks smaller because we usually judge the size of an object by contrasting it with the objects around it.

Pages 28 and 29: Both grey areas have the same intensity. The white lines, though, make the area on the left seem brighter.

Page 30, top: Measure it. The curved lines force our eyes to move to the left of the true center.

Page 30, bottom: It is exactly in the center.

Page 31, top: The cross-bars are exactly in the center of the triangles.

Page 31, bottom: No, they are both the same size. This is another example of the difficulty of judging size when angles are involved.

Page 32: Both circles are the same size. The arrows pull our eyes inwards in the top circle, and our eyes follow the arrows outwards in the lower one.

Page 33: All the objects are the same length.

Page 36:

Page 37: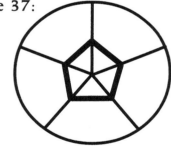

Page 38: No. To best visualize her path, let's undo the cube into its component flattened faces. From this diagram, you can see that the shortest distance between two points is a straight line. That line does not coincide with her planned path (shown as a dotted line).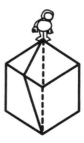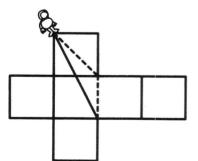

Page 39:

Page 39, bottom:

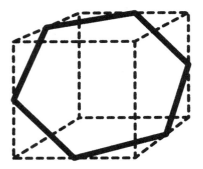

Page 40: Just open the bottom link. The top two links are not attached to each other.

Page 41: It will come free of the pipe. To visualize this action, start at the pipe. From there, trace the pipe's path out from the center. After a few turns, the pipe exits freely at the opening on the right side of the maze.

Page 42:

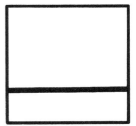

Page 43: Part I: Twenty-two sides. Part II: Thirty-six sides.

Page 44: C.

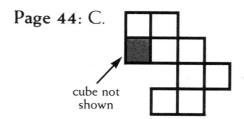

cube not
shown

Page 45, top: B is the only pattern that will produce a four-sided triangular pyramid.

Page 45, bottom: Six. At every half hour of the journey, you'll pass an incoming train. If you count the inbound train in the Metropolis station and don't count the inbound train in the Gotham City station, you'll pass six trains.

Page 46: 27 triangles: 16 one-cell triangles, 7 four-cell triangles, 3 nine-cell triangles, and 1 sixteen-cell triangle.

Page 47:

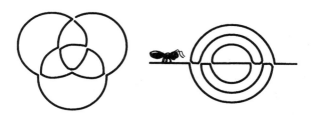

Page 48: Eighteen, but you don't have to trace out each one. The easiest way to solve this puzzle is to start at the beginning and determine the number of paths that can get you to an intersection. The number of paths to each successive intersection is equal to the sum of the paths that are "attached" to it.

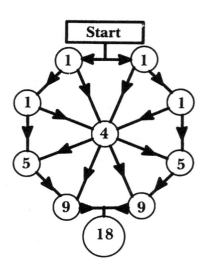

Page 49, top: 21. As you move clockwise around the circle, the number on each section is equal to the sum of the two previous sections.

Page 49, bottom: Fifteen handshakes. The first person would have shaken hands five times. The next person only needed to make four handshakes, since the handshake with one person had already been completed. The next person required only three, and so on. That gives us $5+4+3+2+1=15$.

Page 50: E.

Page 51: 56 pages. Here's how the numbers are arranged on each double sheet.

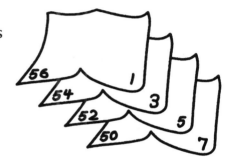

Page 52: Cubes A and D.

Page 53: Pattern D.

Page 54, top: Since they have the same number of teeth, they will spin at the same speed. Cog C does not affect the rate of teeth passage; it only transfers the passage of teeth from cog B to cog D.

Page 54, bottom: The bottom-row center hand is unlike the others. It alone is a right hand.

Page 55: No, the belts are arranged in a pattern that doesn't allow them to move.

Page 56: D.

Page 57: The dial arrow located in the middle of the bottom row is most unusual. In contrast to the rest, it has two heads and only one tail.

Page 60:

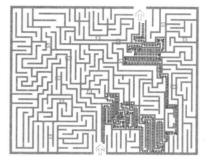

Page 61:

Page 62:

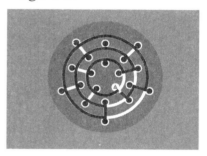

Page 64:

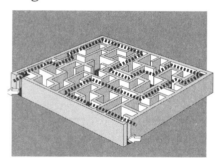

Page 65:

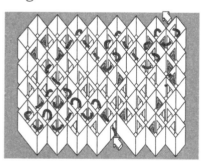

Page 66:

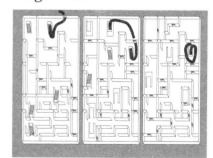

Page 67:

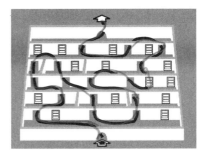

Page 68:

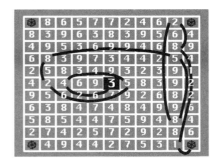

Page 69:

Page 71:

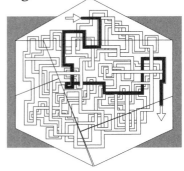

Page 72:

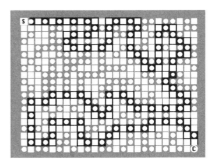

Page 73:

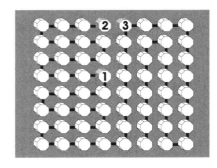

Page 76: It depends on which you saw first—the horizontal A, B, C, or the verticle 12, 13, 14.

Page 77: The ball appears to spin around!

Page 78: You see a black skull in a white frame.

Page 79: The three donkeys have only three ears between them!

Page 80: Either one. The design reverses.

Page 81: Look at the left-hand side of the picture.

Page 82: Both. The design "flip-flops."

Page 83: The girl feeds the goose.

Page 84: Guess first, and then use a ruler to line up the lines. Yes, it's "Y".

Page 85: First count the flames — 5. Now count the base of each candle, and you'll find there are 7.

Page 86: His mouth looks like a bird and his eyes and nose look like a bat.

Page 87: Turn the page upside down to find the answer. It says "Life."

Page 88: Take your pick!

Page 89: Joseph Stalin.

Page 90: Take your pick!

Page 91: Actually, the back wheel has been drawn as an oval shape, to give the picture the correct perspective.

Page 92: This is an example of "closure." Your brain fills in the missing bits.

Page 93: The two cards are the Eight of Clubs and the Queen of Hearts.

Page 94: Between them, these strange fish have only one head.

Page 95: Each tube can be seen to open in different directions.

Page 96: Look closely and you'll find profiles of Adam and Eve.

Page 97: It's an impossible elephant. Look at its legs — can you figure them out?

Page 98: Either one.

Page 99: Turn the page so that the arrow points upwards, and you'll see a scene from the circus.

Page 100: Close one eye and bring the other eye close to the page. The checkerboard will straighten out.

Page 101: Turn him upside down.

Pages 102 and 103: You can see this any way you want.

Page 104: The wheels on the bicycle appear to spin and revolve.

Page 105: They are both the same size, but the white one looks larger because darker things seem smaller than lighter ones.

Page 106: Either one — this is another illusion where the design flip-flops.

Page 107: A beggar holding out a hand — or the profile of a goofy face.

Page 108: They are both the same size, but the curves make #1 look larger.

Page 109: No, it's a series of circles within circles. Check it by tracing them with your finger. This illusion is known as the Fraser Spiral.

Page 110: They form an impossible triangle! The idea was first drawn in Sweden in 1934 by Oscar Reutersvard.

Page 111: It depends on how you look at it.

Page 112: Because this pattern can be viewed from either direction, the brain alternates from one view to the other.

Page 113: After you make a guess, use a ruler to check. In this illusion, the outside lines help to convince us that the bottom fish is bigger.

Page 114: To find out, turn the page upside down.

Page 115: Each circle will seem to revolve on its axis. The inner cog wheel will appear to rotate in the opposite direction.

Page 138:

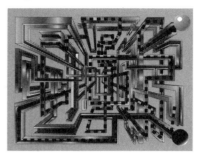

Page 139:

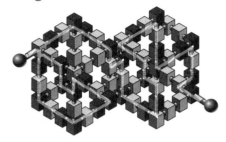

Page 140:

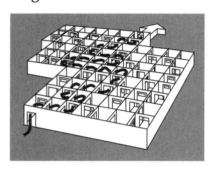

Page 141:

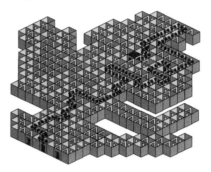

Page 142:

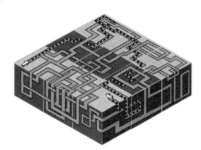

Page 143:

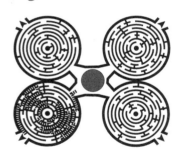

Page 144:

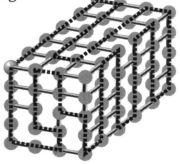

Page 145:

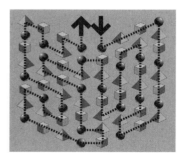

Page 146:

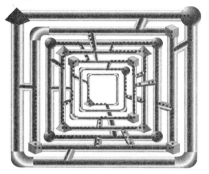

Page 147:

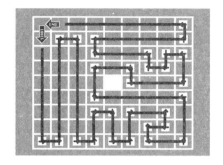

Page 148:

Page 149:

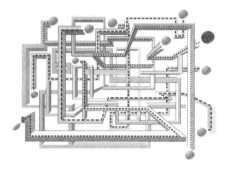

Page 150:

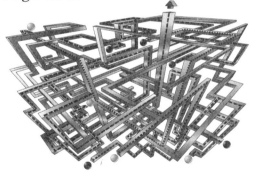

Page 151:

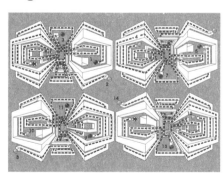

Page 196: 56.

Page 197: Eye brow.

Page 198, a: They are the same size, but the arrows make us think that the lower lizard is bigger than its friend.

Page 198, b: Believe it or not, the little heart is right in the center of the line. If you don't believe it, take a ruler and measure.

Page 199: No, it just looks that way. The vertical and horizontal lines form a perfect square. It's the backgound lines that make it seem as if they are bulging out.

Page 200: No, it too is a perfect square. The background lines are what make the top look narrower.

Page 201: This picture has not been finished, but our brain finishes it for us. We are able to visualize the edges of the pages of this stack of books. This is another example of "closure."

Page 202: Turn the page upside down to see.

Page 203: Turn the page so that the arrow points upward, and you will see one word repeated across the design.

Page 204: These are impossible pencils, so that while you can draw them, you can't use them!

Page 205: Turn the page upside down to find him.

Page 206: It looks like the one on the right, but they are both the same size. What tricks us is the petals around the center.

Page 207: Turn on the light — it's the impossible candelabra! A number of the holders seem to be suspended in mid-air!

Page 208: If you turn the page upside down and look very carefully, you will see the mother's head. The baby's diaper becomes the mother's bandanna.

Page 209: Guess first, then measure. The star is midway between the point and the base.

Page 210, a: They can be seen as either vertical or horizontal.

Page 210, b: The letters flip-flop, so that we can see them pointing up to the right or down to the left.

Page 211, a: Place a small coin on the head of duck #1, and the ducks will seem to move to the right. Now place the coin on the head of duck #2, and the ducks will travel to the left.

Page 211, b: "Minimum."

Page 212: You can make this box open in many different ways— depending on which way you want it to open.

Page 213: The blocks are exactly the same size, though the white one looks bigger. This is another illusion in which the background design confuses us.

Page 214: It's perfect.

Page 215: Turn the page upside down. They're bordering the stem of the glass.

Page 216: They join up perfectly.

Page 217: Our brain is trying to make sense of what we see, so it leaps ahead, closes up the top of the second H, and reads it as an A.

Page 218: The hoop is actually a circle shape, but here it has been drawn as an oval to give the picture the correct perspective.

Page 219: A mouse — or a man's head.

Page 220: No, it's a perfect square. It looks like it's sagging because of the diagonal lines.

Page 221: Either way. This is another design that flip-flops.

Page 222: Slowly bring the page close to your face, and then slowly take the page away from it. There you are — a painless extraction!

Page 223: Just turn the picture upside down.

Page 224: Yes, it's impossible. Count the number of steps. You'll count either 9 or 5 or 3.

Page 225: Turn the page upside down to find him.

Page 226: Nothing, it's perfect — but the sides of it look as if they are bending in. That's because of the background of circles.

Page 227: Either one.

Page 228: To find it, just turn the page upside down.

Page 229: The words in the black panels have horizontal symmetry. That means the letters have the same shape on the top and on the bottom.

Page 230: It is a "magic square." Each horizontal line adds up to 264 — and so do the vertical and diagonal lines. It also works if you turn it upside down!

Page 231: Yes, but they look different because of the way they have been placed in the angle.

Page 232: Turn the page upside down to see what he looked like.

Page 233: A small grey disk appears in the center of the spokes.

Page 234: Both sets are the same, but lighter objects look bigger than darker ones.

Page 235: Either one.

Page 236: It's an impossible fork! You couldn't make one, but maybe you can draw it…

Page 237: A black cat down a coal mine eating a stick of licorice at midnight.

Page 238: Turn the picture upside down to see how the painting got its name.

Index

GIANT BOOK OF PENCIL PUZZLES

By
PETER GORDON, MIKE SHENK,
MAYME ALLEN, JANINE KELSCH,
MARK DANNA, JAMES RICHARD SUIKACH,
& The DIAGRAM GROUP

Sterling Publishing Company, Inc.
New York

10 9 8 7 6 5 4 3 2

Published In 1999 by Sterling Publishing Company, Inc.
387 Park Avenue South, New York, N.Y. 10016

Material in this collection was adapted from
Solitaire Battleships
© Peter Gordon and Mike Shenk
Little Giant Encyclopedia of mazes
© The Diagram Group
101 Word Games
© Mayme Allen and Janine Kelsch
Word Search Puzzles for Kids
© Mark Danna
and
Challenging Whodunit Puzzles
© James Richard Sukach

Distributed in Canada by Sterling Publishing
c/o Canadian Manda Group
One Atlantic Avenue, Suite 105
Toronto, Ontario, Canada M6K 3E7

Distributed in Great Britain and Europe by Cassell PLC
Wellington House, 125 Strand
London WC2R 0BB, United Kingdom

Distibuted in Australia by Capricorn Link (Australia) Pty Ltd.
P.O. Box 6651, Baulkham Hills, Business Centre,
NSW 2153, Australia

CONTENTS

TRICKY TRIOS

GENERAL INSTRUCTIONS

For the games that follow, list as many words as you can, using the designated letters in the sequence specified. You can use only one form of each word—for example, *telegraph* shouldn't also be listed as *telegraphing*. Words with different meanings, however, such as *desert* and *desertion*, can be used, even if they have the same root. No proper nouns allowed in these games.

Solutions—Pages 207-209

1 "EGR"

The letters "egr" appear in this sequence in at least 25 words—list as many as you can.

_____ _____ _____
_____ _____ _____
_____ _____ _____
_____ _____ _____
_____ _____ _____
_____ _____ _____
_____ _____ _____
_____ _____ _____
_____ _____ _____

2 "OXY"

The letters "oxy" appear in this sequence in at least 21 words—list as many as you can.

_____ _____ _____
_____ _____ _____
_____ _____ _____
_____ _____ _____
_____ _____ _____
_____ _____ _____
_____ _____ _____

3 "ADI"

The letters "adi" appear in this sequence in at least 90 words—list as many as you can.

_____ _____ _____

4 "ERT"

The letters "ert" appear in this sequence in at least 115 words—list as many as you can.

_____   _____   _____
_____   _____   _____
_____   _____   _____
_____   _____   _____
_____   _____   _____
_____   _____   _____
_____   _____   _____
_____   _____   _____
_____   _____   _____
_____   _____   _____
_____   _____   _____
_____   _____   _____
_____   _____   _____
_____   _____   _____
_____   _____   _____
_____   _____   _____
_____   _____   _____
_____   _____   _____
_____   _____   _____
_____   _____   _____
_____   _____   _____
_____   _____   _____
_____   _____   _____
_____   _____   _____
_____   _____   _____

5 "AZI"

The letters "azi" appear in this sequence in at least 19 words—list as many as you can.

6 "OQU"

The letters "oqu" appear in this sequence in at least 16 words—list as many as you can.

_____	_____	_____
_____	_____	_____
_____	_____	_____
_____	_____	_____
_____	_____	_____
_____	_____	_____

7 "ICO"

The letters "ico" appear in this sequence in at least 95 words—list as many as you can.

_____	_____	_____
_____	_____	_____
_____	_____	_____
_____	_____	_____
_____	_____	_____
_____	_____	_____
_____	_____	_____
_____	_____	_____
_____	_____	_____
_____	_____	_____
_____	_____	_____
_____	_____	_____
_____	_____	_____
_____	_____	_____
_____	_____	_____
_____	_____	_____

_____ _____ _____
_____ _____ _____
_____ _____ _____
_____ _____ _____
_____ _____ _____
_____ _____ _____
_____ _____ _____
_____ _____ _____
_____ _____ _____
_____ _____ _____
_____ _____ _____
_____ _____ _____
_____ _____ _____
_____ _____ _____
_____ _____ _____
_____ _____ _____
_____ _____ _____
_____ _____ _____

8 "LPH"

The letters "lph" appear in this sequence in at least 11 words—list as many as you can.

_____ _____ _____
_____ _____ _____
_____ _____ _____
_____ _____ _____

9 "EME"

The letters "eme" appear in this sequence in at least 63 words—list as many as you can.

_____	_____	_____
_____	_____	_____
_____	_____	_____
_____	_____	_____
_____	_____	_____
_____	_____	_____
_____	_____	_____
_____	_____	_____
_____	_____	_____
_____	_____	_____
_____	_____	_____
_____	_____	_____
_____	_____	_____
_____	_____	_____
_____	_____	_____
_____	_____	_____
_____	_____	_____
_____	_____	_____
_____	_____	_____
_____	_____	_____
_____	_____	_____

LETTER PERFECT

GENERAL INSTRUCTIONS

In the puzzles that follow, the definitions give clues to words that begin and end with a designated letter. The last letter of the preceding word is also the first letter of the next word. Always work in the direction of the numbers. With these puzzles, it's okay to use proper nouns.

Solutions—Pages 209-210

13

1

In this puzzle, the definitions give clues to words that begin and end with "T."

1. Easily understood; obvious
2. Substandard apartment building
3. _____ is fair play
4. Halloween custom
5. Fruit-filled pastry
6. Firm belief in person or thing
7. Unspoken; silent
8. One of three
9. Disposition; frame of mind
10. One who goes to the other side
11. In geometry, a nonintersecting line
12. Surgical procedure
13. Small corner tower
14. Temporary; passing with time
15. Writing paper fastened at one end
16. Absent without permission
17. William Hurt film, "The Accidental _____"
18. Multitalented individual, "triple _____"
19. Tense; not slack
20. Canvas shelter
21. Fish at the end of the rainbow

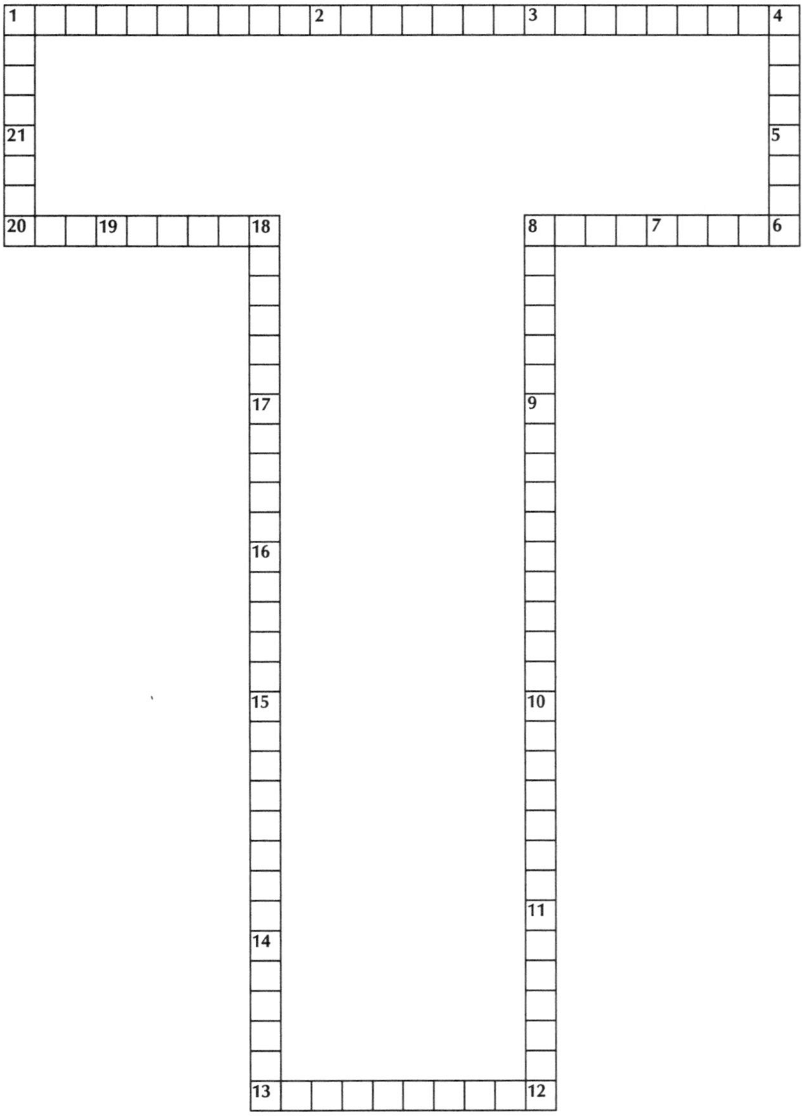
1
2
3
4
5
6
7
8
9
10
11
12
13
14
15
16
17
18
19
20
21

2

In this puzzle, the definitions give clues to words that begin and end with "E."

1. Baked clay containers; dishes
2. Large, imposing building
3. Small group of musicians
4. Keep apart; remove
5. Cut or etch letters on object
6. Shaky natural disaster
7. Vivid, forceful speech or writing style
8. Steal
9. Count one by one; list
10. Something that proves an allegation
11. Walkway along shoreline
12. Drive out evil spirits
13. Treat as equal
14. Roof edge
15. Slip by; pass
16. Get away from; flee
17. Free from blame
18. Tasteful and dignified manner
19. One with discriminating taste in food or wine
20. Give hope or confidence
21. French sandal or shoe
22. Bubbles in beverages
23. Teach; train
24. Insert opinions in factual article
25. Explain in greater detail

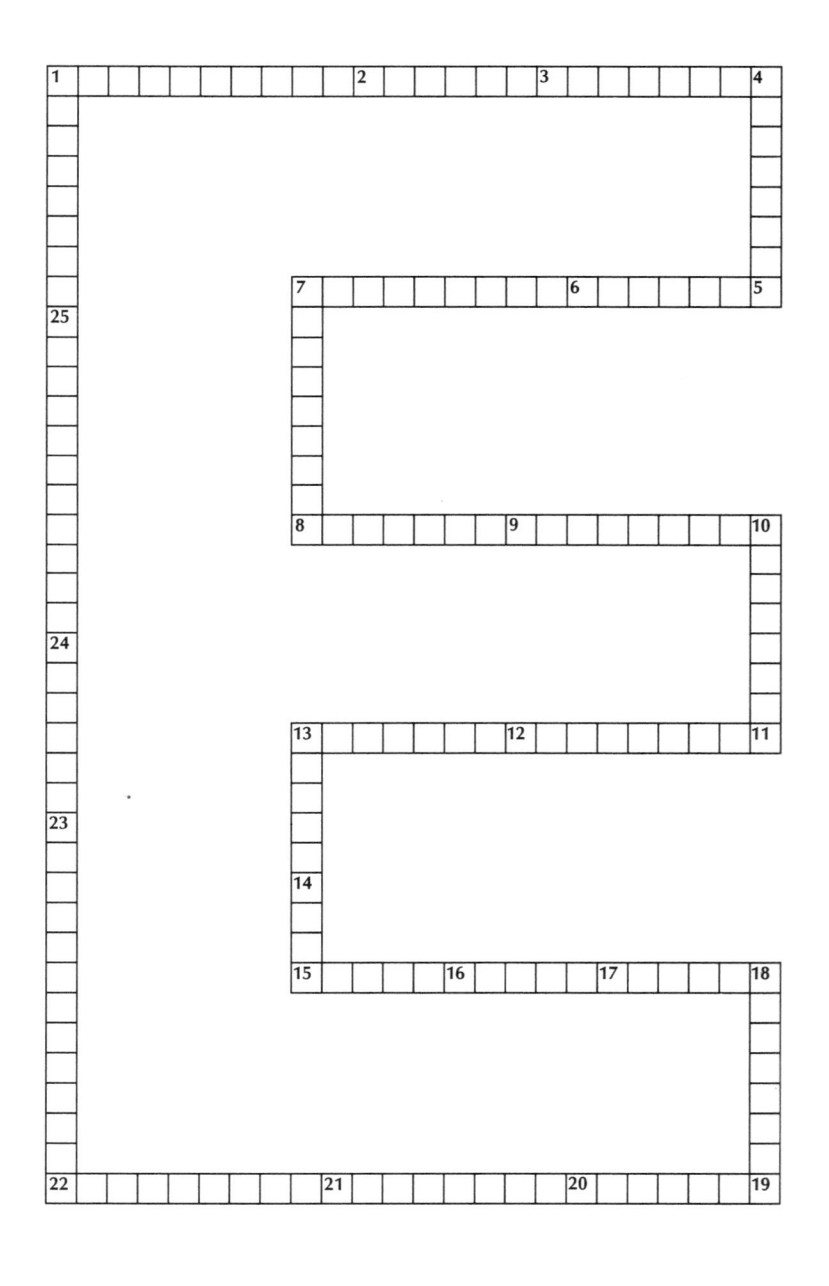

3

In this puzzle, the definitions give clues to words that begin and end with "L."

1. The Beatles' hometown
2. Garbage under layer of soil
3. Kind of evergreen shrub
4. Room deodorizer
5. Slander
6. In football, pass parallel to goal line
7. Part of the pea family
8. Political term for reciprocal voting
9. To classify as; identify
10. Opposite of conservative
11. Quiet; interval
12. Exact; precise
13. Miss Langtry's nickname
14. Faithful; true
15. Mel Gibson movie hit "_____ Weapon"
16. Lounge about
17. Listless; languid
18. Extension of jacket collar
19. Expressing feelings through song
20. Confined to a particular place
21. Uses correct reasoning

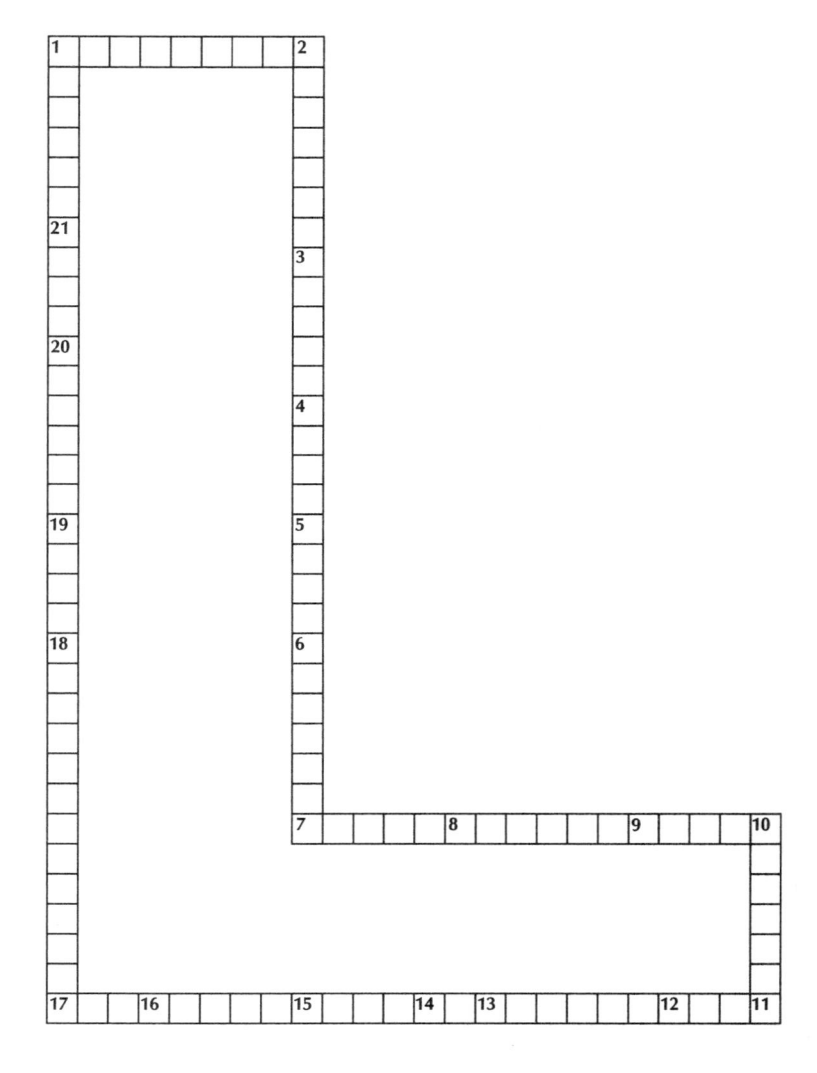

4

In this puzzle, the definitions give clues to words that begin and end with "N."

1. Female version of pajamas
2. Head (slang)
3. Has nine angles, nine sides
4. Women's stocking material
5. Male member of nobility
6. Wayne or fig
7. Colorless gas found in earth's atmosphere
8. Chemical element; component of all living things
9. Covers lap during meal
10. Famous blue-eyed thespian
11. Idea
12. Small ear of corn
13. Gary Cooper western "High _____"
14. One _____ indivisible
15. 18 + 1 =
16. 37th U.S. president
17. French general and emperor
18. Strikeout king Ryan
19. Day-old baby
20. Sister Kate is one
21. Country singer Willie _____
22. Uncharged atom part
23. Five-cent movie theater
24. Proton or neutron in atom's nucleus

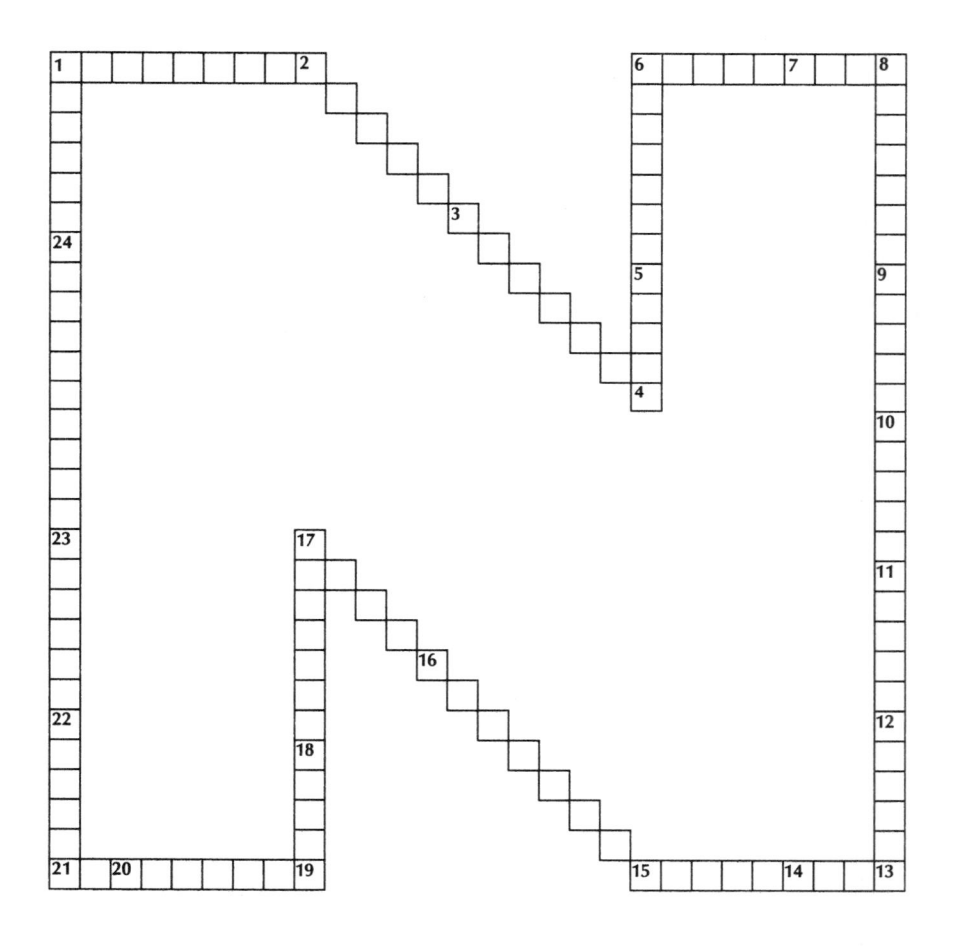

5

In this puzzle, the definitions give clues to words that begin and end with "H."

1. Hip and upper thigh
2. Seasoning; plant of mustard family with pungent root
3. Situated far above ground
4. Game involving moving from one compartment to another
5. Liquor; alcoholic beverage (slang)
6. Chopped mixture of cooked meat
7. Refuse fed to farm animals; swill
8. Canopied seat for riding on elephant or camel
9. Plant of lily family distinguished by bell-shaped flowers
10. Exclamation of praise to God
11. Stone or brick floor of fireplace
12. Very short distance
13. Turkish confection of seeds and nuts
14. Woody Allen character played by Mia Farrow
15. Make quiet or silent
16. Tahoe hotelier
17. Word with same spelling but different meaning and origin
18. From this moment on
19. Premonition; feeling about upcoming event
20. Cheer; shout of joy
21. "Leave It to Beaver" star _____ Beaumont
22. Part of racetrack between last turn and finish line
23. Physical and mental well-being
24. Fasten with hook or knot
25. Drug made of Indian hemp
26. Pen or coop for animals

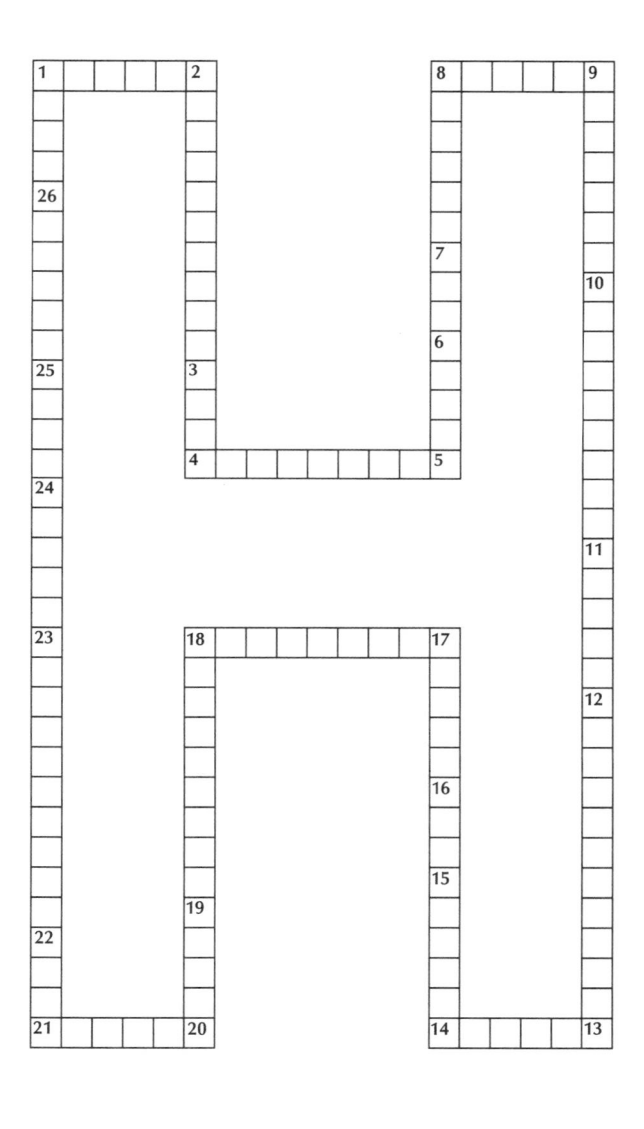

6

In this puzzle, the definitions give clues to words that begin and end with "R."

1. Person skilled at telling stories or anecdotes
2. Appointed to hold funds of others
3. Unconfirmed story; hearsay
4. Male domestic fowl
5. Extreme harshness or severity
6. Cattle thief
7. Natural stream of water
8. Water-filled device for radiating heat
9. Santa Claus' transportation team
10. Bring to maturity by educating, nourishing
11. Loud, deep, rumbling sound
12. Warden who patrols government forests
13. Savior
14. Pistol with cylinder containing several cartridges
15. French painter
16. Tool of measurement
17. Continuing, bitter hate; ill will
18. Restaurant in style of German tavern
19. Wood or metal hinged vertically at ship's stern
20. Clinging rose
21. CBS news anchorman
22. Slender two-edged sword
23. Occur again after an interval
24. Reclaim or get back
25. Give or pay as due
26. Used to indicate direction and distance of object
27. Characterized by conformity, order

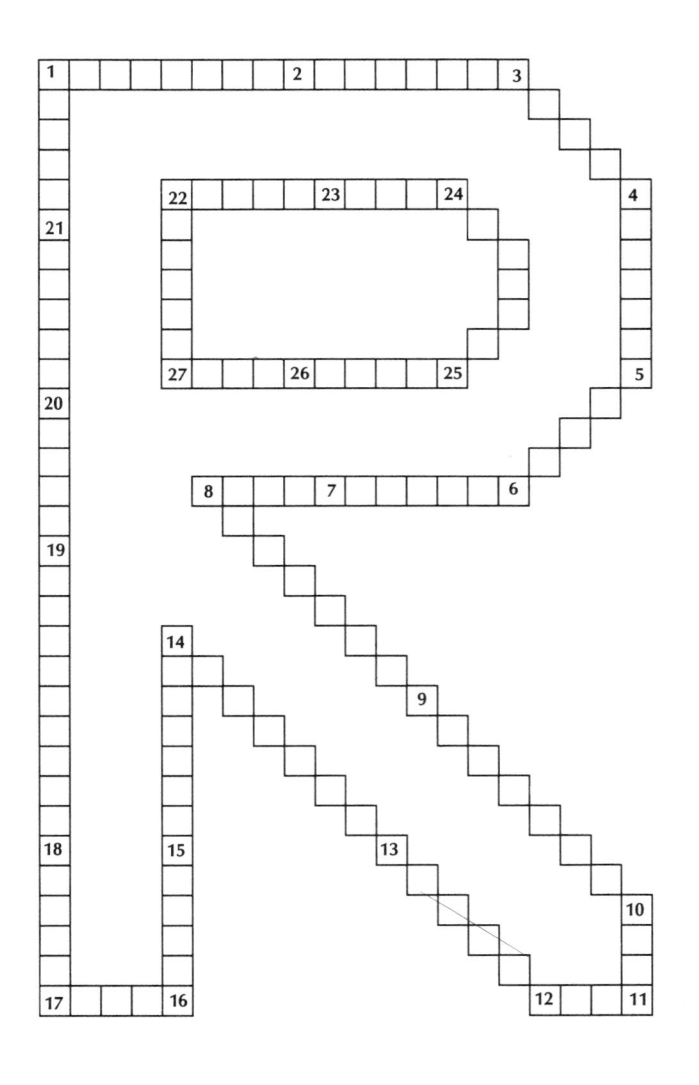

7

In this puzzle, the definitions give clues to words that begin and end with "D."

1. No longer living
2. Small dog with long body and short legs
3. Second king of Israel
4. Neglected; broken down
5. Hardest known mineral
6. Gadget; bauble
7. Wood nymph in Greek mythology
8. Stretch out; expand
9. Completely without
10. Intense fear, apprehension
11. Slight; treat without due respect
12. Sum of money divided among stockholders
13. Cartoon character _____ Bumstead
14. Automobile panel with instruments, gauges
15. The Magic Kingdom
16. Bomb that fails to explode
17. Without life
18. Misshapen
19. Country star Parton's theme park
20. Father
21. Move from higher to lower place
22. Document that states property transfer
23. Disagreement; clash
24. Mean, skulking coward
25. Member of Celtic religious order
26. Minor deity; partly divine

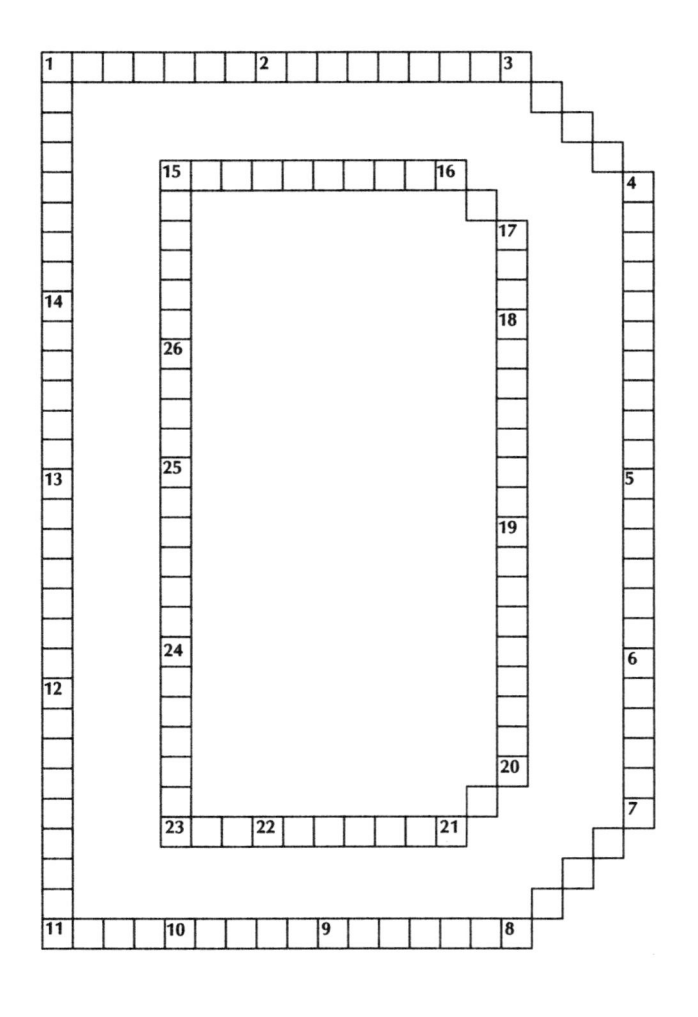

8

In this puzzle, the definitions give clues to words that begin and end with "S."

1. Disrespectful to things held sacred
2. Moved by natural feeling or impulse
3. Small telescope
4. Greek tragic dramatist
5. Phonograph needle
6. Quell; put down by force
7. Excessive; more than needed
8. Absence of
9. Working steadily; diligent
10. Strain; pressure
11. Advantageous coexistence of two dissimilar organisms
12. Italian violin craftsman
13. Contest involving common fund
14. Fond of study; attentive
15. Air carrier in skull opening to nasal cavities
16. Shameful; shocking
17. Brief, general review; summary
18. Characterized by false, malicious statements
19. Native of Switzerland
20. Having no backbone
21. Clandestine; secret

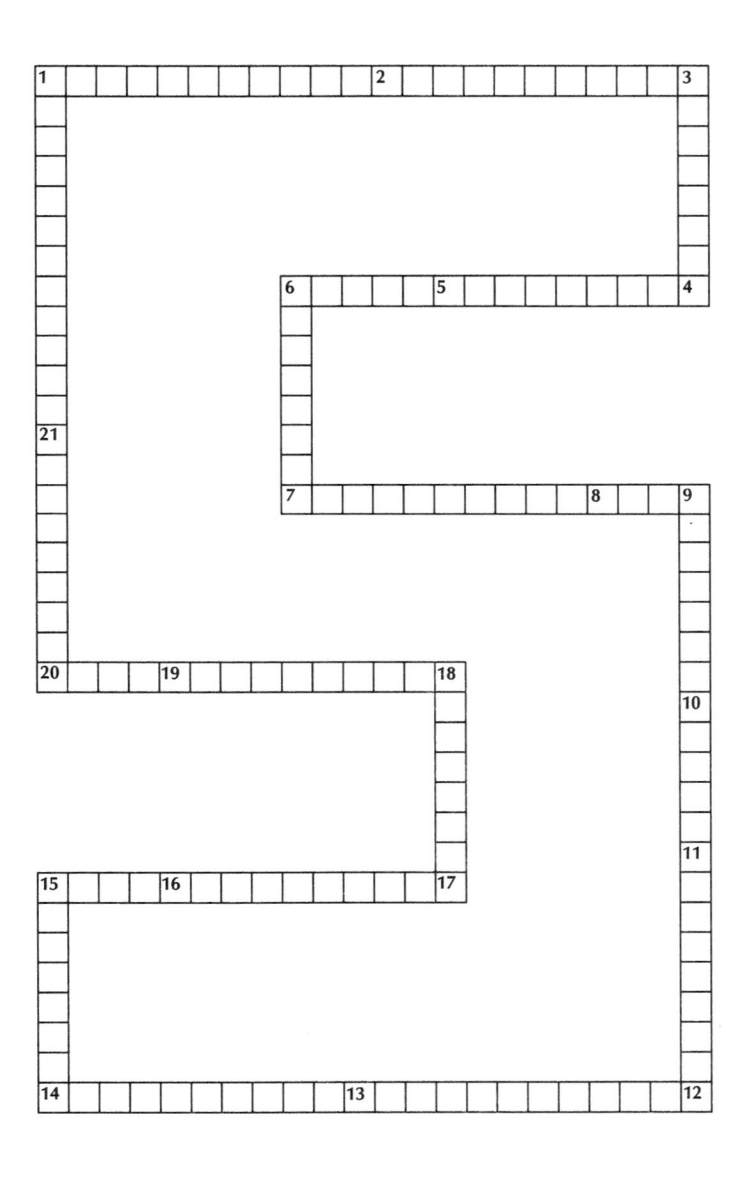

29

SOLITAIRE BATTLESHIPS: SEAMAN

GENERAL INSTRUCTIONS

Battleships puzzles are a solitaire version of the classic paper-and-pencil game of the same name. The object of each puzzle is to find the locations of the 10 ships in the fleet hidden in a section of ocean represented by the 10-by-10 grid. The fleet consists of one battleship (four grid squares in length), two cruisers (each three squares long), three destroyers (each two squares long), and four submarines (one square each).

    The ships may be oriented either horizontally or vertically in the grid, but no two ships will occupy adjacent grid squares, *even diagonally*. The digits along the side of and below the grid indicate the number of grid squares in the corresponding rows and columns that are occupied by vessels.

The Fleet:

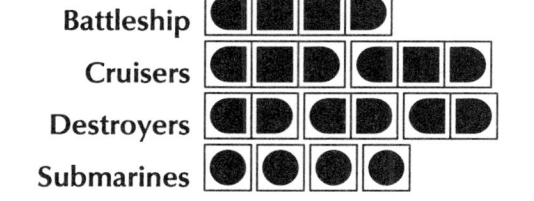

Battleship

Cruisers

Destroyers

Submarines

Solutions—Pages 211-212

In nearly all Battleships puzzles, the contents of a few of the squares have been revealed to start you off. These "shots" come in four types:

 Water This square contains no ship.

Submarine This square consists of a submarine, and thus must be surrounded by water.

End of a ship This square can be oriented in any of four directions. It indicates the end of either a destroyer, cruiser, or battleship. The square adjacent to the flat side must be occupied by a ship segment. All other surrounding squares are filled with water.

Middle of a ship This is either the middle segment of a cruiser, or one of the two middle segments of the battleship. Either it has the squares to the left and right occupied by ship segments and the ones above and below it empty or the squares above and below are occupied by ship segments and the ones to the left and right are empty. In both cases, the diagonally adjacent squares are filled with water. In fact, any time a square is occupied, all of the diagonally adjacent squares must have water in them, because ships can't touch diagonally.

The most basic strategy to Battleships solving has three parts:

1. Fill in what you know in squares adjacent to given ship segments.

2. Fill in water in rows and columns that have all of the ship segments already in place.

3. Fill in ship segments in rows and columns that must have all of their remaining empty spaces filled in order to equal the corresponding number.

For the simplest Battleships, this is all that is needed to solve the puzzle. Take a look at the puzzle in Figure 1.

Throughout this chapter, columns of the grid will be referred to with uppercase letters A through J, while rows will be referred to with letters K through T. In this way, any square in the grid can be referenced with two letters: AK means the upper left square where column A crosses row K. In the example on the right, there are ship segments at CT, EM, and EQ, and water at IR.

To solve this puzzle, start with strategy 1: Fill in squares adjacent to the given ships. You know that the flat side of an end of a ship must have a ship segment next to it, so you can fill in DQ with a ship segment—it must be the other end of a destroyer because the row

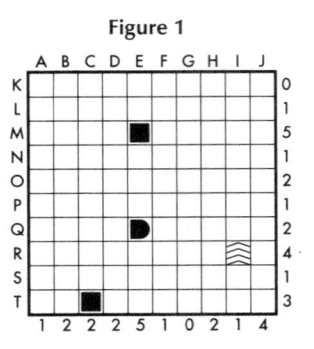

Figure 1

31

can only contain two ship segments. You can then fill in the spaces surrounding the destroyer with water. The ship segment at CT must be the middle part of a cruiser or one of the middle sections of the battleship. The ship must be horizontal (if it were vertical, it would extend below the bottom edge of the grid), so the squares to the left and right of CT (BT and DT) must have ship segments in them. Since row T can only have a total of three ship segments in it, BT-CT-DT must be a cruiser. The squares surrounding it can be filled in with water. The filled-in square at EM is also the middle section of a cruiser or one of the middle sections of the battleship. You don't know which yet, but you know that the four squares that touch a ship segment diagonally must be water, because ships never touch diagonally. Keep this in mind at all times for easier solving. Your grid should now look like Figure 2.

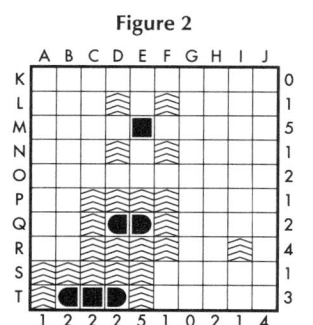

Figure 2

Now use strategy 2. Rows K, Q, and T, and columns D and G have all of their ship segments accounted for, so you can fill all the blank squares in those rows and columns with water. Your grid should now look like Figure 3.

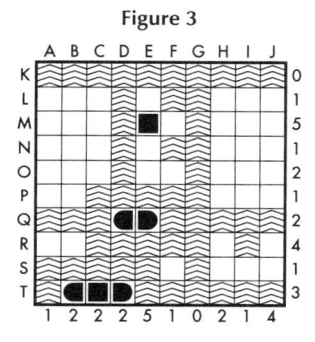

Figure 3

Now look at EM. It must be part of a ship that goes vertically because DM is water, and the ship can no longer extend to the left. You could have figured this out using strategy 3 instead, since column E has only three blank spaces, all of which need to be filled with ship segments to reach the five needed. Since four segments in a row in column E are filled, that must be the battleship. Row R also has to have all of its empty spaces filled with ship segments. The left part, AR-BR must be a destroyer. The right part, HR and JR, must have ship segments in them, too. Don't make the mistake of filling them in with submarines—although they may be submarines, each one could also be the top half of a destroyer. To indicate that it's filled in with an unidentified ship segment, use a small dot in the middle of the square. Your grid should now look like Figure 4.

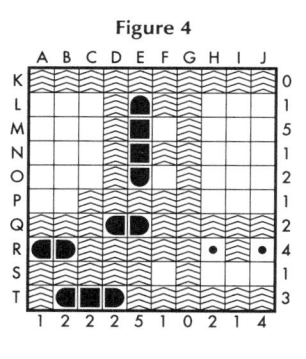

Figure 4

Whenever you fill in a ship segment, go back to strategy 1. Here, you can put water in FM and FO, and IS, too, since it touches a ship segment diagonally. And using strategy 2, you can put water in what's left of columns A and B and rows L and N, to get Figure 5.

It's time to use strategy 3 again. Column F must have a submarine in that empty space (it can't be some-

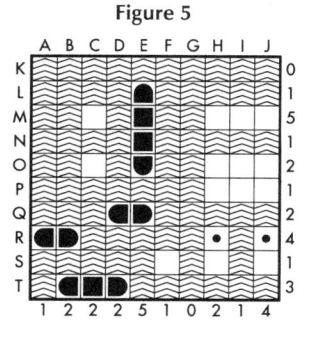

Figure 5

thing bigger because it's surrounded by water), and row M must have all four of its empty spaces filled with ship segments, making a submarine on the left and a cruiser on the right. This gives you Figure 6.

When you return to strategy 1 this time, you'll find it doesn't help, but strategy 2 does: You can fill in the blank spaces of columns C, H, and I and row S with water, since they already contain the required number of ship segments. Your grid now looks like Figure 7 .

The dots in row R are surrounded by water, so they must be submarines. And since you need two more ship segments in column J and have two spaces available, you can finish off the puzzle by filling those spaces with a destroyer. A quick double check verifies that you have all the required ships, so you're done (Figure 8).

The three basic strategies, though certainly important, will take you only so far. When you've reached a point at which the basic strategies provide no further help, the simplest advanced strategy is to try placing the largest ship that hasn't yet been located. If you haven't found where the battleship goes, try finding a spot for it. If the battleship is already in place, then look for spots for the cruisers. Here's an example (Figure 9).

First, of course, you should fill in what you can using the basic strategies. Your grid should now look like Figure 10.

Now, consider where the battleship can go. It must go in a row or column that has a four or higher. Only two qualify: row L and column E. It can't fit in row L, though—that row already contains a ship that can't be the battleship since there's only room for it to be a cruiser or destroyer, and the battleship can't go in the right part of the row since then there would be more than four

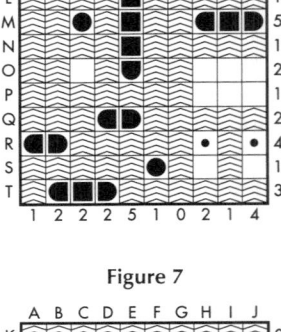

Figure 6

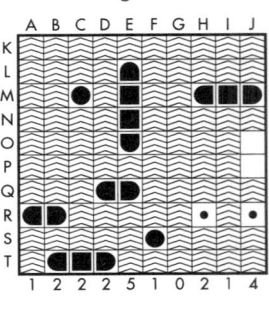

Figure 7

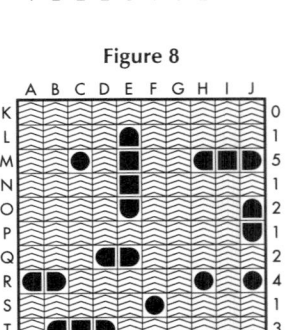

Figure 8

Figure 9

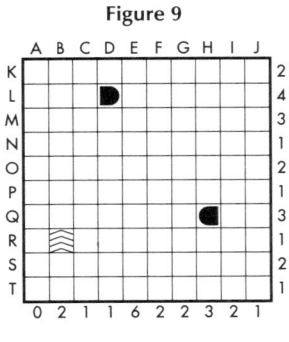

Figure 10

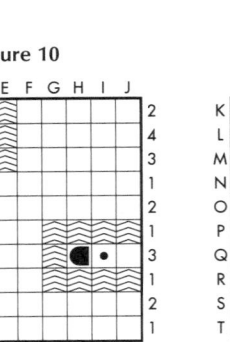

Figure 11

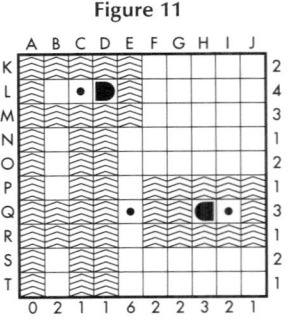

spaces filled by ships. So the battleship must go in column E. But where in the column? Its top can be at either EN, EO, EP, or EQ. You don't know which, but if you look at those four possibilities, you'll notice that in every case EQ is filled with a ship segment. So you can put a dot in EQ. Any time you put a dot in a square, you can immediately put water in the diagonally adjacent squares (since ships never touch diagonally), so fill in FP and FR with water. And look at row Q. It has its three ship segments, so the rest of it must be water—fill them in (Figure 11, page 33).

When you've filled in all the spaces surrounding a square that contains a dot, you can convert the dot to its proper ship segment. Here, square IQ must be the right end of a destroyer. Whenever you make a change using an advanced strategy, go back to you basic strategies to see if you can use them. Row R has only one empty space, and it has a one at the end of it, so that empty square must be filled with a ship segment. Since you don't yet know what type it is, put a dot in it. That dot gives you water in FS. Your grid should now look like Figure 12.

Now you'll need to think. Consider the four places the battleship can go. The first is EN-EO-EP-EQ. That's not possible because to put it there, ER would have to contain water, but it doesn't. The next possibility is EO-EP-EQ-ER. It fits, but putting it there would require water in EN and ES, leaving only one more blank space in column E, and two are needed to bring the total number of ship segments to six. So that possibility is out, too. The next possibility, EP-EQ-ER-ES, has the same problem—EO and ET would need to be water, leaving only one blank space (at EN), when two are needed to bring the total to six. So the last possibility, with the battleship at EQ-ER-ES-ET, must be correct; fill it in. That allows you to put water at EP and FT (Figure 13).

Now go back to the basic strategies. Fill in square BP with a dot (remember not to assume it's a submarine—it could extend upward!), and EN-EO with a destroyer. This puts water at FM, FN, and FO (Figure 14).

Continue using the basic strategies. Column F must contain a destroyer at FK-FL, and water must go in GK, GL, and GM. Now look at row M. HM-IM-JM must be a cruiser. This puts water in HL, IL, JL, GN, HN, IN, and JN. You can also fill in BN, IK, IO, IS, IT, JK, JO, JS, JT, BT, GT, and HT with water, giving you Figure 15.

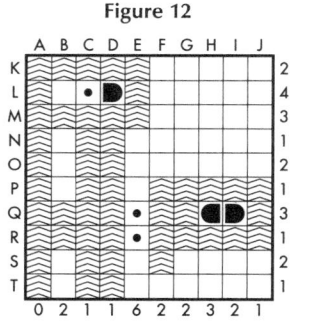

Figure 12

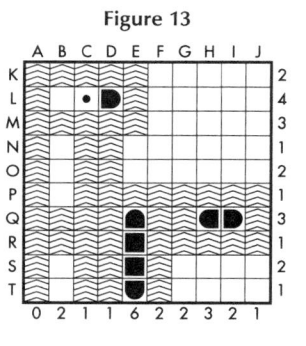

Figure 13

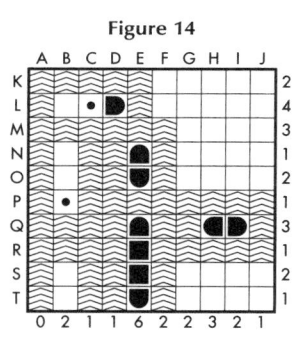

Figure 14

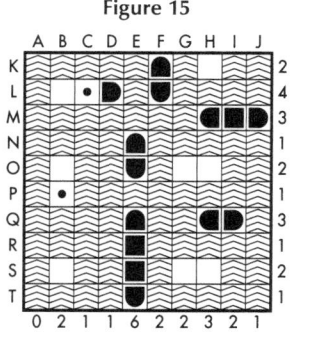

Figure 15

You can complete the puzzle with the basic strategies. Finish rows K and L first, and then columns B, G, and H. When you're done, your solution should look like Figure 16.

This example illustrates how a typical Battleships puzzle of medium difficulty can be solved. You start with the three basic strategies, then use some logical thinking to break through to the next step, and finish by again using the basic strategies. More difficult puzzles require more of these thought steps (Figure 17).

Using the basic strategies, you can get to the point shown in Figure 18.

Now try the advanced strategy of finding where the biggest remaining ship goes. In this case, the biggest ship not yet placed is the battleship. It can only go in column I (the only row or column with a four or higher), at either IK-IL-IM-IN or IL-IM-IN-IO. In both cases, IL, IM, and IN have ship segments in them, so you can fill those in. You can also put water in IT, since the battleship in the top of column I will use up all four allotted ship segments (Figure 19).

As always, after using an advanced strategy, you should reapply the basic strategies. You'll find you can put water in all the empty spaces of rows L and N, as well as in HK, HM, HO, JK, JM, and JO since they're diagonally adjacent to ship segments (Figure 20).

This is as far as you'll get with the basic strategies. It's time to try advanced strategy again. You know roughly where the battleship goes (somewhere at the top of column I); consider now where the cruisers can go. Only rows and columns with a three or higher are possibilities. You can rule out column I (since the battleship accounts for all four segments there), row M (since, after

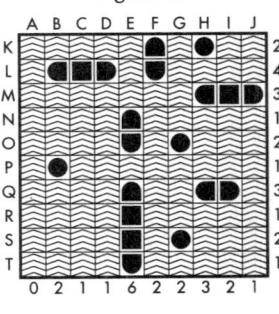

Figure 16

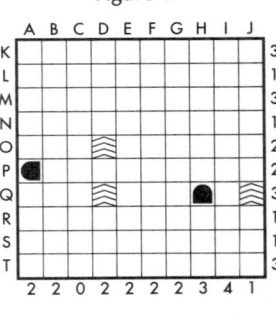

Figure 17

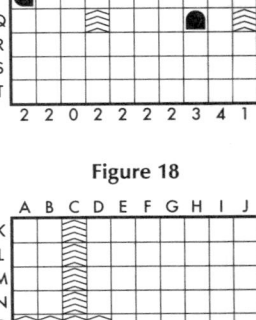

Figure 18

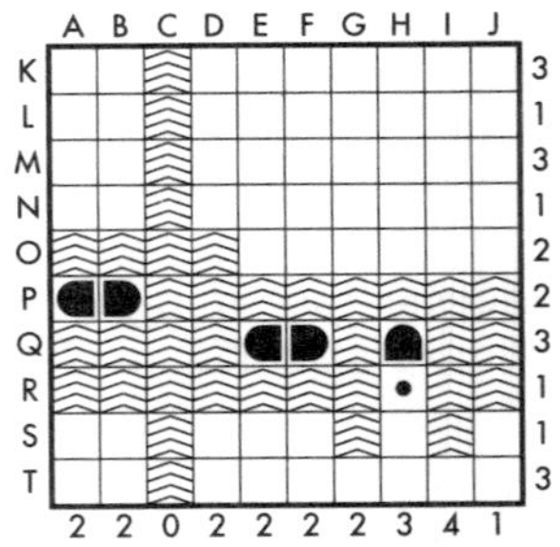

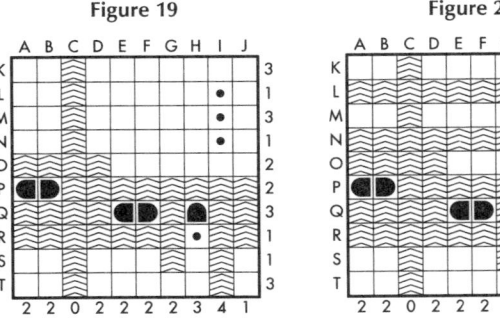

Figure 19

Figure 20

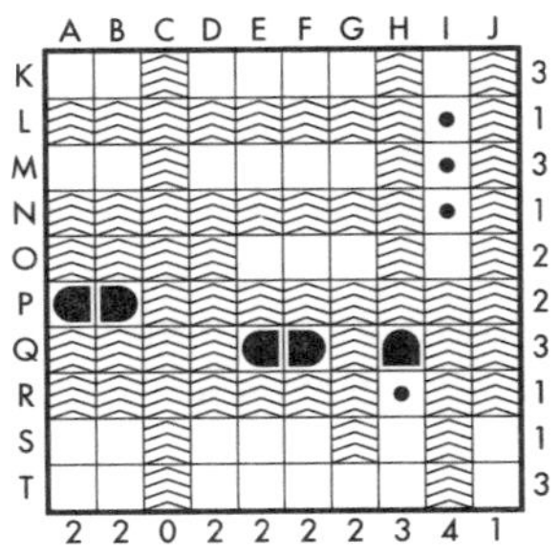

Figure 21

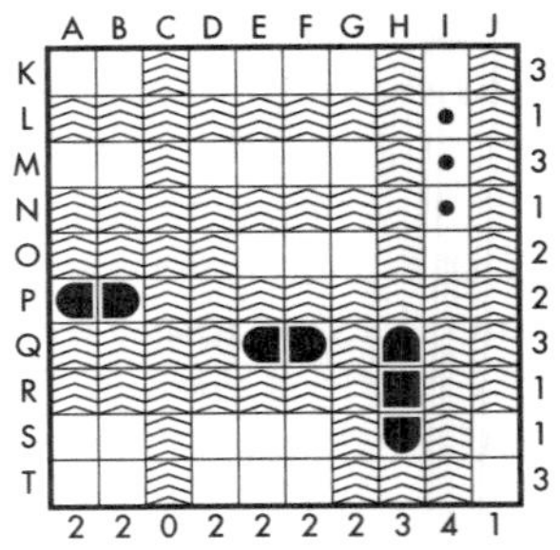

35

the component of the battleship is taken into account, there are only two more ship segments in that row), and row Q (which already has its three ship segments). That leaves column H, row K, and row T as possibilities. Two of those three must contain cruisers. If a cruiser goes in row K, it can only fit in the center section of four consecutive white squares. No matter where a cruiser fits in those four squares, square FK will have a ship segment in it. Similarly, if a cruiser goes in row T, it can only fit in the center section of five consecutive white squares. No matter where it fits in those five squares, square FT will have a ship segment in it. Since column F already contains one ship segment (FQ), the two cruisers can't go in both rows K and T at the same time, or else column F would have one too many ship segments in it. So one of the cruisers must be located in column H (and the other in either row K or row T). Column H can have only three ship segments in it, so the cruiser must be a part of what's already there. Fill it in with the surrounding water (Figure 21, page 35).

Now back to the basic strategies. Fill in water in the remaining spaces of row S; then it's clear that JT is a submarine (Figure 22).

Bingo! You now know the cruiser can't go in row T, since there's already a submarine in it, leaving only two remaining ship segments. So the cruiser must be in row K. You don't know its exact location; there are two possibilities, but in either case EK and FK must contain ship segments, and AK, BK, and IK must contain water, since all three ship segments in that row will be used up by the cruiser (Figure 23).

Back to the basic strategies. The battleship location has been determined in column I. You can fill the empty spaces in columns E and F with water, making GO a submarine (Figure 24).

Basic strategies still haven't finished off the puzzle. So again, look for a place for the largest remaining ship. You need one more destroyer. Row K is out—it's reserved for the cruiser. There are only two places left on the board with two adjacent white spaces: AM-BM and AT-BT. If the ship went in AM-BM, then AT and BT would contain water, leaving row T with at most two ship segments in it, which isn't enough. So the destroyer must instead be at AT-BT (Figure 25).

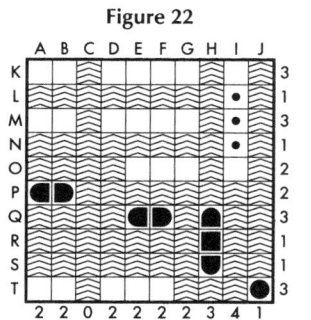

Figure 22

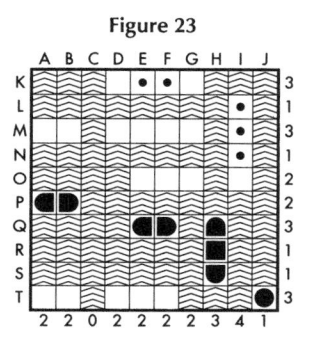

Figure 23

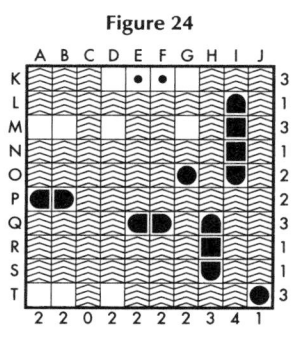

Figure 24

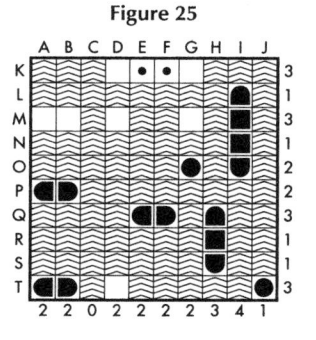

Figure 25

And now, at last, you can finish the puzzle with the basic strategies (Figure 26).

By now, you should know enough to get through all but the toughest of Battleships puzzles. Further advancement requires practice and more advanced strategies. Take a look at the next puzzle (Figure 27).

After using the basic strategies, the puzzle should look like Figure 28.

The biggest ship not yet placed is the battleship. Where can it go? Plenty of places: It could fit in one place in row N, one place in column B, or in any of four places in column J. You probably don't want to try that many possibilities. It's time for a different strategy: Look around the board for rows and columns that are almost determined. In particular, look for rows and columns in which the number of ship segments left to place is one less than the number of empty spaces. In this puzzle, row N needs four ship segments and has only five empty spaces. Row O needs three ship segments in the four remaining empty spaces. You'll find a similar condition in row Q, but for this puzzle you should concentrate on rows N and O. Consider square CN. If it's filled with a ship segment, then both BO and DO would have to contain water (since they're diagonally adjacent to CN). But that would leave only two empty spaces in row O for three ship segments—an impossibility! So CN can't contain a ship segment; fill it in with water. After filling CN with water, the basic strategies will take you a long way (Figure 29).

Now you go back to the first advanced strategy: Where can the biggest remaining ship go? In this case, you still need to place two destroyers. You can fit one of them in column C and the other in row K. They can't go anywhere else, so that's where they must be. The destroyer in row K must go at FK-GK, so CK is water, leaving CS-CT for the other destroyer (Figure 30).

From here, you just need to make the dot at CL a submarine and fill the blank squares with water, and you're done (Figure 31, page 38).

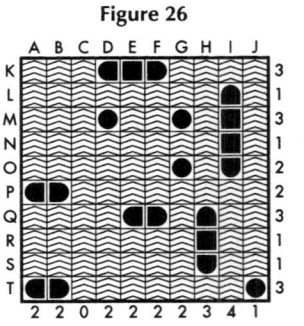
Figure 26

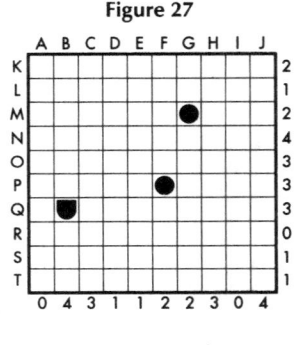
Figure 27

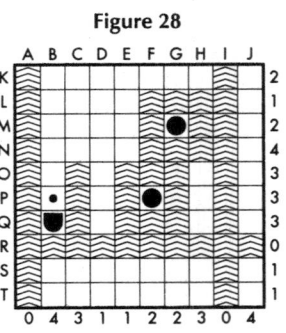
Figure 28

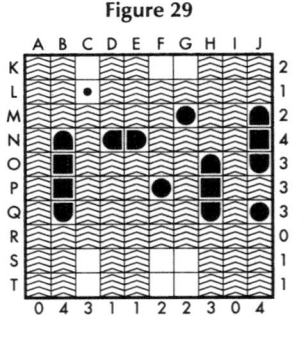
Figure 29

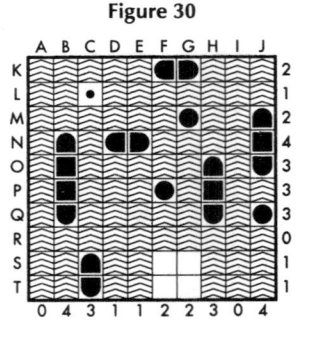
Figure 30

It's time for a toughie (Figure 32).

By now, the basic strategies should be second nature to you; applying them, your grid should look like Figure 33.

Now you'll need some deep thought. Where can the battleship go? Only in row M or row N. But you can be even more specific than that. It can't go at BM-CM-DM-EM because then AN, BN, CN, DN, EN, and FN would contain water, not leaving enough spaces for four ship segments in row N. Similarly, it can't go at BN-CN-DN-EN, because then row M would be impossible. So either the battleship goes at ABCD in one of these rows (M or N) with F and HIJ occupied in the other *or* it goes at CDEF in one of these rows with A and HIJ occupied in the other. In either case, the one at the bottom of column A is filled in row M or N, as is the one of column D and the one of column I. So you can put water in all the empty spaces in columns A, D, and I other than those in rows M and N (Figure 34).

Back to the basic strategies—they'll bring you to Figure 35.

You already know the battleship and one of the cruisers will go somewhere in rows M and N. Where will the other cruiser go? The only possibility is column B. Row Q and column E can be ruled out for obvious reasons. Columns C, H, and J are out because, as discussed above, at least one square in each of those columns will be part of a horizontal ship in row M or N. The cruiser in column B will account for all three hits in the column, so the battleship must go at CDEF of either row M or N, and either AM or AN must be a submarine. You can now place the cruiser in column B. Since it must include BP, its top is at BN, BO, or BP. If it were at BN or

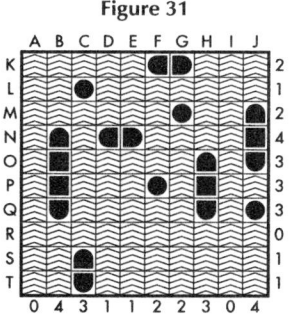

Figure 31

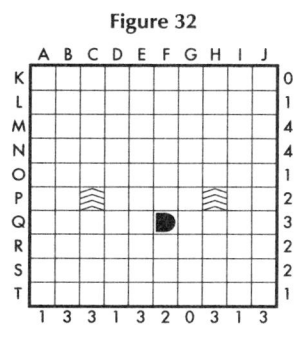

Figure 32

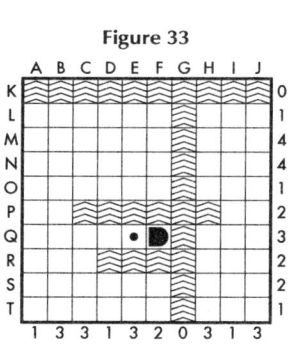

Figure 33

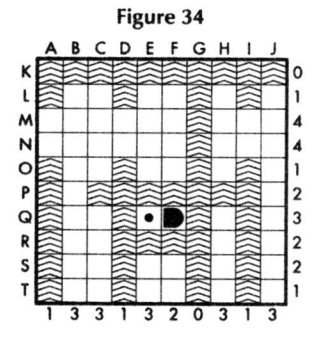

Figure 34

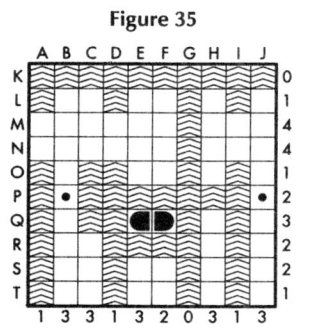

Figure 35

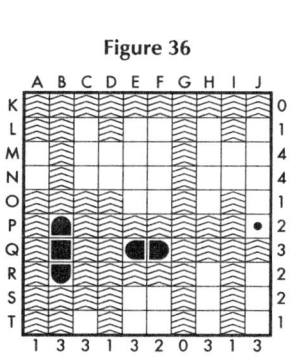

Figure 36

38

BO, then both AN and CN would contain water, making rows M and N impossible to finish, so the top of the cruiser must be at BP. Placing the cruiser at BP-BQ-BR and—of course—applying the basic startegies, yields Figure 36 (page 38).

Now look at column C. Three of those four squares must have ship segments. The battleship fits horizontally into either row M or N, taking up one of those three spaces. If it went in row M, then CL and CN would both contain water, making column C impossible. So the battleship goes at CN-DN-EN-FN. With basic strategies, you'll get Figure 37.

Check out the submarines—they've all been placed. That means the dot at JP can't be a submarine, so it must be part of a destroyer. And that gives you enough information to finish the puzzle (Figure 38).

One more puzzle (Figure 39) and then you're on your own to discover new, more advanced strategies.

Basic strategies don't help much (Figure 40).

Our advanced strategies don't help much either. The battleship can go in a number of places, and none of the rows or columns are within one of being filled. Sometimes solving the really hard puzzle requires trial and error.

The battleship can go in two places in column G and in six places in column I. Try them until one works. As soon as one works you can stop, because all Battleships have unique answers. Try the first of two locations in column G, namely GP-GQ-GR-GS. After surrounding the battleship with water, and completing column G with water, the next step is to complete column H with a cruiser at HL-HM-HN and complete column F with a ship segment at LF. But wait! Now row L has two ship

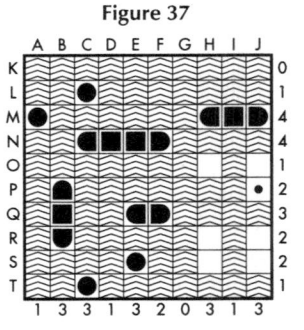

Figure 37

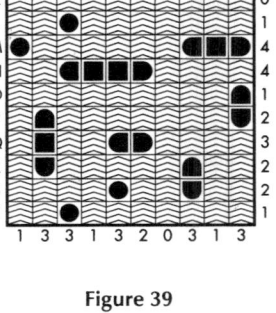

Figure 38

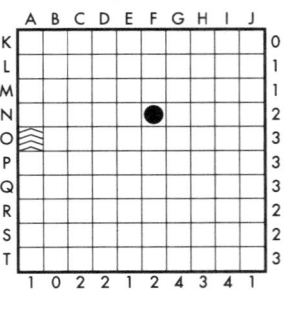

Figure 39

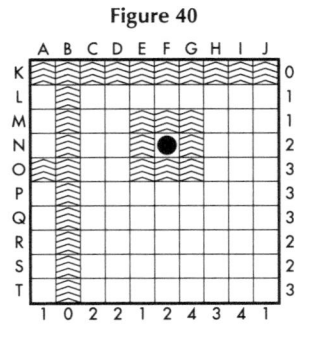

Figure 40

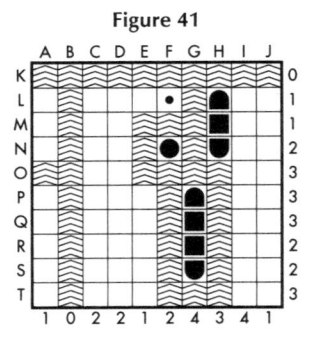

Figure 41

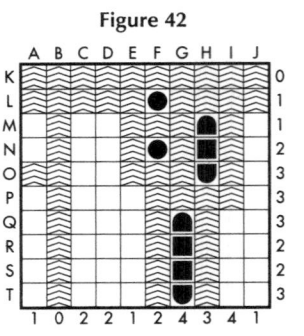

Figure 42

segments (Figure 41, page 39), which is one too many, so the battleship doesn't go at GP-GQ-GR-GS.

Moving on, try the battleship at the bottom of column G. Surround the ship with water and complete column F with a ship segment at FL and complete column G with water at GL. Now look at row L. Make the ship segment a submarine and complete the row with water. Now complete column H with a cruiser at HM-HN-HO and surround it with water. This leaves column I with four consecutive spaces that need to be filled, but the battleship can't go there since it's already in column G (Figure 42, page 39).

You now know the battleship is in column I. Try placing it next to the top, at IL-IM-IN-IO. (It can't start at IK since row K has no ship segments.) Surround the ship with water, and complete column I with water. Complete rows L, M, and N with water, and complete row O with a destroyer at CO-DO. Fill in the water surrounding the destroyer and complete row P with a submarine at AP and a destroyer at FP-GP. Surround that destroyer with water, and complete columns A and F with water. Now row Q must have a destroyer at CQ-DQ and a submarine at JQ. Surround the destroyer with water and complete columns C, D, and J with water. At last, there is an impossibility. Row R must have another destroyer in it, but there are none left. Also, columns G and H must both have cruisers in them adjacent to each other (Figure 43).

Onward you go, to IM-IN-IO-IP. Start by surrounding the battleship with water and completing its column with water. Next, complete column H with a cruiser at HR-HS-HT and surround it with water. This makes column G impossible (Figure 44).

Next up is IN-IO-IP-IQ. Start by surrounding the battleship with water and completing its column with water. Next, complete column H with a submarine at HL and a destroyer at HS-HT. Complete row L with water and surround the destroyer with water and column G becomes impossible (Figure 45).

Just three more possibilities. At this point you may start worrying that none of these three will work and that you'll have to go back and redo everything you've done so far to find your mistake. That's the wrong way to think. Have confidence! Keep working.

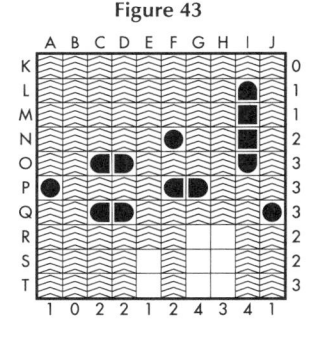

Figure 43

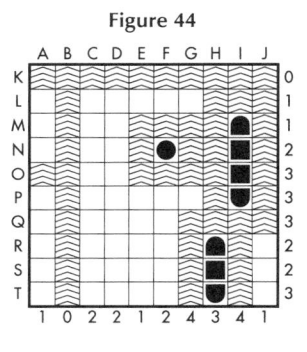

Figure 44

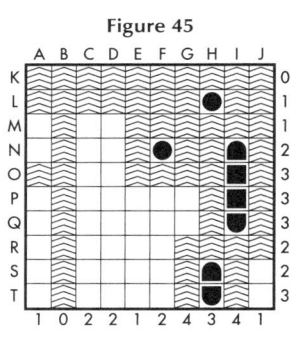

Figure 45

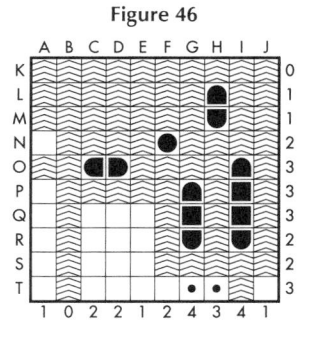

Figure 46

Moving down one more spot yields IO-IP-IQ-IR. As usual, surround the battleship with water and complete its column with water. Then complete column H with a destroyer at HL-ML and a ship segment at HT. Complete rows L and M with water and fill in water at GS (since it's diagonally adjacent to HT). Complete column G with a cruiser at GP-GQ-GR and a ship segment at GT, and surround the cruiser with water. Row O can be completed with a destroyer at CO-DO, and the water surrounding it can be filled in. Now both AN and AP must have ship segments to complete rows N and P, but column A can only have one ship segment in it, so it's yet another impossibility (Figure 46, page 40).

The next possibility is IP-IQ-IR-IS. This one doesn't last long at all. After surrounding the battleship with water and completing its column, there's an impossibility in row O (Figure 47).

So you are left with only one possibility, namely IQ-IR-IS-IT. It had better work! Basic strategies don't take you too far (Figure 48).

Don't be discouraged, though. You've made it this far. You'll sink this fleet yet! Move on to advanced strategy. Where can the longest not-yet-placed ship go? The cruisers can only go in column G, column H, or row P. If it went in row P though, row O would be impossible. Here's why: If the cruiser were at CP-DP-EP or at DP-EP-FP, then CO and DO would have to be water, leaving too few empty spaces in row O. If the cruiser were at EP-FP-GP, then DO and HO would have to be water, again leaving too few empty spaces in row O. Since those are the only three places where the cruiser can go in row P, it must not go.there. That leaves you only two places for the two cruisers, so they must go in those places:

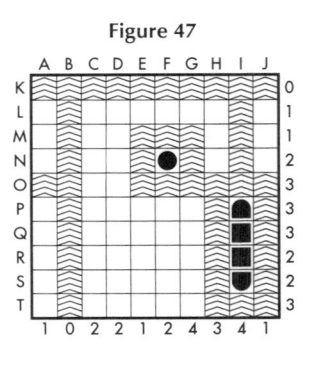

Figure 47

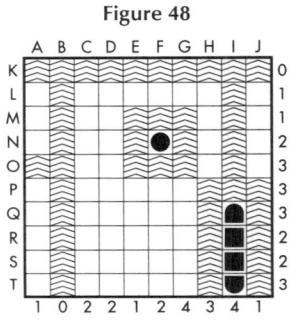

Figure 48

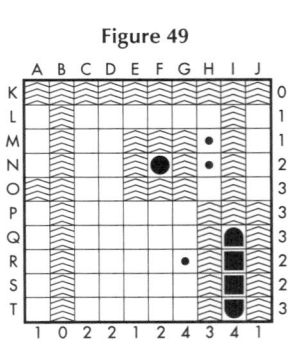

Figure 49

Figure 50

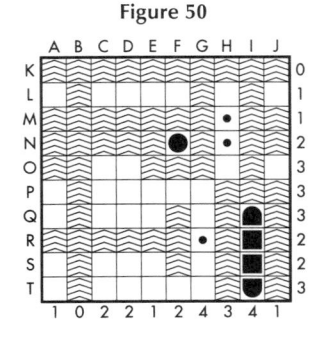

Figure 51

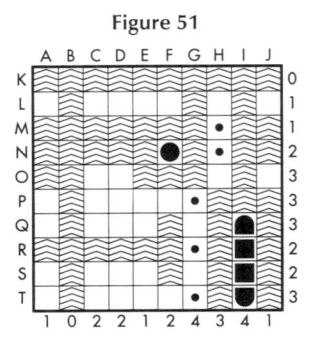

Figure 52

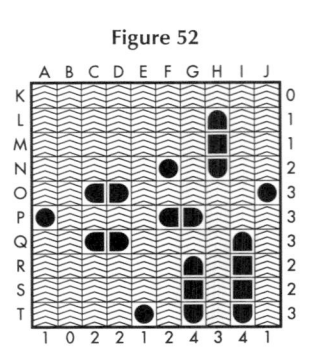

columns G and H. You don't know exactly where, but you do know that GR must contain a ship segment, as well as both HM and HN (Figure 49, page 41).

Using basic strategies now, you get Figure 50 (page 41).

Now, if GP were empty, then column G would need a battleship to fill it. But you've already used the battleship, so GP must have a ship segment. Similarly, GT can't be empty or else column G would need a battleship, so it too has a ship segment (Figure 51, page 41).

From here you can use basic strategies (starting off with water in HO since it's diagonally adjacent to GP, which has a ship segment in it) to finish up (Figure 52, page 41).

So there you have it. There are plenty of other strategies to use, depending on the puzzle. For example, if all the submarines are already in place, then every remaining ship segment must be a part of a longer ship, and if there's a column with a one that crosses a row with a one then it must contain water, since if it contained a ship, it would be a fifth submarine. Similarly, if three submarines are in place and there's a row with a two that has both adjacent rows filled with water, then you know the row with the two has to be a destroyer, not two submarines, since only one submarine is left to place. And then there's the case when ... well, you get the idea. Part of the fun is discovering new strategies.

And the best way to develop new strategies is to solve lots of puzzles.

1

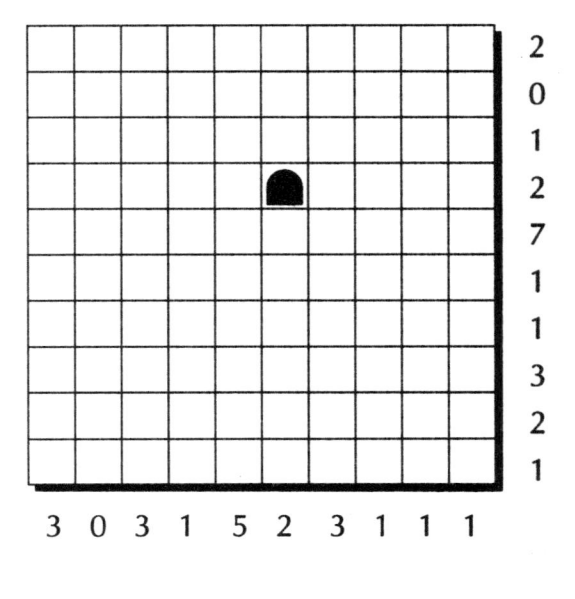

Battleship
Cruisers
Destroyers
Submarines

2

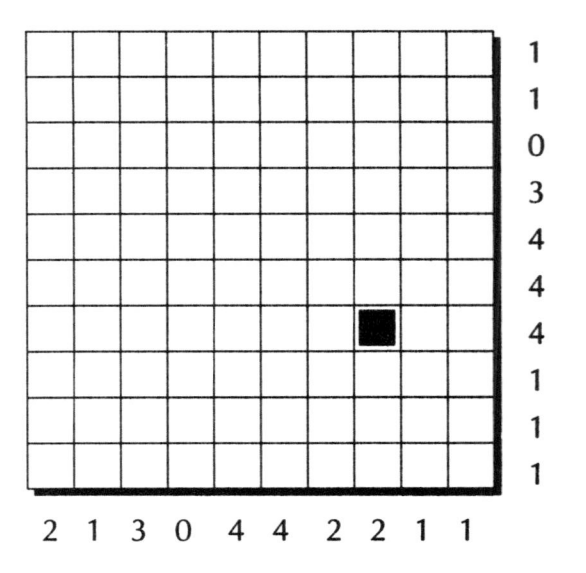

3

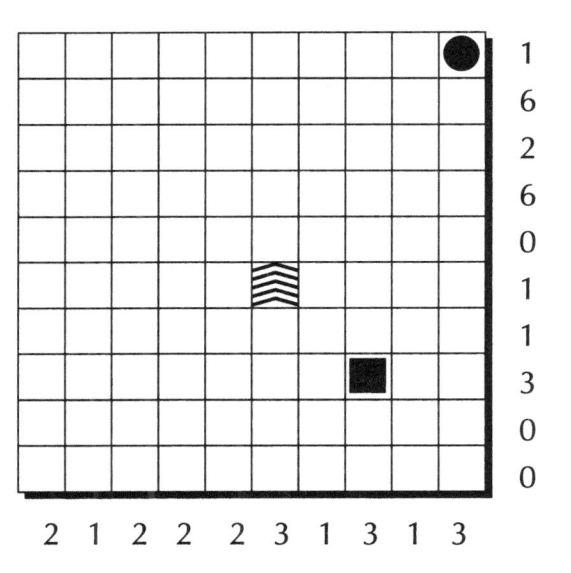

Battleship
Cruisers
Destroyers
Submarines

4

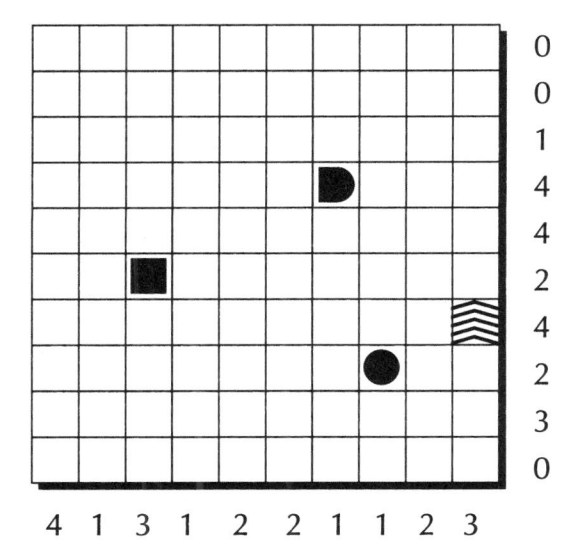

5

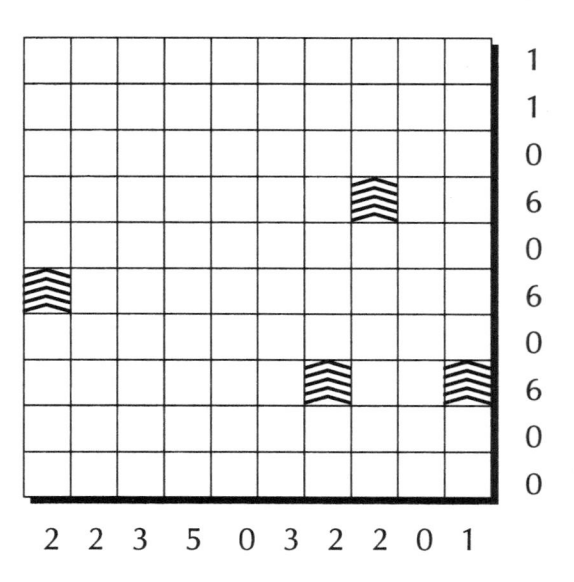

1
1
0
6
0
6
0
6
0
0
0

2 2 3 5 0 3 2 2 0 1

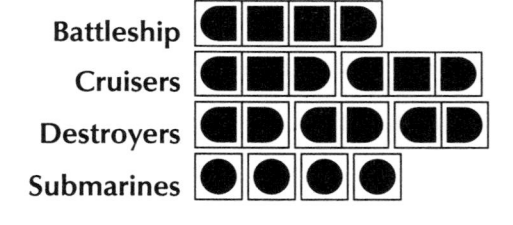

Battleship
Cruisers
Destroyers
Submarines

6

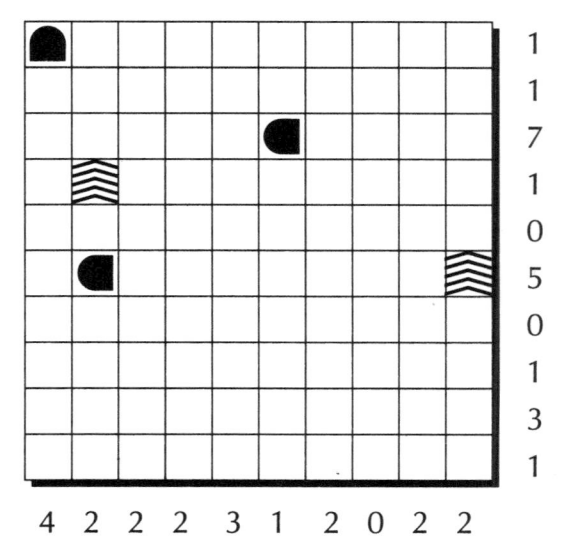

1
1
7
1
0
5
0
1
3
1

4 2 2 2 3 1 2 0 2 2

7

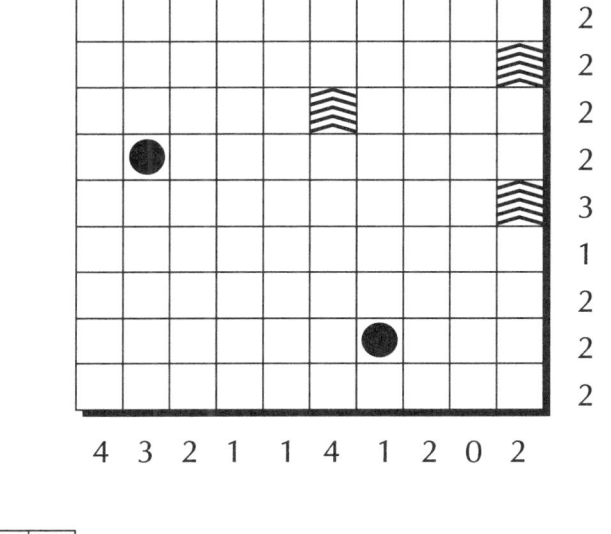

2
2
2
2
2
3
1
2
2
2

4 3 2 1 1 4 1 2 0 2

Battleship
Cruisers
Destroyers
Submarines

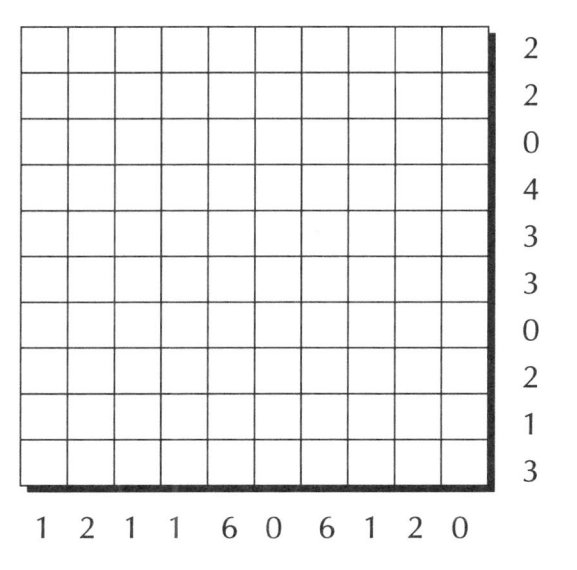

8

2
2
0
4
3
3
0
2
1
3

1 2 1 1 6 0 6 1 2 0

9

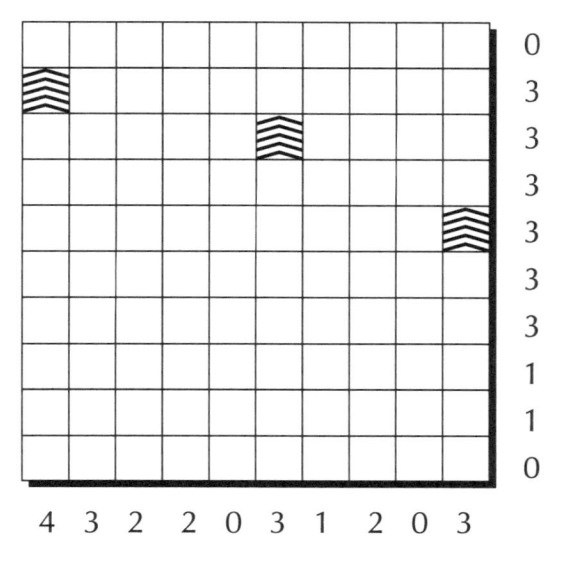

Battleship	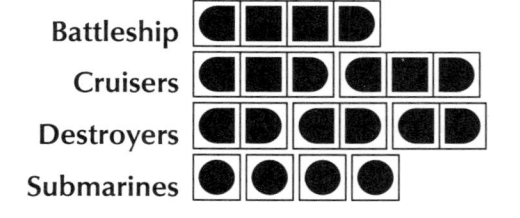
Cruisers	
Destroyers	
Submarines	

10

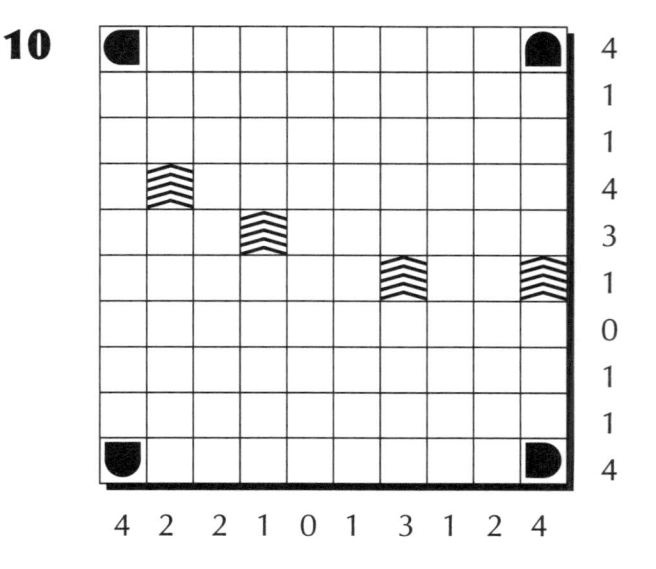

11

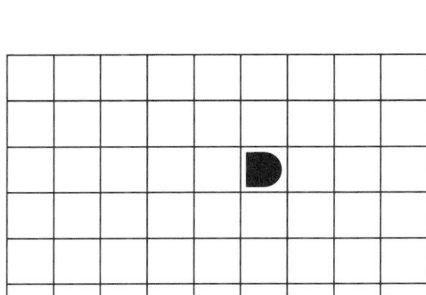

Grid 11 column totals (left to right): 1 1 2 1 3 2 6 2 1 1

Grid 11 row totals (top to bottom): 3 2 5 0 3 1 2 2 1 1

Battleship
Cruisers
Destroyers
Submarines

12

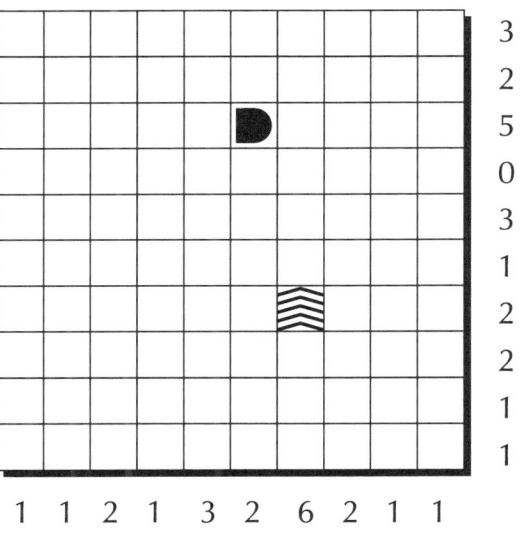

Grid 12 column totals (left to right): 2 0 2 3 1 1 3 3 2 3

Grid 12 row totals (top to bottom): 2 1 4 3 4 2 2 1 1 0

48

TRICKY MAZES

GENERAL INSTRUCTIONS

Where no specific instructions are given, find the route from A to B. One way to solve them is to start at B and color in all the blind alleys until you have the clear route.

Solutions—Pages 220-224

A Find a route from A to B that passes no more than four dots.

1

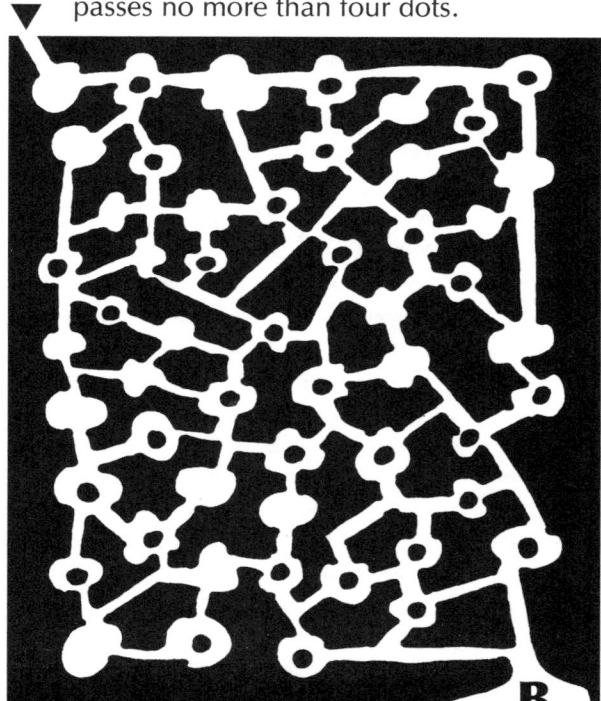

50

B

A

2

4

Draw a continuous line from A to B that passes through every one of the diamonds and none of the circles. The line may pass through each diamond once only.

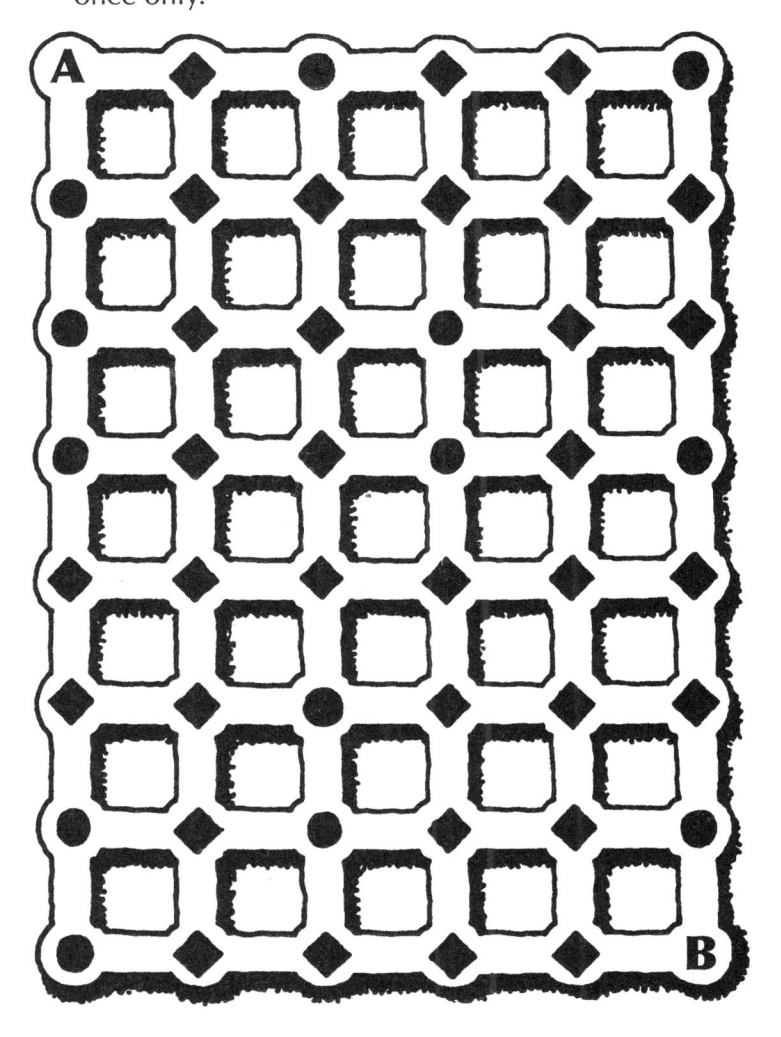

Which of the entrances at the bottom
leads to the exit at the top?

9

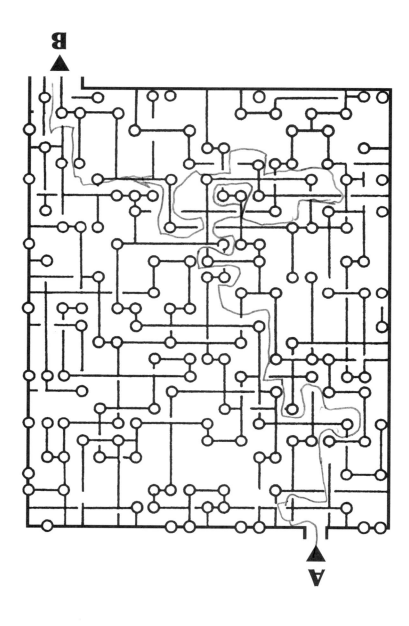

8

10

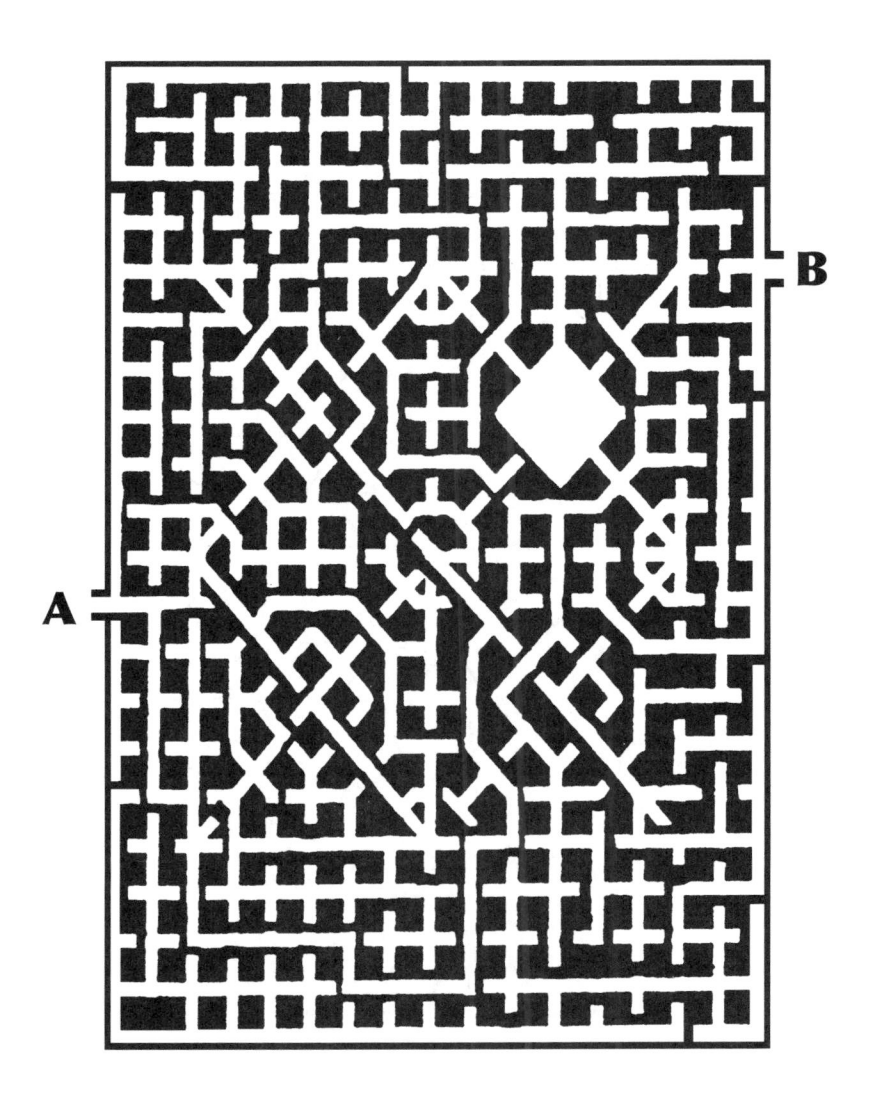

11

12

B　　　　**C**

D　　　　**A**

Find a route from A to B
that avoids C and D.

13

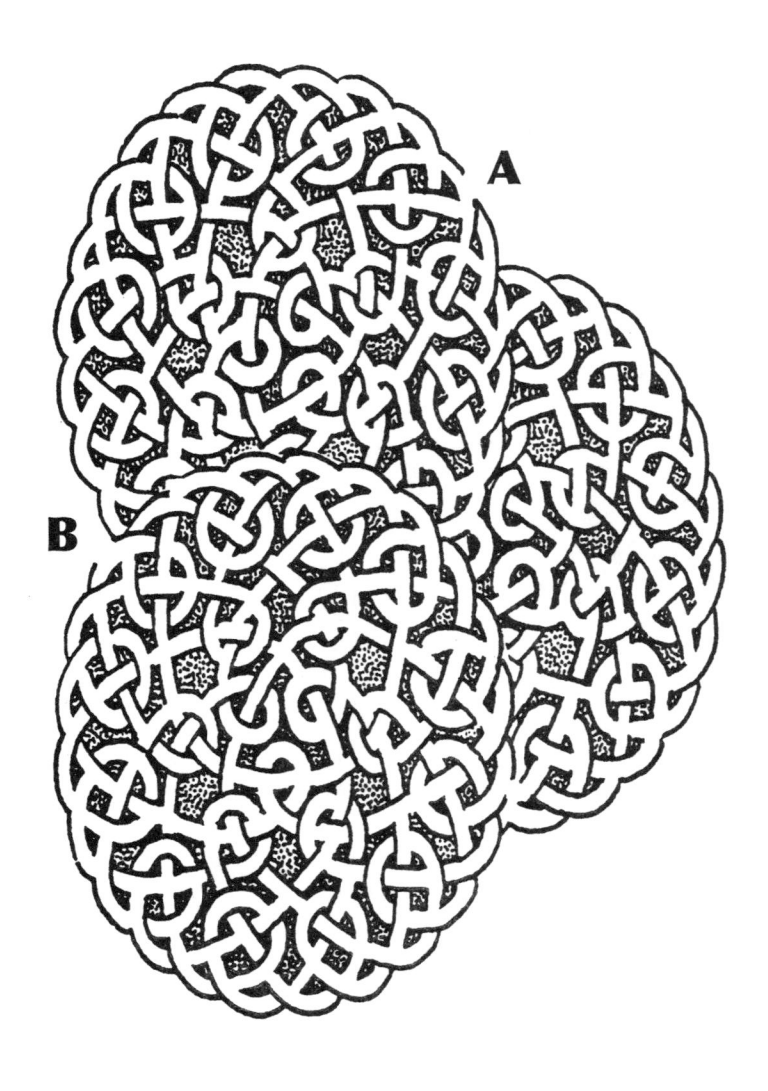

14

A

B

15

A

B

16

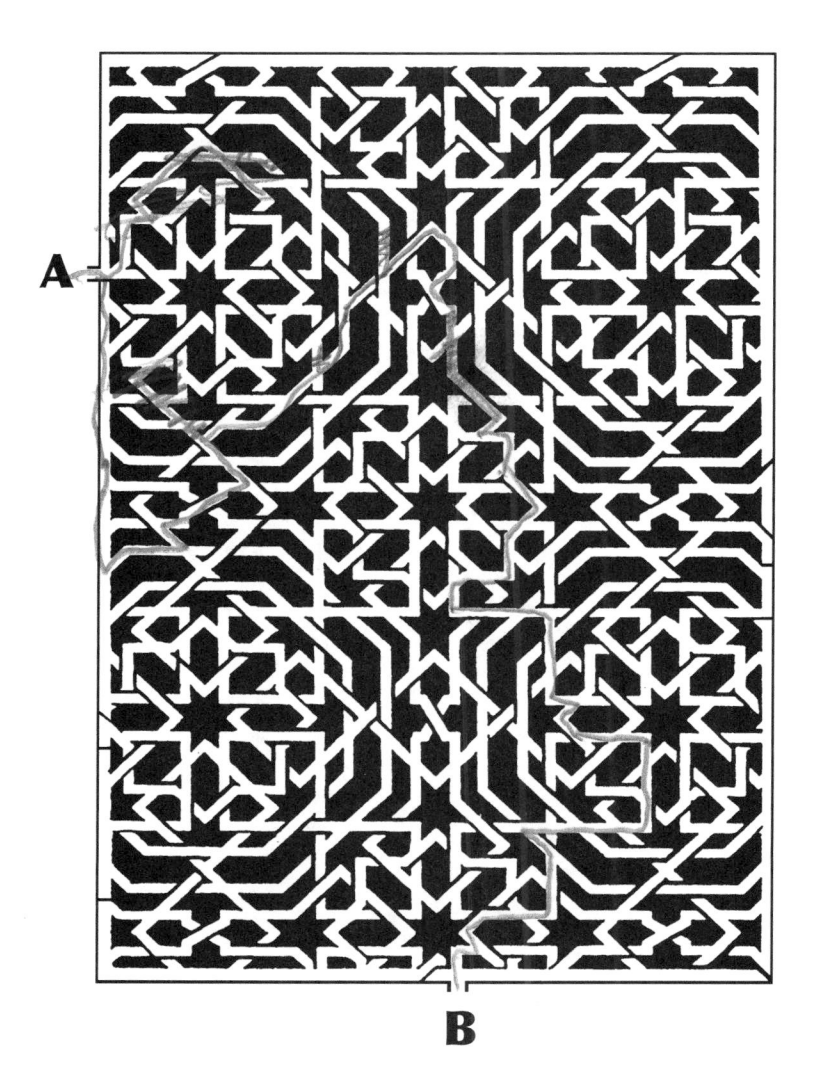

A

B

17

A

B

18

A   B

WHODUNITS

DR. J. L. QUICKSOLVE

Dr. Jeffrey Lynn Quicksolve, professor of criminology, retired from the police force as a detective at a very young age. Now he works with various police agencies and private detectives as a consultant when he isn't teaching at the university.

He certainly knows his business, solving crimes. Many people are amazed at how he solves so many crimes so quickly. He says, "The more you know about people and the world we live in, the easier it is to solve a problem."

His son, Junior, enjoys learning too, and he solves a few mysteries himself.

Read, listen, think carefully, and you can solve these crimes too!

Solutions—Pages 228-229

MURDER BETWEEN FRIENDS

The apartment building was an old house near the university. It had been divided into four apartments. The owner of the building, Gracious Host, lived in a large apartment downstairs. She rented out the three apartments upstairs. Dr. J. L. Quicksolve had heard the call over the police radio and arrived before the officers.

Gracious described her tenants to Dr. Quicksolve. She said Tweeter Woofer was a young "hippie type" who sometimes played her music too loudly. "I told her, one more complaint and she would be out on the street." Baby Blossom was hearing impaired, but "she reads lips." Terry Cloth was dead.

Gracious said she was sure only her three tenants were in the building when she heard the shots and discovered the body.

The hall was quiet when Dr. Quicksolve walked upstairs. The woman in the bathrobe lay against the wall, as if she were taking a nap. The three red stains told him the nap would last forever.

Dr. Quicksolve heard music in the back of the apartment and smelled burning incense when Tweeter Woofer opened her apartment door to let him enter. Miss Woofer was shocked when he explained what had happened. As they stood inside the door, she said, "This is so upsetting. Who would shoot Terry?" She said she did not hear anything and did not see anything.

Dr. Quicksolve knocked quietly on Baby Blossom's door. She and her dog , a yellow Labrador, came to the door. He explained what happened. "I was a little afraid to open the door because I thought I heard shots," she said. "I guess I was right."

When Dr. Quicksolve went back downstairs, the policemen had arrived. "I have a good suspect," he told them.

Which woman did he suspect?

INHERITANCE

"A small turtle sundae, please," Dr. J. L. Quicksolve told the waitress. He was the last to order. His friend, Fred Fraudstop, had invited Dr. Quicksolve and his son, Junior, for an ice cream treat to celebrate Fred's move into town. Fred ordered a chocolate-marshmallow sundae, and Junior ordered a "freight train"—two banana splits in separate glass bowls pulled by a glass train engine. If you ate the whole thing, you got to keep the glass engine. Junior had five of them at home.

"That reminds me of a railroad tycoon who died recently. He was an only child and a bachelor who kept to himself, though he loved to travel through the West when he was younger. Studying

the Old West was a hobby of his. We had to hunt for his next-of-kin," Fred said as Junior's ice cream was brought out by two waitresses wearing conductor's caps and red bandannas.

"Did you find anybody?" Junior asked, reaching for his spoon.

"They found us, " Fred said, "which wasn't surprising considering the money they stood to inherit. I've narrowed it down to two people. The rest are obviously just pretending to be relatives, hoping to get the money."

"Who are they?" Junior asked.

"One is a niece from Chicago, and the other is a cousin from North Dakota. They're the only ones who don't have a previous record of fraud of some sort or another. I still have to check out their claims, though. Would you like to talk to them with me?" he asked Dr. Quicksolve.

"Sure; it sounds interesting," the detective answered. "Let's start with the one from North Dakota."

Why did Dr. Quicksolve want to talk to the relative from North Dakota?

STRIKEOUT

Dr. J. L. Quicksolve and Junior were meeting Fred Fraudstop for lunch. Fred said he had to stop and question a man about a burglary at the Strikeout Sportscard Shop. Dr. Quicksolve decided to go with him because Junior was a baseball card collector and would be interested in the shop, not to mention Quicksolve's curiosity about the burglary.

"We were broken into overnight," Homer Hitter, the shop owner, told them. "They took a bunch of cards, but mostly money," he said, showing them the back door that had been jimmied open and the empty moneybox. "We close late, so I usually take the money to the bank in the morning," he said.

"Did you lock up last night?" Dr. Quicksolve asked him. Junior was looking at a display of Mickey Mantle cards. He showed his dad the 1953 rookie card that had a price of $300 on it. "Save your money," Dr. Quicksolve said.

"No, my clerk, Art Dunn, closed up last night. He always closes up. He bolts the back door and goes out the front. I let him have his own key. I don't think he would do anything like this." Then he noticed Junior looking at the cards. "You like Mickey Mantle?" he asked Junior. He reached below the counter and brought out a card that showed Mantle standing at the left side of the plate as if he were waiting for a pitch. "Without all those injuries he would have been the Home Run King."

"What do you think of the Strikeout Sportscard Shop?" Fred asked Junior as they walked out onto the sidewalk.

"I don't think I'd buy anything from that guy," Junior said, "and you probably should doubt what he tells you about the robbery."

Why does Junior mistrust Homer?

CODDLED COED

Three college coeds rented the house next to Dr. J. L. Quicksolve. Brenda Broadcloth and Cherry Ripple, two of them, ran up to Dr. Quicksolve in front of his house just as he was saying goodbye to Sergeant Rebekah Shurshot. Brenda said they had been robbed.

   The three roommates had shopped together. They had bought their groceries, including cod for that night's dinner because Holly Mackeral loved fish. Brenda chose asparagus for the vegetable, and Cherry chose vanilla ice cream for dessert.

"I had the money, but I put it back in the cookie jar when we got home," Brenda said. "Then I went upstairs to call my boyfriend. That was about three o'clock."

"I fed the cat and went out to work in the backyard. I decided to get bananas for the ice cream," Cherry said, "so I went to the cookie jar for the money around four-thirty. The money was gone. I guess someone came into the house and took it."

Holly came walking up with their dog Furball on a leash. Brenda told her about the robbery. Sergeant Shurshot asked Holly what she did after they came back from shopping.

"I unwrapped the fish and put it on the counter to thaw a little. Then I went to the basement to read. Shortly after four I put the fish in the oven and took the dog for a walk. I didn't see anybody," she said.

"Will you check the cookie jar for fingerprints?" Brenda asked Sergeant Shurshot.

"I don't think that will be necessary. This was an inside job," Sergeant Shurshot responded.

What did Sergeant Shurshot mean?

TELEPHONE RING

Dr. J. L. Quicksolve and Junior sat in the airport waiting for Captain Reelumin's plane to arrive. Junior liked to watch the people going by. He liked to guess things about who they might be and where they were going.

Dr. Quicksolve watched people make phone calls at a round table filled with telephones, each with its tiny "booth," small dividers that separated the phones. He noticed one man kept a phone to his ear with one hand. He held a pencil with the other hand, as if he was getting instructions or directions, but he had not written anything down. A man in a jacket took the phone in the adjoining booth. He took a card out of his pocket that he looked at as he spoke into the telephone. The first man finally wrote something down.

"See those two men?" Dr. Quicksolve asked his son.

"Yes," Junior said, noticing that his father was staring at the two men by the phones. The one in the jacket walked away, and the other man suddenly hung up his phone. Then he held it to his ear again and began making another call, talking into the phone as he looked down at his notepad.

"Get that man," Dr. Quicksolve said quietly, pointing to the man in the jacket who had just walked by them. Dr. Quicksolve walked up behind the man on the telephone and looked over his shoulder.

What did he expect to see?

BEN BOINKT

Dr. J. L. Quicksolve walked in the open door, passed a man lying on the couch with an icepack on his head, and proceeded into the dining room, following the voices he heard.

"That's Ben Boinkt out there on the couch," Officer Longarm said to Dr. Quicksolve.

A woman sat at the table. She had so much makeup on, Dr. Quicksolve wondered what she really looked like. Then, through the doorway that led to the kitchen, he saw the body of a woman.

"Mrs. Boinkt is dead," Officer Longarm said, answering the unspoken question. "This is Miss Glenda Cheatenheart," he said, indicating the woman at the table. "She lives next door. She found the Boinkts lying on the floor in the kitchen."

Dr. Quicksolve looked into the kitchen, where the body lay. The back door lock had been broken, and the door was open.

"I heard the crash of the door in the kitchen," Mr. Boinkt said as he stood in the dining-room doorway holding the icepack to his head. Then I heard my wife falling down when the thugs hit her from behind. There were two of them. They never said a word and they wore masks. I turned to run, but they caught me from behind and knocked me out cold. They went upstairs to the wall safe in our bedroom. They took my wife's jewels and about $200 in cash."

"I saw what happened in the kitchen through my window next door," Glenda said. "I called the police right away and ran over here with my gun, but they were gone."

Dr. Quicksolve looked at Ben and Glenda. He walked up the stairs without saying a word. When he came down, he said, "I think Mr. Boinkt needs his head examined."

What did he mean?

SOCKS

Bobby Socks looked menacing sitting in Mr. Paddlebottom's office when Junior and Kimberly Kay walked into the principal's office. Bobby wore his jeans tucked into baseball socks just below his knees. Most kids thought it looked funny. That suited Bobby fine because he used every excuse he could think of to start a fight. He had beaten up almost every boy in school at one time or another over some imagined insult. Junior was one of the few boys Bobby would not mess with, though. Junior figured Bobby was afraid to pick on the son of the famous Dr. J. L. Quicksolve. It was as if he had something to hide and was afraid Junior would figure it out. He was right.

Kimberly's new skateboard had been stolen from her garage yesterday afternoon. She was sure she had seen Bobby in his baseball uniform pushing her bike away. Mr. Paddlebottom wanted to talk to Kimberly and Bobby before he called Bobby's parents or the police. Kimberly had asked Junior to go with her to the office for moral support.

"It was seven o'clock," Kimberly said when the principal asked her the time she thought she saw Bobby taking her bike. "I was looking out the front door for my girlfriend. Her dad was going to take us shopping," she said.

"I was playing baseball in the park at seven," Bobby said. "We were playing those bums from Jackson. We were just getting our last bats. We were ahead five to nothing when I hit my second home run of the game. Then I walked home with Michael Thomas. You can ask him."

"You can't believe Bobby's story, Mr. Paddlebottom," Junior said to the principal.

Why doesn't Junior believe Bobby is telling the truth?

WORD SEARCHES 1

GENERAL INSTRUCTIONS

Welcome to the wonderful world of word searches. (Say *that* three times fast!) Sure, words are used primarily to communicate, but let's face it—they're a lot of fun to play with, too. And there are lots of ways to play with them.

A word search puzzle is like a game of hide-and-seek. We hide the words—you go seek them. If you've never solved a word search, no problem. We'll explain all the rules shortly. If you have done word searches, keep reading. You'll learn about the twists we've added for some extra fun.

A word search puzzle is made up of two main parts: a grid and a word list. The usually rectangular-shaped grid is filled with what looks to be a meaningless jumble of letters. Actually, that jumble hides all the words and phrases given in the word list, which appears on the same page.

Hidden words and phrases always go in a straight line, but may run horizontally, vertically, or diagonally. Horizontal words (words that go across) may run forward or backward. Vertical words may go down or up. Diagonal words (top left to lower right, or top right to lower left) may run up or down along their angle. So words may run in any of eight possible directions. Also, be aware that the same letter may be used more than once when words cross it in two or more directions. Furthermore, ignore all punctuation and spaces in the word list when searching in the grid. For example, "That's all,

Solutions—Pages 230-238

folks!" would appear in the grid, in some direction, as THATSALLFOLKS. If all that sounds confusing, don't worry—it won't be for long. All it takes is a little practice.

You can tackle a word search in many ways. Some solvers start by searching for the across words. Others look for the long words first or words containing less common letters such as Q, Z, X, or J. Still others begin at the top of the word list and methodically work their way to the bottom. Whatever works for you is fine.

The same holds true for marking the grid. You can loop the hidden words, draw a straight line through them, or circle each individual letter. Whatever you choose, we recommend you cross off the words on the word list as you find them in the grid.

Each of these puzzles has a different theme and about the same level of difficulty. All but three of the grids are in the shape of a rectangle with 11 letters across and 15 letters down. (That's useful to know. If a word or phrase is more than 11 letters long, it is too long to go across or diagonally and so it must run vertically.) Each word list, except one, has 20 words or phrases.

Each puzzle contains a hidden message! After you've found all the words in a grid, read the unused letters left to right, row by row, from top to bottom and you'll discover that they spell out a hidden message relating to the puzzle's theme. (There's no punctuation, so you'll have to figure that out, too.) Hidden messages contain silly sayings, puns, riddles, amazing facts, quotations, definitions, or interesting observations.

Another puzzle-within-a-puzzle may be the theme itself. Sometimes the puzzle's title will make the theme obvious. Other times, you'll need to use a little imagination to see what the title means.

There are other added twists. A few grids have shapes related to their themes. One contains numbers. And some puzzles, when completed, display specially designed loop patterns.

If you draw loops (and most solvers do), make sure the loop contains only the letters in the word you've found and no other letters. Otherwise, you'll end up missing letters from the hidden message.

GETTING STARTED

```
D E C A R G Y A S T D
N R T Y O I F V E A R
S O S H D A F D O K V
O I I C E A O R E E W
P D L T N G E A G A E
E M N G I H E R R D I
N N E E T D T M T E S
T D B T E F U O R E E
H P I U U P K A D P G
E H T P T R U I I B N
B D E T A E S E B R G
O M E B H K O U K E P
O T M A C I H P L A N
K E I I L N N G C T W
E A P H C T E K S H R
```

AUDITION	PACK
BE SEATED	PICK SIDES
DEAL	PLAN
EMBARK	SAY GRACE
ENLIST	SKETCH
GET READY	TAKE A DEEP BREATH
GET UP	TEE OFF
GO HIDE	THINK
HIT THE ROAD	WAKE UP
OPEN THE BOOK	WARM UP

CHECK THIS OUT

```
I  F  B  Y  N  G  O
D  R  A  O  B  A  W  U  P
L  A  E  B  M  E  T  A  M
A  N  T  B  I  S  H  O  P
Y  K  I  Y  C  T  A  K  E
H  T  H  F  E  S  C  S  A
   L  W  I  M  O  V  E
   O  S  L  T  A
   R  C  E  N  Y
   C  H  E  C  K
   D  E  O  C  N
   U  R  A  U  I
Q  A  L  A  C  G  H
E  S  B  S  N  W  H  U  T
K  I  N  G  N  I  L  T  S  A  C
```

BISHOP	KING
BLACK	KNIGHT
BOARD	MATE
BOBBY FISCHER	MOVE
CASTLING	PAWN
CHECK	QUEEN
CLOCK	RANK
DRAW	TAKE
GAMBIT	WHITE

FATHER'S DAY

```
D  F  O  R  E  F  A  T  H  E  R
T  A  P  O  P  C  O  R  N  S  P
H  T  D  E  B  R  E  A  S  G  O
T  H  P  O  P  A  R  T  D  E  P
H  E  A  O  O  W  D  P  D  L  S
O  R  M  Y  P  D  W  O  O  G  I
P  F  U  I  L  A  D  P  L  N  C
O  I  W  Y  T  D  D  O  I  O  L
N  G  N  P  A  R  L  O  P  L  E
P  U  P  P  O  L  E  O  S  Y  P
O  R  G  O  I  U  P  H  E  D  L
P  E  A  P  R  T  I  P  T  D  D
T  Y  O  C  O  P  O  P  L  A  R
O  P  N  P  T  P  E  S  D  D  F
T  Y  D  D  A  D  R  A  G  U  S
```

CRAWDAD	POPCORN
DADA	POPEYE
DADDY-LONGLEGS	POPGUN
DOODAD	POPLAR
FATHER FIGURE	POPPY
FATHER TIME	POPSICLE
FOREFATHER	POP-TART
HOP ON POP	POP-TOP
LOLLIPOP	SODA POP
POP ART	SUGAR DADDY

AT THE MALL

```
T R U O C D O O F T A
L L P A A E S W O R B
A U R L S R A W E A S
S T A R B U C K S P C
S R H A T W C A L A O
Y N T E O O H E D G W
A C F I L E N E S E S
D T L T G I W A R H D
I U O A N L M C L T L
R O A T I S J I T S A
F G S H K R H A T T N
I N S R R M E O A E O
G A L L A M R S P A D
T H J C P E N N E Y C
L L N O R D S T R O M
```

ARCADE
BROWSE
CARTS
CLAIRE'S
FILENE'S
FOOD COURT
FOOT LOCKER
HANG OUT
J.C. PENNEY
J. CREW

MCDONALD'S
NORDSTROM
PARKING LOT
SEARS
SHOP
STARBUCKS
STORE
T.G.I. FRIDAY'S
THE GAP
THE LIMITED

X MARKS THE SPOT

```
X O B D N A S A B H B
O I O X E R A P E U A
S T S E L I F X E H T
P T T P H E A L L M T
H I O X E G O O E E L
I A N F O E K U N I E
N X R N T R D I O E A
X I E P X A H S H L X
E Y D N O C D X P O R
I X S C A M E I O H O
E A O M C R A V L X C
Y L X D O H E R Y O I
X A I X U N T G X F X
F G R H E S E I C E E
B O X X I N E O H P M
```

AXLE
BATTLE-AX
BOSTON RED SOX
DEEP-SIX
EXODUS
FAX MACHINE
FOXHOLE
GALAXY
HARPO MARX
HEXAGON

LOUIS XIV
MEXICO
OXYGEN
PHOENIX
SANDBOX
SPHINX
THE X-FILES
XEROX
X-RAY
XYLOPHONE

THE SIMPSONS

```
D  L  E  I  F  G  N  I  R  P  S
T  O  D  H  E  O  S  P  A  A  R
Y  E  N  R  A  B  B  C  P  E  E
B  A  A  U  L  I  E  M  N  S  N
W  A  K  H  T  O  A  S  I  E  N
H  M  R  B  U  R  N  S  D  J  I
Y  O  A  T  G  W  U  F  N  P  K
H  O  B  N  O  M  L  C  E  C  S
C  A  A  S  K  A  I  I  L  A  R
T  O  P  N  N  R  G  A  S  R  U
A  R  P  D  E  G  U  I  O  K  O
R  A  E  N  A  E  L  S  N  T  M
C  R  L  M  G  Y  H  C  T  I  Y
S  A  N  D  O  K  O  O  D  Y  E
O  S  S  R  E  H  T  I  M  S  S
```

BARNEY	MAGGIE
BART	MARGE
DONUT	MR. BURNS
EDNA KRABAPPEL	NED FLANDERS
GRAMPA	NELSON
HOMER	OTTO
ITCHY	SCRATCHY
JIMBO	SEYMOUR SKINNER
KRUSTY	SMITHERS
LISA	SPRINGFIELD

CIRCLING THE BASES

```
          B  T  C
       A  E  H  E  A
    S  T  R  I  K  E  T
 E  E  Y  I  E  V  R  U  C
 H  O  I  U  P  N  R  E  M  O  H
 I  G  E  R  S  M  T  M  T  A  C  J  E
T  T  R  O  E  P  U  R  E  T  T  A  B  K  R
P  N  R  E  S  O  U  T  F  I  E  L  D  L  B
L  U  O  N  D  E  C  K  P  H  E  A  G  A  U
 B  E  E  L  I  R  D  F  O  U  L  C  B
 W  K  R  A  L  S  E  N  A  K  G
    E  O  I  F  S  R  I  S  F
    W  H  T  E  R  T  E
       H  C  A  O  C
       N  P  R
```

BACKSTOP	FOUL
BALK	HOMER
BASE HIT	NO-HITTER
"BATTER UP!"	ON DECK
BUNT	OUTFIELD
CATCHER	SLIDER
CHOKE UP	STRIKE
COACH	UMPIRE
CURVE	WILD PITCH
ERROR	WORLD SERIES

"IT'S ABOUT TIME!"

```
T R A E Y T H G I L I
M O O E N E H I S T L
H N E G D O C S M O A
S T H G I N T R O F I
S I M T T V A N A O D
A M L I U D W H O A N
L E B M N L L E G W U
A T H E I U A N G I S
R A L R B M T A I N B
M A C A N I I E N S P
C O H O U R G L A S S
L E N N D T I B S K H
O R E T A L D E E O P
C H R A H S T E C N U
K S S T O P W A T C H
```

ALARM CLOCK	LATER
BIG BEN	LIGHT-YEAR
BIG HAND	MINUTE
CALENDAR	MONTH
DIGITAL WATCH	"NOT NOW!"
EGG TIMER	ON TIME
EONS	SOON
FORTNIGHT	STOPWATCH
HOURGLASS	SUNDIAL
"IN A SEC!"	WEEK

AT THE MOVIES

```
O A D P O P C O R N T
T N N T O H A E M E O
N V A S I E S D K Y O
E U T D B A L C O N Y
E E S P A A I Y T S O
R S N M A T I N E E N
C I O T I N E T H O E
S T I C K Y F L O O R
P D S A H H H S R D A
K R S W I T G O O H T
Y A E L O N G L I N E
B D C V I L B D O T D
B O N M I Y F O S T P
O R O A A E B U T S G
L C C N C G W T E R S
```

BALCONY
CANDY
COMING SOON
CONCESSION STAND
DOLBY
LOBBY
LONG LINE
MATINEE
ON A DATE
POP CORN

POSTER
PREVIEW
RATED PG
SCREEEN
"SHHH!"
SODA
SOLD OUT
STICKY FLOOR
STUB
TICKET

SURFING THE WEB

```
S M W H S E N I J A G
R E T T E L N I A H C
I S A R L T R S V H B
E S N R E Y D U A S E
Y A A R C A N T E L W
E G N C T H R R O N E
I E I P R O F I L E D
T B C D O O M E S A I
W O E M O D E M O S W
E A N A G R E L T N D
B R I U H A P T O S L
S D L F J U E G M I R
I A N L E E O M A A O
T I O B U L C M I S W
E M A N N E E R C S L
```

CHAIN LETTER	PRODIGY
CHAT ROOM	PROFILE
E-MAIL	SCREEN NAME
INTERNET	SEARCH
JAVA	SIM CLUB
JUNO	UPLOAD
LOG ON	U.R.L.'S
MESSAGE BOARD	WEB SITE
MODEM	WORLD WIDE WEB
ONLINE	YAHOO

LIFE'S A PICNIC

```
B A D O S P O A P D I
L U C T N U I I C A M
A E N A N S S R D L C
N A T S A T F E U A N
K E E G T A I G R S R
E I K O O C M R E O A
T B S C F D O U O T W
O D A F I T T B I A H
S L B R S H L O L T C
E E C T B D C S H O I
C H I P S E E O O P W
U C N P T L C L I N D
K G C O O R E U E A N
S Y I C T R A S E K A
P A P E R P L A T E S
```

ANTS	COOKIE
BARBECUE	COOLER
BLANKET	HOT DOG
BUNS	PAPER PLATES
BURGER	PICNIC BASKET
CARROT STICK	PIES
CATSUP	POTATO SALAD
CHICKEN	RADIO
CHIPS	SANDWICH
COLE SLAW	SODA

PIECE A PIZZA

```
        N O O O M A E F T
        T T A N C H O V I E S
        T E L A R A H O I W I T Y
    O S U G A S L M I L N C E A
    B U E M U S H R O O M I
    R R T R Y E O U R R
    O C L H E G A E
    C I L R A G P
    C V A E T P R O
    O O B A E L D U M I
    L S T P T A T H B I S P
    I W A A A N P A R M E S A N
        S E U M T S A U S A G E E
        M A C O S Y T A S H P
        I E E T O N I O N
```

ANCHOVIES	ONION
BROCCOLI	OREGANO
CRUST	PARMESAN
EGGPLANT	PEPPERONI
FETA	PESTO
GARLIC	ROMANO
HAMBURGER	SALT
MEATBALL	SAUCE
MUSHROOM	SAUSAGE
OLIVE	TOMATO

MONOPOLY GAME

```
E T N E R M Y P O N B
O S K R O W R E T A W
S E U P O O L Y N P R
O H P O P E R K T O I
E C O E H N E K O T M
S Y R R O R A R E N K
L T X A T Y R U X U L
Y I A M E L A E D D A
A N A F L T I E I R W
S U T J R C L N C E D
E M T S H I R N E A R
R M T A L A O M N T A
D O N O T P A S S G O
I C L C C G D I T Y B
E C A L P K R A P N J
```

BANKER	LUXURY TAX
BOARDWALK	MONEY
CHANCE	PARK PLACE
COMMUNITY CHEST	PROPERTY
DICE	RAILROAD
DO NOT PASS GO	RENT
GAME	ROLL
HOTEL	SHORT LINE
HOUSE	TOKEN
JAIL	WATER WORKS

A BAND WE'D LIKE TO HEAR

```
B  F  L  U  G  E  L  H  O  R  N
M  A  R  O  U  S  I  C  A  O  I
S  T  N  E  L  G  N  A  I  R  T
B  G  X  J  M  H  E  D  U  N  P
I  A  A  V  O  I  R  E  R  S  E
A  L  S  O  L  O  C  C  I  P  N
L  A  O  S  C  U  N  L  G  U  N
L  A  N  C  D  G  T  E  U  M  Y
C  Y  A  O  T  R  F  E  A  D  W
H  U  R  D  Y  G  U  R  D  Y  H
I  M  P  E  M  A  A  M  E  N  I
M  K  O  I  P  C  N  F  D  L  S
E  O  S  M  A  R  I  M  B  A  T
S  N  G  S  N  F  F  E  L  L  L
O  S  E  P  I  P  G  A  B  W  E
```

ACCORDION	HURDY-GURDY
BAGPIPES	LUTE
BANJO	LYRE
BASS DRUM	MARACAS
CHIMES	MARIMBA
DULCIMER	PENNYWHISTLE
FIFE	PICCOLO
FLUGELHORN	SOPRANO SAX
GONG	TRIANGLE
HARP	TYMPANI

THINGS THAT SPIN

```
H W E E R A D R E A S
T P E D A E H R U O Y
R I B N R N C G I R N
A G S V O O E N P O N
E U I R O R C R A O W
E S R E N F O E T D A
H T F N E P S A R G G
T O O A E D B O R N E
M R A L L I M D N I W
V I L P E S L W D V L
S E I T D L K R L L E
R P I N I A Y A A O E
M J O U E E A B T V H
C E N T R I F U G E W
M E S S D R O T O R R
```

AUGER	RECORD
BALL	REVOLVING DOOR
BATON	ROTOR
CENTRIFUGE	SKATER
DANCER	STUNT PLANE
DERVISH	THE EARTH
DREIDEL	TOPS
DRYER	WHEEL
FRISBEE	WINDMILL ARM
PROPELLER	YOUR HEAD

CAMP SIGHTS

```
H Y A D S T N E R A P
O C R A M P K S O R N
R G S E A I S N D T S
S W I M H C H A G S R
E Y S O T C O O O A K
B C R S M O R E S N T
A I O Q E F T A U D U
C T R U N K S B S C O
K A R I N E H F U R S
R N A T R S E S P A T
I N N O O U E N I F H
D S I N N E T L D T G
I T B A H E I C O S I
N A A M R N P F I R L
G R C E G A T E M A N
```

ARCHERY
ARTS AND CRAFTS
BUNK
CABIN
COUNSELOR
FROG
HIKE
HORESEBACK RIDING
"LIGHTS OUT!"
MOSQUITO

NAMETAG
PARENT'S DAY
RAIN
SAILING
SHORT-SHEET
S'MORES
SWIM
TAPS
TENNIS
TRUNK

HINKY PINKY

A Hinky Pinky is a two-word rhyming phrase in which each word has the same number of syllables. A simple example is DAN RAN. In this case, just one letter—the first—changes from word to word. We think that more variety adds more fun, so in the list below, each word in the pair is spelled significantly different from the other.

```
Y  E  K  R  U  T  Y  K  R  E  J
S  E  I  X  H  L  I  P  E  C  S
K  T  O  O  F  E  W  T  S  H  S
F  N  W  H  A  L  E  J  A  I  L
D  O  G  R  S  P  O  Q  Z  N  E
S  I  A  H  T  E  S  I  W  J  T
H  T  A  E  O  W  U  E  E  U  Y
W  O  E  M  A  S  R  L  O  R  N
E  M  T  X  D  G  N  T  B  E  N
N  N  H  Y  U  E  E  G  A  G  E
K  A  O  O  A  R  H  R  E  I  P
O  E  L  C  E  C  P  G  T  N  Y
H  C  K  P  N  I  H  Y  I  G  N
W  O  E  A  E  W  R  T  K  E  A
S  T  O  R  E  D  O  O  R  R  W
```

ANY PENNY	NEAR PIER
BLUE SHOE	OCEAN MOTION
DRY TIE	OWN CONE
HIGH FLY	SHAQ'S WAX
HOT YACHT	STORE DOOR
INJURE GINGER	TOO FEW
I SPY	WEIGHED MAID
JERKY TURKEY	WHALE JAIL
LOU GREW	WHO KNEW
MEET PETE	WISE THAIS

WORDWORKS

GENERAL INSTRUCTIONS

In the games that follow, vocabulary fiends can find many hidden words in the designated word for each game. Use only words of four or more letters and no proper nouns.

Solutions—Pages 239-243

1 "GAMESTER"

Find up to 82 words in the playful noun above. A score of 40 deserves a red ribbon; 50, a blue one; and 60, the dictionary hall of fame!

(4 letters)

(5 letters)

(6 letters)

(7 letters)

2 "FAVORITE"

Find at least 50 words in this shining example. Score 30 to be a tough contender; go for broke with 35; find 45, and you'll be favored in any word race!

(4 letters)   **(5 letters)**

3 "BETROTHAL"

There are 114 words concealed here. Finding 70 means you're a real word lover; 80, you're totally committed; and 90 or more gets the brass ring!

(4 letters)   **(5 letters)**   **(6 letters)**

                                                  (7 letters)

4 "DEVELOPMENT"

Seek out the 94 words concealed here. Get 60 words for a good foundation; 70, and you've done the framework; 80 or more, and you're a master wordsmith!

(4 letters)   **(5 letters)**   **(6 letters)**

(7 letters)   **(8 letters)**

(9 letters)

5 "EXEMPLARY"

Search for the 68 words hidden here. Finding 40 is outstanding; 50 makes you a truly superb player; 55, and you are a paragon of games-manship!

(4 letters)   **(5 letters)**   **(6 letters)**

(7 letters)

6 "POPULARITY"

Find at least 100 words in this fun-fest. Come up with 75, and you're hot; nail 85, and you're totally rad; 90 or more, and you're a party animal!

(4 letters)   **(5 letters)**   **(6 letters)**

(7 letters)   **(8 letters)**

7 "HISTORICAL"

Hidden in this stumper are at least 112 words. Locate 70, and you're a scholar; score 80, and be a professor; discover 90, and you've got tenure!

(4 letters)   **(5 letters)**   **(6 letters)**

(7 letters)   **(8 letters)**

8 "CONCENTRATION"

At least 150 words can be found in the word above, including one 11-letter word! A total of 75 is good; 90 is excellent; and 110 means your powers of concentration are awesome!

(4 letters)

(5 letters)

(6 letters)

(7 letters)

(8 letters)

(9 letters)

(10 letters)

(11 letters)

9 "XYLOPHONE"

This noteworthy number will reveal at least 40 words. Find 25, and you've made the band; 30 hands you the baton; 35, you're Lionel Hampton!

(4 letters)   (5 letters)   (6 letters)

10 "NASTURTIUM"

As you tiptoe through the hothouse, look for at least 84 new words. Uncover 55, and you've got a green thumb; find 65, you're president of the garden club; cultivate 75, and you are a wordiculturist!

(4 letters)   **(5 letters)**   **(6 letters)**

(7 letters)   **(8 letters)**

11 "WHISPERING"

You are likely to discover at least 84 words hiding here. Find 50, you're the sly one; uncover 60, and you're quite the detective; 70 proves you to be a master sleuth!

(4 letters)

ring

wing

(5 letters)

(6 letters)

(7 letters)

(9 letters)

12 "POLITICIAN"

The word above is concealing at least 86 words. A score of 40 is good; 50, excellent; and 60 means you win by a landslide!

(4 letters)   **(5 letters)**   **(6 letters)**

(7 letters)

SOLITAIRE BATTLESHIPS: ENSIGN

13

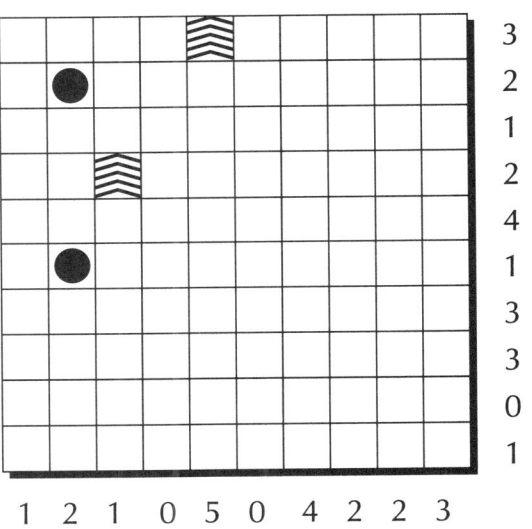

Battleship

Cruisers

Destroyers

Submarines

Solutions—Pages 213-216

14

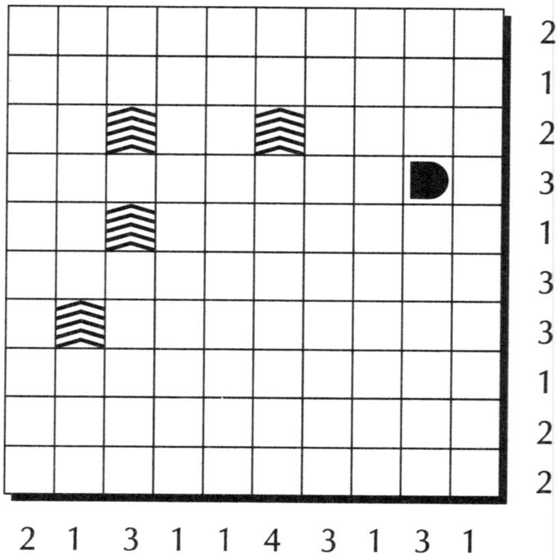

Right-side row clues (top to bottom): 2, 1, 2, 3, 1, 3, 3, 1, 2, 2

Bottom column clues: 2 1 3 1 1 4 3 1 3 1

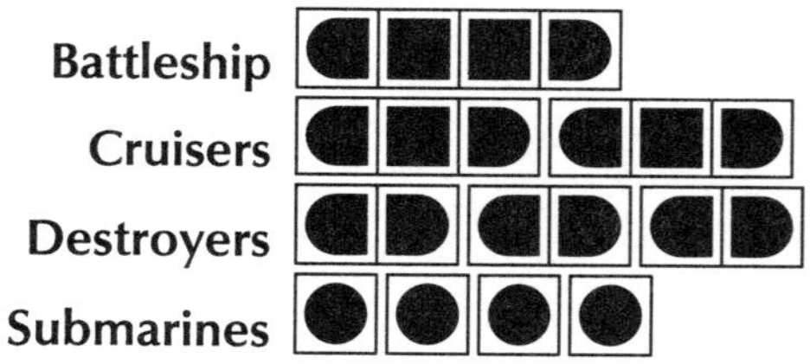

Battleship

Cruisers

Destroyers

Submarines

15

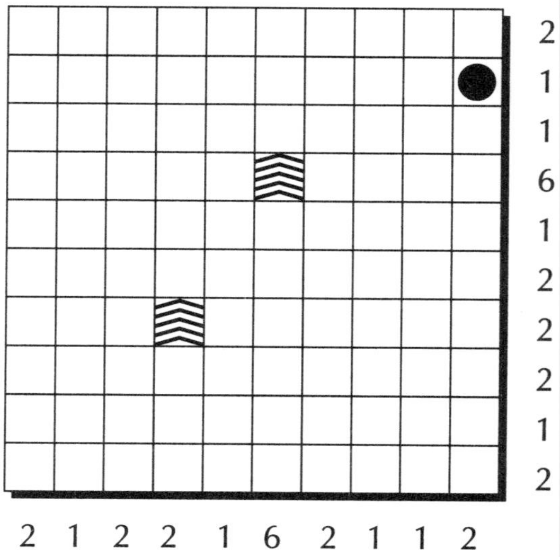

Right-side row clues (top to bottom): 2, 1, 1, 6, 1, 2, 2, 2, 1, 2

Bottom column clues: 2 1 2 2 1 6 2 1 1 2

16

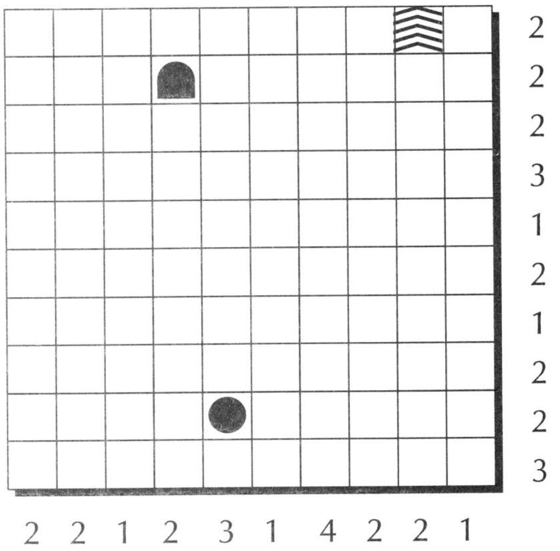
2
2
2
3
1
2
1
2
2
3
2 2 1 2 3 1 4 2 2 1

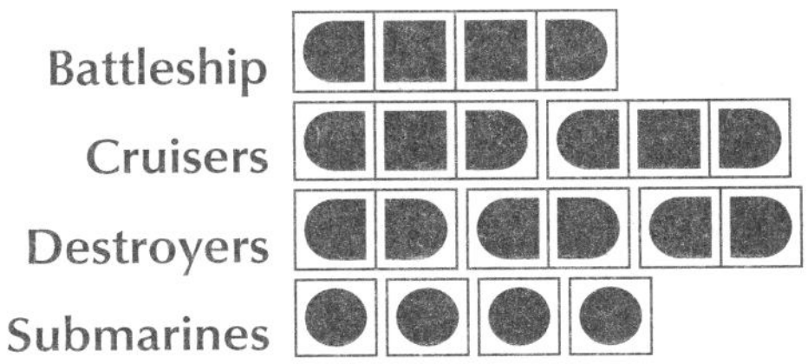
Battleship
Cruisers
Destroyers
Submarines

17

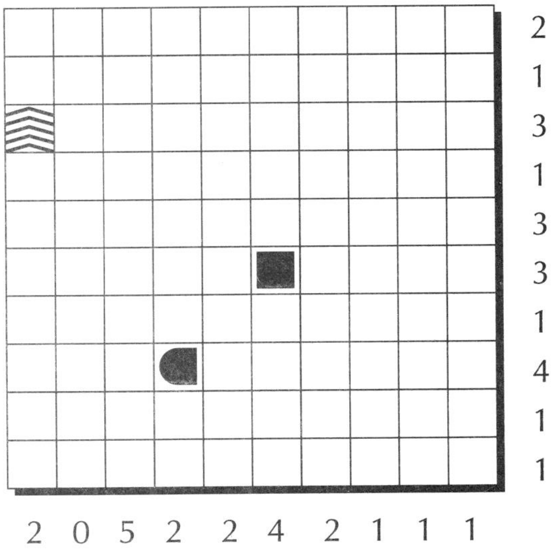
2
1
3
1
3
3
1
4
1
1
2 0 5 2 2 4 2 1 1 1

18

										2
										2
										2
										4
										3
										2
										1
										1
										0
										3

4　1　2　3　3　1　1　1　3　1

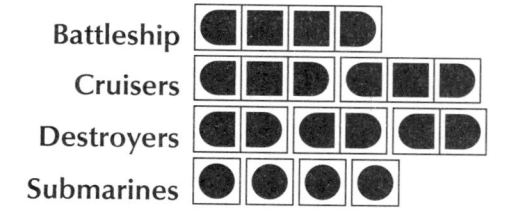

Battleship

Cruisers

Destroyers

Submarines

19

										2
										2
										1
										2
										4
										1
										4
										3
										0
										1

3　1　2　3　1　3　1　2　3　1

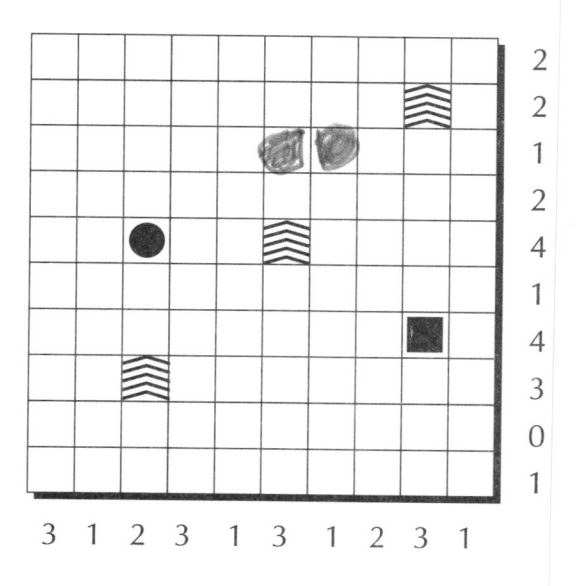

20

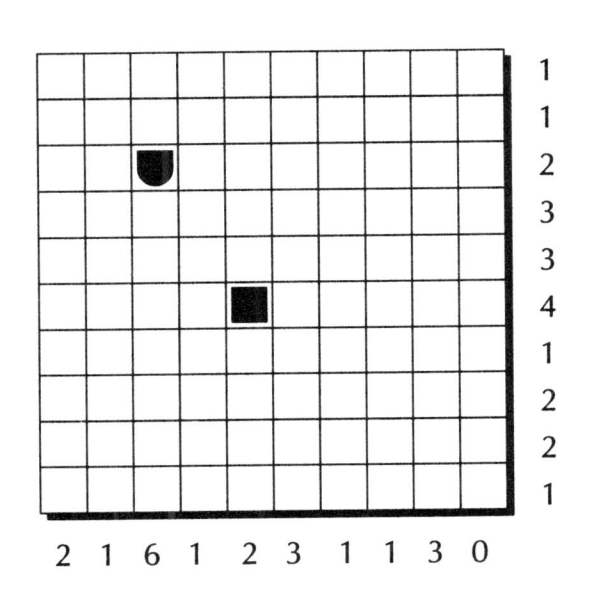

1
1
2
3
3
4
1
2
2
1

2 1 6 1 2 3 1 1 3 0

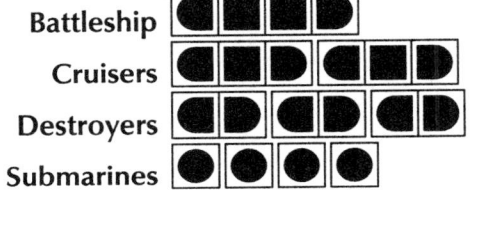

Battleship

Cruisers

Destroyers

Submarines

21

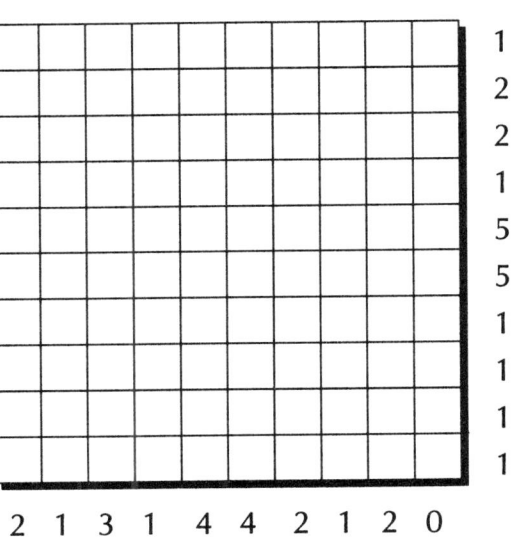

1
2
2
1
5
5
1
1
1
1

2 1 3 1 4 4 2 1 2 0

22

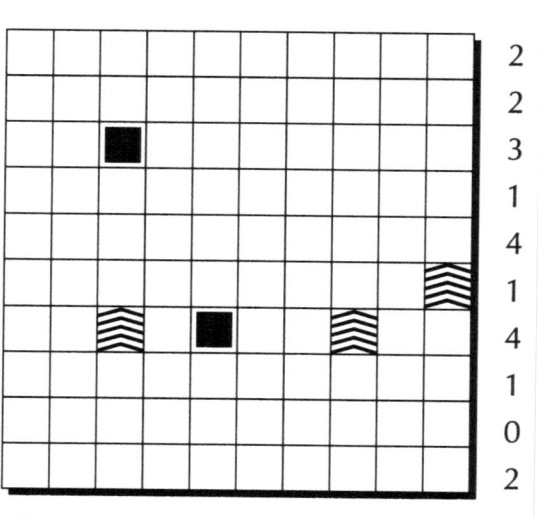

2
2
3
1
4
1
4
1
0
2

0 1 3 5 3 3 0 3 0 2

Battleship
Cruisers
Destroyers
Submarines

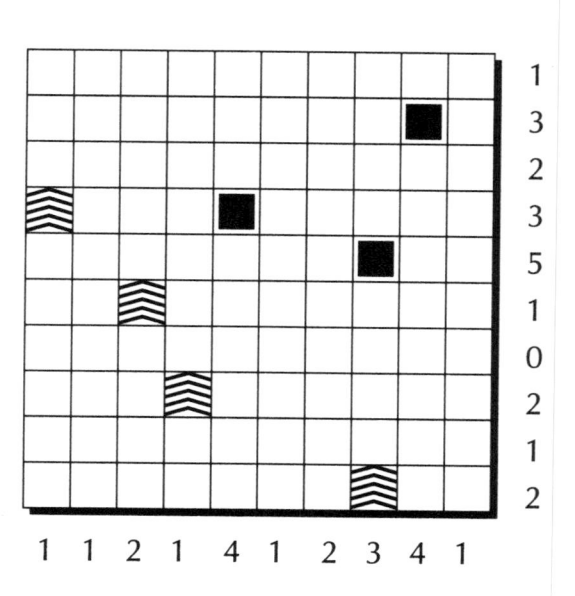

23

1
3
2
3
5
1
0
2
1
2

1 1 2 1 4 1 2 3 4 1

24

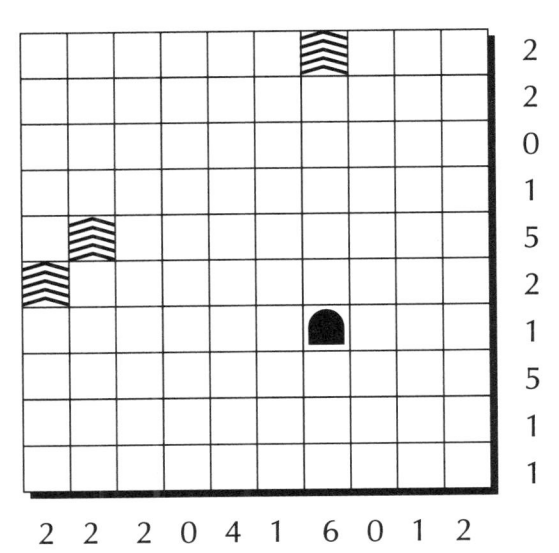

Battleship **Cruisers** **Destroyers** **Submarines**

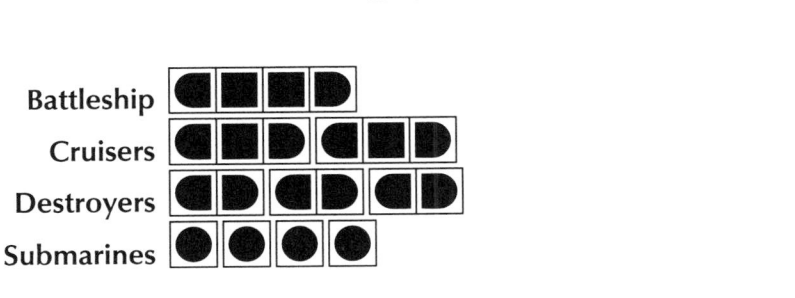

25

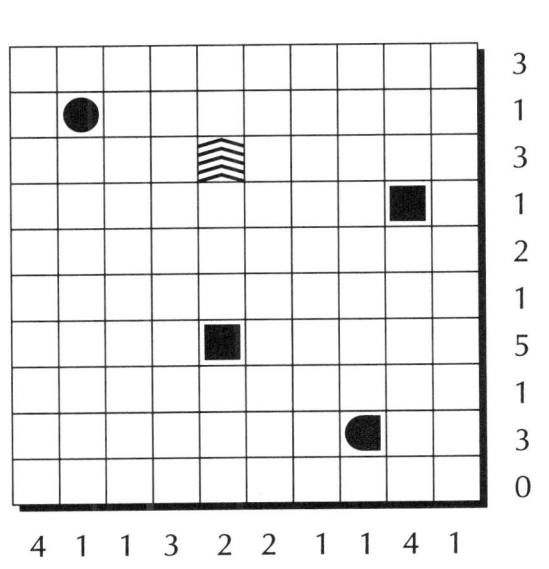

26

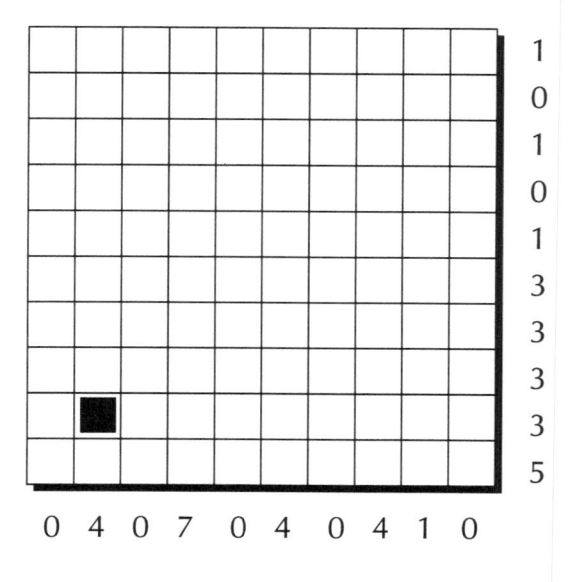

Battleship
Cruisers
Destroyers
Submarines

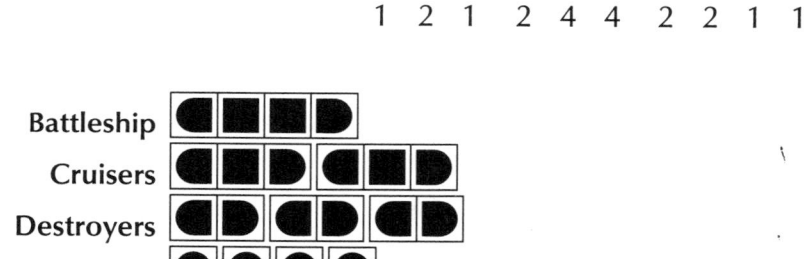

27

28

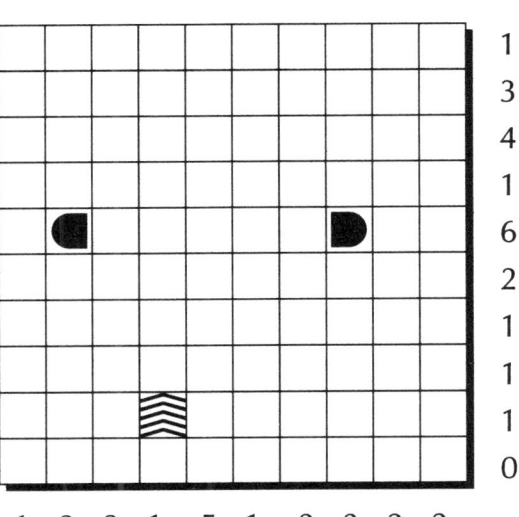

1
3
4
1
6
2
1
1
1
0

1 2 2 1 5 1 2 2 2 2

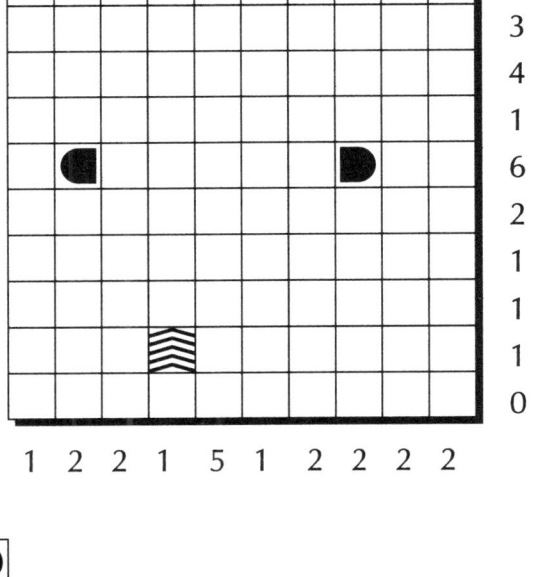

Battleship
Cruisers
Destroyers
Submarines

29

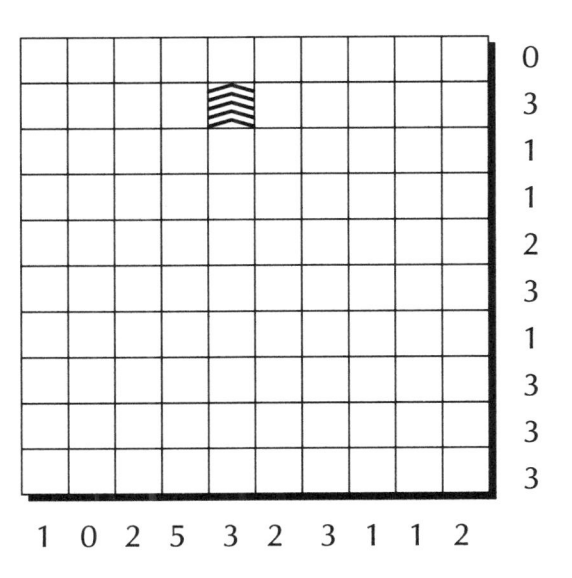

0
3
1
1
2
3
1
3
3
3

1 0 2 5 3 2 3 1 1 2

30

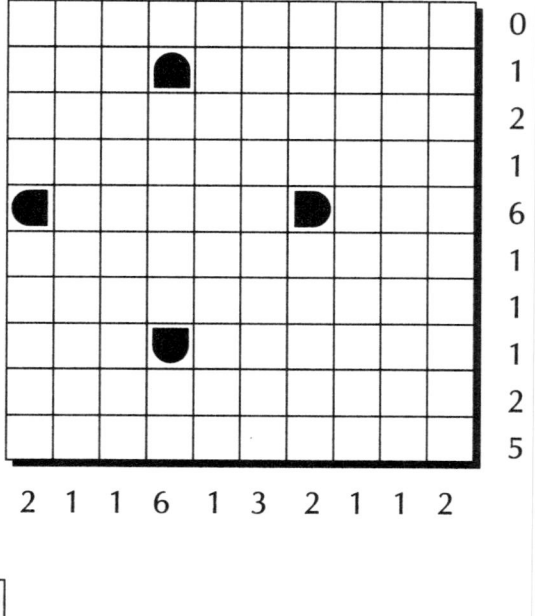

Battleship
Cruisers
Destroyers
Submarines

31

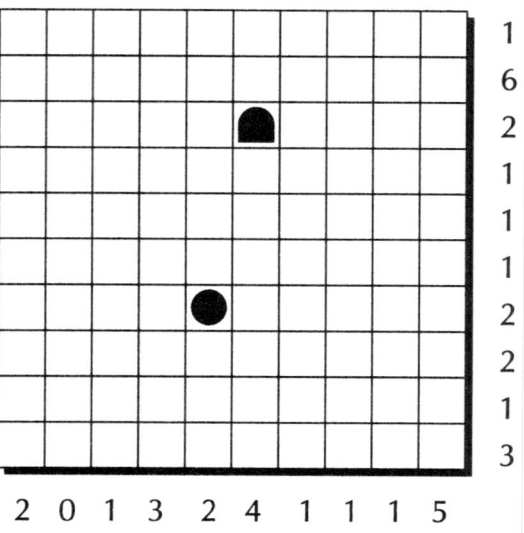

32

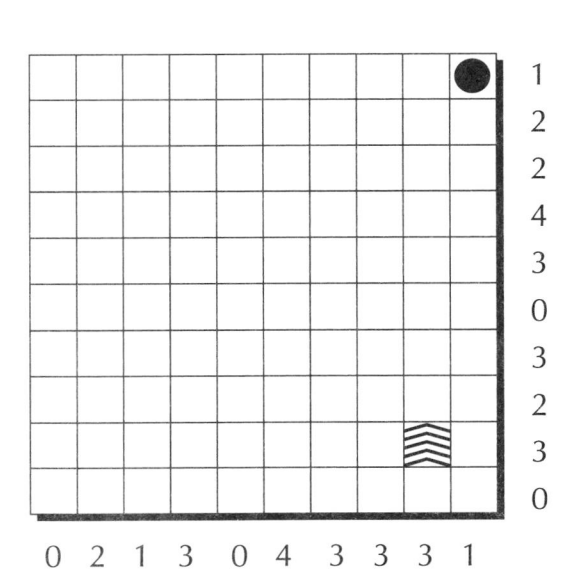

1
2
2
4
3
0
3
2
3
0

0 2 1 3 0 4 3 3 3 1

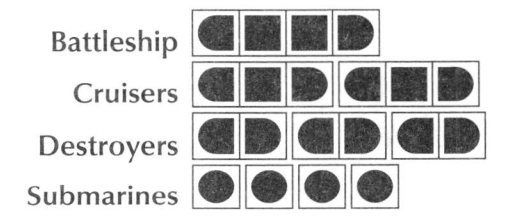

Battleship
Cruisers
Destroyers
Submarines

33

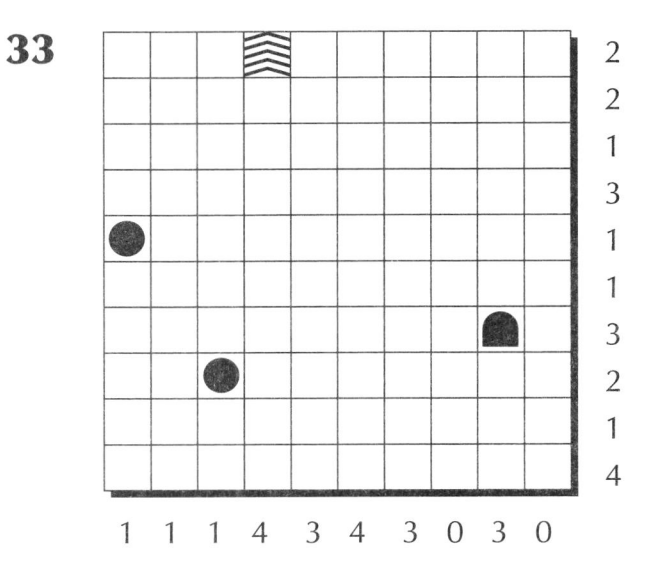

2
2
1
3
1
1
3
2
1
4

1 1 1 4 3 4 3 0 3 0

MORE MAZES

19

A ▶

▶ B

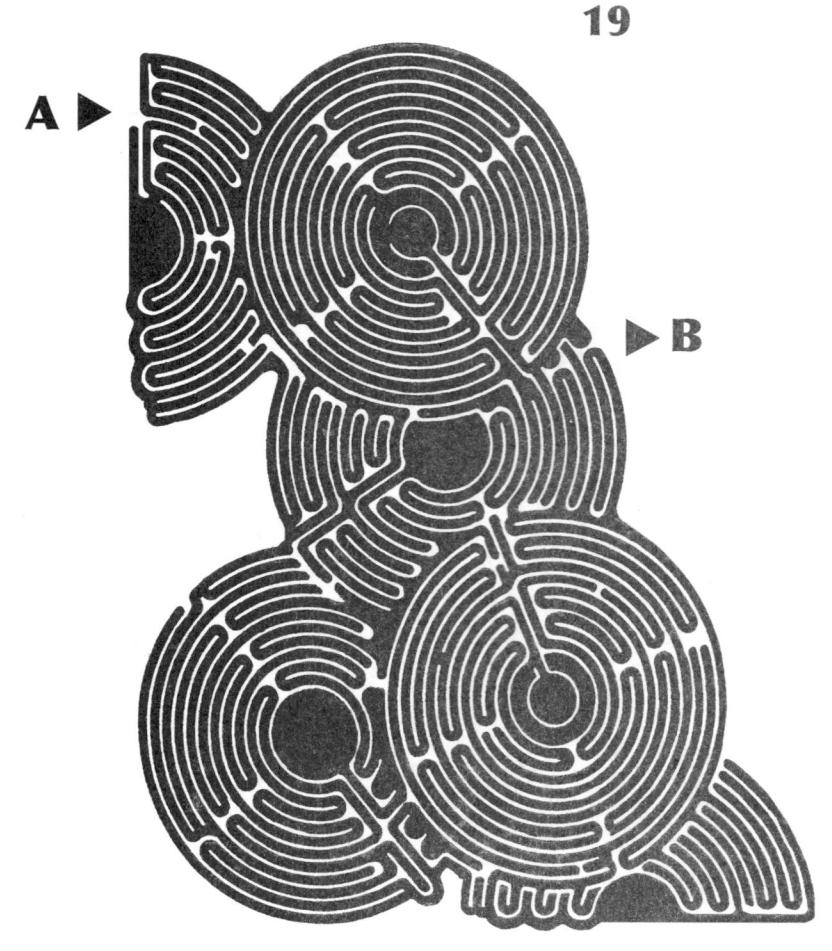

Solutions—Pages 224-227

20

21

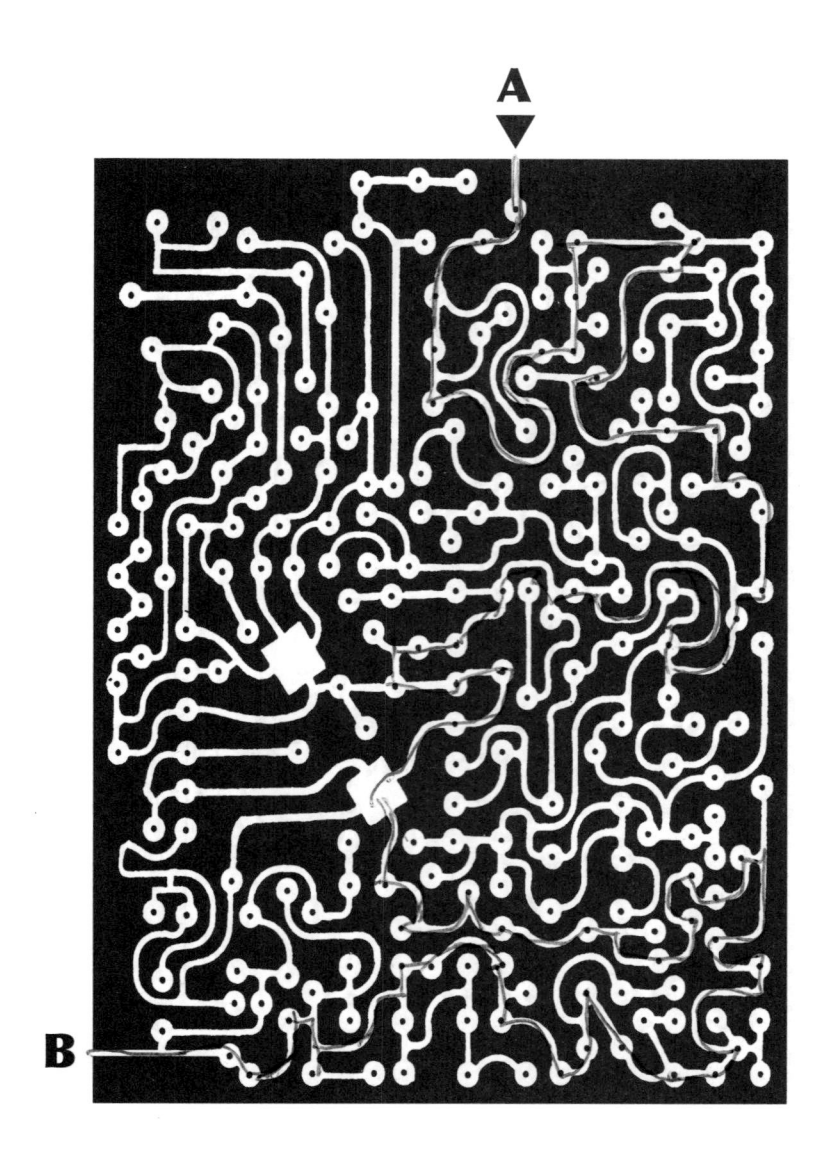

22

Find a route from A to B that passes every one of the stars. The route may pass each star once only.

A

B

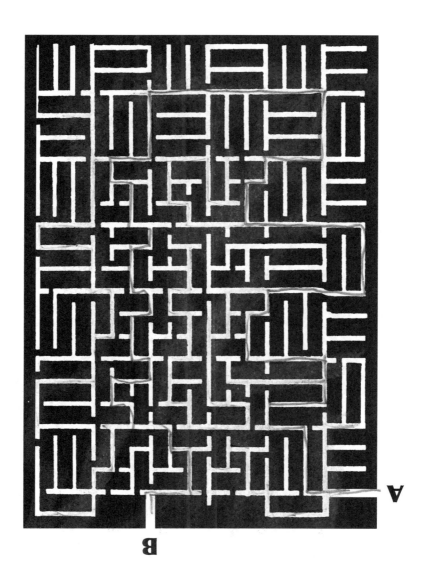

B

▲

▲

A

28

A
▼

▼
B

A B C D E F

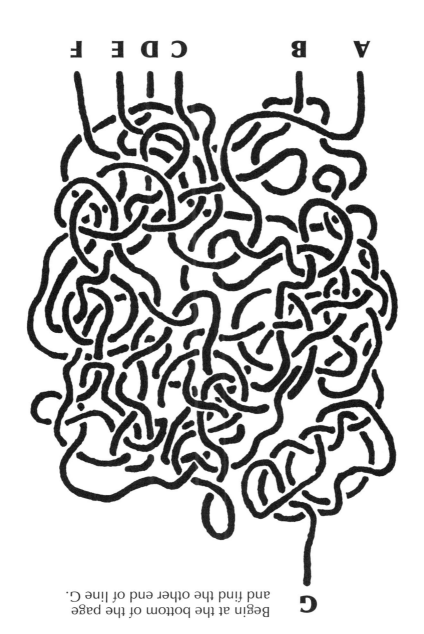

G

Begin at the bottom of the page and find the other end of line G.

30

WORD SEARCHES 2

"Guess the Theme"
GENERAL INSTRUCTIONS

To make things a bit trickier, the theme and the word list of three puzzles are a secret. It's up to you to figure out what the 20 items hidden in the grid are and what they have in common. To get you started, we'll tell you the first letter of each word or phrase and give you the appropriate number of blanks. For example, if the item were APPLE TREE, the hint would be A _ _ _ _   _ _ _ _.

    After you loop an item in the grid, fill in the appropriate blanks below the grid to help you with the word list. If you find a word that doesn't fit in any of the blanks, ignore it: it's not part of the list. You may also find that more than one word will fit a particular set of blanks. If it doesn't have something in common with all the other entries, ignore it, too. To help you, the clue list, when completed, will be in alphabetical order. There is just one correct overall puzzle solution.

    When you're done looping, read the unused letters from left to right, row by row, from top to bottom. They will spell out a message that reveals the theme.

Solutions—Pages 230-238

GUESS THE THEME 1

For instructions on how to solve Guess the Theme puzzles, see page 137. Hint: the grid itself resembles one of the hidden items. The word list is on page 230.

```
N T B H I B   F L U T E
O L I F E S A V E R S
T S R     S E G A G E
E W D     I L E E O E
B S H S C H D B E L H
O S O I R E E H C F C
O E U S C L E E G G S
K R S R T U N O D R S
P C E I D G     E I
A I O H K N N   E W
P A S S C T I H I N S
E N     O G W A R T S
R R     P S E W R T I
T H I H N O S E E T O
N O T T U B L N E S S
```

B _ _ _ _   N _ _ _
   B _ _ _   N _ _ _ _ _ _ _ _ _ _ _ _
B _ _ _ _ _ _ _ _   P _ _ _ _ _ _ _ _ _
   B _ _ _ _ _   P _ _ _ _ _
C _ _ _ _ _ _ _   S _ _ _ _ _ _ _ _ _ _ _
   D _ _ _ _   S _ _ _
   F _ _ _ _   S _ _ _ _ _ _ _
G _ _ _ _ _ _ _ _   S _ _ _ _
L _ _ _ _ _ _ _ _ _   S _ _ _ _ _ _ _ _ _ _
   N _ _ _   T _ _ _

THE LEGEND OF ARTHUR

```
A E R E V E N I U G A
R T X I H U R A M V L
D O S C N E W E A A E
E O S A A B R L L U K
R C A M E L O T L T A
D E T O I N I I P H L
R O U N D T A B L E E
O U L L K R T L U R H
M K N I G H T A H R T
E S N Y W D O N R Q F
C G L D O U N C U T O
M O R G A N L E F A Y
H O U F T H S L G E D
R O M R A T S O T E A
O R U H T R A T N E L
```

ARMOR	LADY OF THE LAKE
ARTHUR	LANCELOT
AVALON	LEGEND
CAMELOT	MERLIN
COURT	MORDRED
EXCALIBUR	MORGAN LE FAY
GUINEVERE	QUEST
HOLY GRAIL	ROUND TABLE
KING	UTHER
KNIGHT	VISOR

FEELING LUCKY?

```
K N O C K O N W O O D
C F L L A B T H G I E
A I N D E M S I C S N
R T H I R T E E N U G
C A C A B K H E V P N
A A H D G S A U P E P
N C A E I N N E M R N
O Y N W B I S O R S T
P H C J I N X R O T U
E O E C G S A H T I S
T T G O U I H L B T R
S I N N R O B G I G
R A B B I T S F O O T
O O O D T B L E U N C
K W H O R S E S H O E
```

BIG BREAK	LOTTO
BINGO	OMEN
CHANCE	RABBIT'S FOOT
CHARM	RAINBOW
CURSE	SEVEN
DICE	STEP ON A CRACK
EIGHT BALL	STREAK
HORSESHOE	SUPERSTITION
JINX	THIRTEEN
KNOCK ON WOOD	WISHBONE

IT'S ELEMENTARY

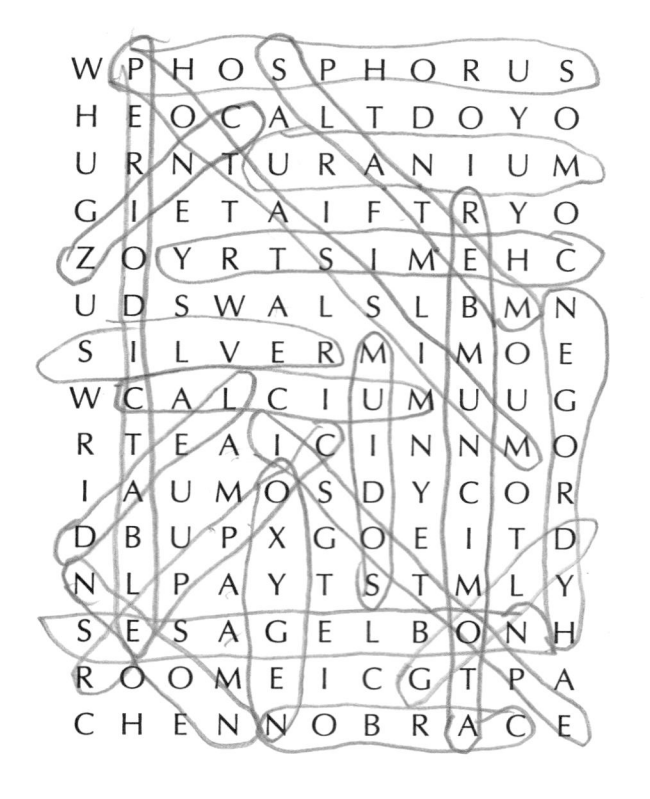

```
W P H O S P H O R U S
H E O C A L T D O Y O
U R N T U R A N I U M
G I E T A I F T R Y O
Z O Y R T S I M E H C
U D S W A L S L B M N
S I L V E R M I M O E
W C A L C I U M U U G
R T E A I C I N N M O
I A U M O S D Y C O R
D B U P X G O E I T D
N L P A Y T S T M L Y
S E S A G E L B O N H
R O O M E I C G T P A
C H E N N O B R A C E
```

ATOMIC NUMBER
CALCIUM
CARBON
CHEMISTRY
COPPER
GOLD
HYDROGEN
ISOTOPE
LEAD
METALS

NEON
NOBLE GASES
OXYGEN
PERIODIC TABLE
PHOSPHORUS
POTASSIUM
SILVER
SODIUM
URANIUM
ZINC

GUESS THE THEME 2

For instructions on how to solve Guess the Theme puzzles, see page 137. Hint: the grid itself could be an item in the list. The word list is on page 230.

```
T  H  R  U  O  F  Y  B  O  W  T
C  L  N  E  L  G  R  E  I  D  A
O  E  N  A  P  W  O  D  N  I  W
M  W  G  M  N  A  D  S  O  A  L
I  O  A  T  L  T  G  H  H  O  D
C  T  V  P  A  E  R  E  L  U  R
S  H  T  I  H  M  E  E  M  E  A
T  C  E  E  E  S  E  T  N  T  C
R  A  R  C  H  S  I  C  E  S  T
I  E  A  E  R  N  C  E  A  D  S
P  B  L  R  O  U  S  R  O  L  O
U  F  A  P  L  L  Y  M  E  R  P
T  R  U  O  C  S  I  N  N  E  T
E  O  C  T  A  N  N  G  U  L  N
C  A  E  P  O  L  E  V  N  E  R
```

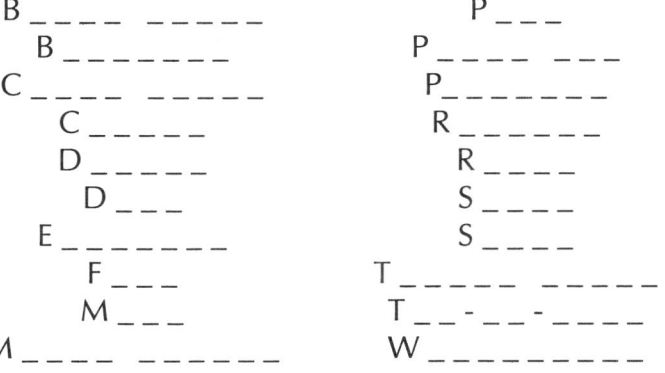

B _ _ _ _ _ _ _ _ _   P _ _ _
  B _ _ _ _ _ _ _   P _ _ _ _ _ _ _
C _ _ _ _ _ _ _ _ _   P _ _ _ _ _ _ _
  C _ _ _ _ _   R _ _ _ _ _ _ _
    D _ _ _ _ _   R _ _ _ _
    D _ _ _   S _ _ _ _
  E _ _ _ _ _ _ _   S _ _ _ _
    F _ _ _   T _ _ _ _ _ _ _ _ _ _
    M _ _ _   T _ _ - _ _ - _ _ _ _
M _ _ _ _ _ _ _ _ _   W _ _ _ _ _ _ _ _

DOG AND CAT SCAN

```
H E A T H C L I F F M
S W S H E N B E I U T
O L D Y E L L E R S R
C E A D L I L R N L Y
K P D P X V A P O J C
S I U M R Y E U I H I
E E N A G W E S E S N
B K O R T S A S T I G
A U Y T I T H I T E A
L D D S A I R N A Y R
I A N D R C I B P I F
N M S E Y T P O G C I
A R C S N T O O D I E
S A A I I N N T T D L
T M R D S E O S G S D
```

ASTRO	MURRAY
BENJI	ODIE
BUDDY	OLD YELLER
CHESHIRE CAT	PUSS IN BOOTS
EDDIE	RIN TIN TIN
FELIX	SNOOPY
GARFIELD	SOCKS
HEATHCLIFF	SYLVESTER
LASSIE	TOP CAT
MARMADUKE	TRAMP

STAR WARS

```
T T H E E M P I R E H
T E D A R K S I D E F
H I L L N M J E S T S
E Y P U A S A E R C T
F E P K B T O I D L O
O A L E H L L I I R
R S W S R O A G O W M
C S T K G D H A R O T
E A S Y P T R O D O R
R O O W S R L I F K O
O D N A L O L E V I O
A O B L F D S E B E P
B E N K E N O B I E E
R T A E R E W A R A R
S D A R T H V A D E R
```

BEN KENOBI
DARK SIDE
DARTH VADER
DEATH STAR
DROID
ENDOR
HAN SOLO
HYPERDRIVE
JEDI
LANDO

LEIA
LIGHTSABER
LUKE SKYWALKER
REBEL
STORMTROOPER
THE EMPIRE
THE FORCE
TRILOGY
WOOKIEE
YODA

"OH-OH!"

```
S O F O O T L O O S E
M E E O O T H O E R B
B A Z O O K A D O I O
U A B O L L E O G R W
K O Y R O D P F S A D
C O C O O N O R R K G
B E C U O O S C O O K
L O O P T H E L O O P
O O O O E T O D A B F
O T T O I S Y O O K O
P O S L A G O O N O O
E C D R O R L O O O O
R B O O B O O M C G
S E D O O A N P O A D
D Y O M O V H D A D V
```

BAZOOKA	IGLOO
BIGFOOT	KAZOO
BLOOPERS	LAGOON
BOO-BOO	LOOP-THE-LOOP
COCOON	OOMPH
COOKBOOK	POOLROOM
DROOL	SNOOZE
FOOLPROOF	VAMOOSE
FOOTLOOSE	VOODOO
GOODY-GOODY	"YOO-HOO!"

145

BEACHY-KEEN

```
S T I U S M I W S A N
T D A E C A D U N E S
T E V L L I N I K I B
E A K S L B R E Q D U
W B I N L E R N R U B
O E O O A T R A H S R
T E C D B L U B E E T
R K H I Y G B S M N G
E V I D E S S S U S
D A N F L A U D R W A
N T I A L T E R A R N
U L O G O O A N E D D
I M N W V A A G T I A
N U A T E D I T W O L
S I O S P L A S H N S
```

BIKINI
BLANKET
BODY SURF
BURN
DIVE
DUNE
FLOAT
LIFEGUARD
LOW TIDE
RAFT

SANDALS
SPLASH
SUNBLOCK
SUNGLASSES
SWIMSUIT
TOWEL
UMBRELLA
UNDERTOW
VOLLEYBALL
WAVES

GUESS THE THEME 3

For instructions on how to solve Guess the Theme puzzles, see page 137. The word list is on page 230.

```
T  H  T  N  A  E  G  R  E  S  W
E  D  G  R  B  R  I  E  D  T  A
E  I  I  S  I  F  B  I  I  L  R
L  L  E  A  L  E  R  E  G  I  T
O  D  W  I  L  T  S  H  Z  I  S
P  A  T  B  I  P  E  M  N  S  C
R  Q  M  B  A  R  C  O  D  E  A
E  U  T  H  R  A  C  C  O  O  N
B  A  T  A  D  A  T  B  A  E  D
R  F  L  I  B  W  A  A  Y  E  Y
A  R  K  L  A  W  S  S  O  R  C
B  E  S  F  L  F  K  S  O  E  A
R  S  O  F  L  U  R  T  E  F  N
N  H  H  A  N  A  V  A  E  E  E
S  T  R  K  I  P  G  E  P  R  S
```

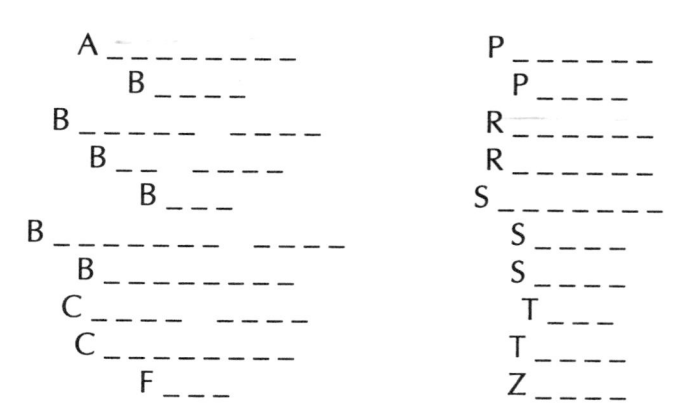

A _ _ _ _ _ _ _ _   P _ _ _ _ _ _ _
    B _ _ _ _   P _ _ _ _
B _ _ _ _ _ _ _ _ _ _   R _ _ _ _ _ _
    B _ _ _ _ _ _   R _ _ _ _ _ _
        B _ _ _   S _ _ _ _ _ _ _
B _ _ _ _ _ _ _ _ _ _   S _ _ _ _
    B _ _ _ _ _ _ _   S _ _ _ _
    C _ _ _ _ _ _ _ _   T _ _ _
    C _ _ _ _ _ _ _ _   T _ _ _ _
        F _ _ _   Z _ _ _ _

CASUAL DRESS

B T E W J S A R T E A
B A S E B A L L C A P
L L A H E N E A T E T
S N T R I B P R C I I
S O U S T R O H S K U
E V R S E S T T S H S
R E T A E W S F A E P
D R L R T S F R T E M
N A E Q I O U T U S U
U L N I T K O O A R J
S L E U H L S M L E N
E S C A U W A I C B L
T E K C A J M I N E D
O I T H A S T H G I T
S L I P P E R S E S M

BASEBALL CAP	OVERALLS
BELT	PAJAMAS
BLOUSE	SHORTS
CULOTTES	SLACKS
CUTOFFS	SLIPPERS
DENIM JACKET	SUNDRESS
JEANS	SWEATER
JUMPSUIT	TIGHTS
KHAKIS	T-SHIRT
MINISKIRT	TURTLENECK

THE LOST WORLD

```
N O J T T X E R T F A
A S L U L C O D O I G
T U N O R T N S G G E
S R A L P A S I U R O
J U I A A I S S T S F
W A R C L A W S K X R
T S W E E R E E I H E
U O G S O R L E S C P
O L M E N E A W E R T
P L A N T E A T E R I
E A T O O H F E O L L
S I N Z L B E E L P E
S T E G O S A U R U S
O F A N G C K H I N C
K E E N Y S E L A C S
```

AGE OF REPTILES
ALLOSAURUS
BONE
CLAWS
EGGS
EXTINCT
FERNS
FOSSIL
JAWS
JURASSIC

PALEONTOLOGY
PLANT EATER
RAPTOR
SCALES
SKELETON
SKULL
STEGOSAURUS
TAIL
T. REX
TRICERATOPS

WRITE ON!

```
S  C  R  E  E  N  P  L  A  Y  D
U  R  T  L  I  N  N  G  A  S  T
S  O  R  C  E  I  O  O  K  H  O
N  C  T  I  E  T  I  I  V  C  D
I  O  I  T  S  A  T  I  R  E  O
B  M  T  R  I  S  P  E  R  E  L
I  P  I  A  Y  G  I  H  R  P  I
O  O  M  E  M  L  R  T  M  S  S
G  S  T  N  O  W  C  E  N  R  T
R  I  I  I  T  R  S  E  M  T  O
A  T  O  Z  R  S  E  V  U  I  S
P  I  L  A  A  S  R  P  L  T  L
H  O  E  G  S  A  P  N  O  D  W
Y  N  E  A  I  L  B  R  C  R  U
R  W  Y  M  R  I  Y  G  H  T  T
```

BIOGRAPHY	NOVEL
COLUMN	POEM
COMPOSITION	PRESCRIPTION
ESSAY	REPORT
LETTER	SATIRE
LYRICS	SCREENPLAY
MAGAZINE ARTICLE	SKIT
MEMO	SPEECH
MESSAGE	STORY
NOTE	TO-DO LIST

SCHOOL SUPPLIES

```
S U S P P K L Y L C H
P A P E R C L I P I C
R D I R S O C A G S N
O T R P E N S H H S U
T C A A E T L A N C P
R M L P O I N R A R E
A D N D G B E I E U L
C P O H F D K K O A O
T D T S N S R C T P H
O E E I E A U A A S I
R N B S M L G P A L C
E A O L K C A K U L B
L R O T A L U C L A C
U A K T O E R A S E R
R T E S T T U B E S R
```

BACKPACK	MARKER
BINDER	PAPER CLIP
BLACKBOARD	PENCIL
CALCULATOR	PENS
CHALK	POINTER
DESK	PROTRACTOR
ERASER	RULER
HIGHLIGHTER	SCALES
HOLE PUNCH	SPIRAL NOTEBOOK
MAPS	TEST TUBES

BY THE NUMBERS

```
E  C  A  R  D  E  G  G  E  L  3
T  H  2  E  E  E  3  2  S  P  2
3  D  5  O  T  9  I  T  E  O  1
2  W  O  H  G  F  4  A  B  E  S
S  S  A  S  B  C  T  S  A  A  A
E  L  L  Y  E  D  E  9  B  1  Y
S  1  S  M  B  V  4  E  Y  E  S
S  E  T  E  I  U  C  O  L  B  A
A  U  Y  L  1  A  L  W  O  A  E
L  Y  9  K  T  T  I  B  N  C  C
G  4  H  C  L  U  B  K  5  O  E
D  T  H  U  2  S  O  1  L  N  A
3  2  1  B  L  A  S  T  O  F  F
2  B  Y  2  O  E  4  I  N  N  G
7  4  4  1  7  5  E  K  A  T  1
```

BABYLON 5	1, 2, BUCKLE MY SHOE
CATCH-22	R2-D2
COLT .45	TAKE 5
EASY AS 1, 2, 3	3-D GLASSES
49ER	3-LEGGED RACE
4-EYES	3-PEAT
4-H CLUB	3-2-1 BLASTOFF!
9 LIVES	3-WAY BULB
9 TO 5	2-BY-4
1-ON-1	2 IF BY SEA

GREAT BEGINNINGS

GENERAL INSTRUCTIONS

With these games, use the definitions to help you identify the words that begin with the specified letters.

Solutions—Pages 244-245

1 "IN"

Using the definitions listed below, identify these words that begin with IN.

1. Stimulus; motive   IN_____
2. True identity concealed or disguised   IN_____
3. Reliable; never wrong   IN_____
4. Establishment providing food and lodging   IN_____
5. Itemized list of goods   IN_____
6. Unafraid; bold; fearless   IN_____
7. Person who meddles in others' affairs   IN_____
8. Abnormal inability to sleep   IN_____
9. To receive as an heir   IN_____
10. Person confined to an institution or asylum   IN_____
11. Feebleness; weakness   IN_____
12. Measure of length; equal to $\frac{1}{12}$ foot   IN_____
13. To hurt or inflict physical harm   IN_____
14. Inactive; without power to move   IN_____
15. To examine by formal questioning   IN_____
16. Very young child; baby   IN_____
17. To sit on and hatch, as in eggs   IN_____
18. Raging fire; hellish   IN_____
19. Deep violet-blue   IN_____
20. The Hoosier state   IN_____
21. Group of foot soldiers   IN_____
22. Legally charge with a crime   IN_____
23. Colored liquid used for writing   IN_____

2 "EX"

Using the definitions listed below, identify these words that begin with EX.

1. To dismiss; to _____ from school   EX_____
2. The way out   EX_____
3. Free from obligation; excused   EX_____
4. "Bill and Ted's _____ Adventure"   EX_____
5. Overstate; make something better than it is   EX_____
6. More or better than normal   EX_____
7. Test or quiz   EX_____
8. Process to discover something unknown   EX_____
9. Facial movement that reveals thoughts   EX_____
10. Minimize; apologize   EX_____
11. Second book of the Old Testament   EX_____
12. Costly; high priced   EX_____
13. Prolonged banishment   EX_____
14. Precise; accurate   EX_____
15. King Arthur's sword   EX_____
16. E.T. is one; alien being   EX_____
17. Enlarge; grow   EX_____
18. Great fatigue or weariness   EX_____
19. Highway for high-speed traffic   EX_____
20. One who carries out death penalty   EX_____
21. To send goods from one country to another   EX_____
22. Not an introvert   EX_____

3 "QU"

Using the definitions listed below, identify these words that begin with QU.

1. Wet, boggy ground — QU _____
2. A group of four — QUad _____
3. Bedcover stitched in patterns — QUilt _____
4. Sound a duck makes — QUack _____
5. Shake; tremble — QUake _____
6. Not noisy; hushed — QUiet _____
7. Angry dispute — QU _____
8. Wet, deep sand deposit — QU _____
9. Most powerful chess piece — QUeen _____
10. State of uncertainty; dilemma — QU _____
11. Society of Friends member — QU _____
12. Imposed isolation — QU _____
13. Small game bird — QU _____
14. Stone or slate is excavated from this — QUartz _____
15. Nazi collaborator; traitor — QU _____
16. Drink deeply and heartily — QU _____
17. Peculiarity — QU _____
18. Question; inquiry — QU _____
19. Line up — QU _____
20. Pleasingly odd and old-fashioned — QU _____
21. Subdue; allay — QU _____
22. Malaria treatment — QU _____
23. Yellowish apple-shaped fruit — QU _____
24. Football team leader — QU _____
25. Witty remark — QU _____

4 "WA"

Using the definitions listed below, identify these words that begin with WA.

1. Erratic, eccentric, irrational (slang)   WA_____
2. Thin, crisp cracker   WA_____
3. Apple, celery, and walnut mixture   WA_____
4. Carry or propel lightly   WA_____
5. Female who serves restaurant patrons   WA_____
6. Four-wheeled vehicle   WA_____
7. Child without home or friends   WA_____
8. Massive sea animal of the seal family   WA_____
9. Small kangaroo   WA_____
10. Roundish nut with two-lobed shell   WA_____
11. Unchaste; lewd   WA_____
12. Person looking on at a dance   WA_____
13. Yellow substance secreted by bees   WA_____
14. Fleshy flap of skin hanging from throat   WA_____
15. Person's supply of clothes   WA_____
16. Frame with ridged metal used for cleaning   WA_____
17. Sing like a bird   WA_____
18. Path taken by North American Indians on warlike expedition   WA_____
19. First U.S. president   WA_____
20. Sorcerer; wizard   WA_____
21. Longing or urge to travel   WA_____
22. Ballroom dance   WA_____

5 "SH"

Using the definitions listed below, identify these words that begin with SH.

1. Darkness cast upon a surface   SH_____
2. Frozen watered fruit juice and sugar   SH_____
3. English dramatist and poet; bard of Avon   SH_____
4. Onionlike plant used for flavoring   SH_____
5. Person who uses unethical or tricky methods   SH_____
6. Fragment; broken piece   SH_____
7. Cloth used to wrap corpse for burial   SH_____
8. Neglect; evade an obligation   SH_____
9. Shell fragments scattered by explosion   SH_____
10. Fraud; imitation or counterfeit   SH_____
11. Tomb of saint or revered person   SH_____
12. British silver coin   SH_____
13. Gesture indicating indifference   SH_____
14. County's chief law enforcement officer   SH_____
15. Plant; bush   SH_____
16. Bunch of cut stalks of grain   SH_____
17. Young pig   SH_____
18. Used in baked goods   SH_____
19. Sharp, piercing cry or scream   SH_____
20. Small, long-tailed crustacean   SH_____
21. Nagging, evil-tempered woman   SH_____
22. Scrupulously avoid   SH_____

6 "PO"

Using the definitions listed below, identify these words that begin with PO.

1. Written expression, usually rhyming   PO _em_____
2. White, translucent, hard earthenware   PO _____
3. Spirit; ghost   PO _____
4. Device measuring pulse; lie detector   PO _____
5. To cook unbroken egg in water   PO _____
6. Hawaiian food made of mashed taro root   PO _____
7. Pope or high priest   PO _____
8. Flat portable case used for carrying   PO _____
9. Yellow powderlike cells on flower stamens   PO _____
10. Animal covered with sharp spines   PO _____
11. Painting of person, usually the face   PO _____
12. Position of body parts   PO _____
13. Popular card game   PO _____
14. Nonsense (slang)   PO _____
15. Hairdo; hair swept high off forehead   PO _____
16. Fast dance using specific music   PO _____
17. Body of men who assist sheriff   PO _____
18. The North Star   PO _____
19. Leading Communist Party committee   PO _____
20. Former mail delivery system using horses   PO _____

7 "MA"

Using the definitions listed below, identify these words that begin with MA.

1. Authoritative order or command   MA_____
2. Small South American monkey   MA_____
3. Short love poem that can be set to music   MA_____
4. Hard metamorphic limestone   MA_____
5. Hypothetical inhabitant of Mars   MA_____
6. Man in charge of royal household   MA_____
7. One who chooses suffering rather than compromising principles   MA_____
8. Young Caroline Kennedy's pony   MA_____
9. Fat Tuesday; carnival day in New Orleans   MA_____
10. Manage or plan skillfully; scheme   MA_____
11. Intricate network of pathways   MA_____
12. Disease caused by infectious mosquito bite   MA_____
13. Tract of low, wet soft land   MA_____
14. Tragedy by Shakespeare   MA_____
15. Long distance or endurance contest   MA_____
16. Care of fingernails   MA_____
17. Rhythmic ballroom dance   MA_____
18. Cocktail made of gin and dry vermouth   MA_____
19. Purple and red mixture   MA_____

8 "FO"

Using the definitions listed below, identify these words that begin with FO.

1. Young horse — FO**al**
2. Lack of sense or rational conduct — FO
3. One's strong point — FO
4. Creamy sauce used for dipping — FO
5. Imitate for purposes of fraud — FO
6. Field team game played with pigskin — FO
7. Enemy; opponent — FO**e**
8. Comment or reference at bottom of page — FO
9. For eternity; always; endlessly — FO
10. Bowl holding water in baptismal services — FO
11. Leaves, as of a plant or tree — FO
12. Tract of land covered by trees — FO
13. Small tongs or pincers for grasping, pulling — FO
14. Weakness in character; frailty — FO
15. Coarse food for cattle, horses — FO
16. Chain attached to watch — FO
17. To search for food or provisions — FO
18. Child found after parental abandonment — FO
19. Two weeks — FO
20. Hardened remains of ancient life — FO
21. Plant with small blue flowers — FO
22. Prohibit; rule against — FO

9 "NO"

Using the definitions listed below, identify these words that begin with NO.

1. Flat, narrow strip of dough   NO_____
2. Longing for something long ago   NO_____
3. Eleventh month of calendar year   NO_____
4. Cut in edge or surface   NO_____
5. In the Bible, patriarch commanded to build an Ark   NO_____
6. Party's candidate in election   NO_____
7. Harmful to health   NO_____
8. Casually indifferent; without concern   NO_____
9. Clamor; din   NO_____
10. Special prayers and devotions   NO_____
11. Christmas expression of joy   NO_____
12. Swedish inventor of dynamite   NO_____
13. Loop formed in rope   NO_____
14. Small spout of hose   NO_____
15. Pen name; pseudonym   NO_____
16. Official authorized to attest documents   NO_____
17. Sugar and nut confection   NO_____
18. Brief written statement to aid memory   NO_____
19. Wanderer   NO_____
20. Functioning at night   NO_____
21. Person new to activity; apprentice   NO_____
22. Northern end of earth's axis   NO_____
23. Small knot or rounded lump   NO_____

SAY IT AGAIN, SAM

GENERAL INSTRUCTIONS

In each of the following grids, five synonyms or words similar in meaning can be found. Following the example and using the clue letters provided in each puzzle, complete the words.

Solutions—Page 246

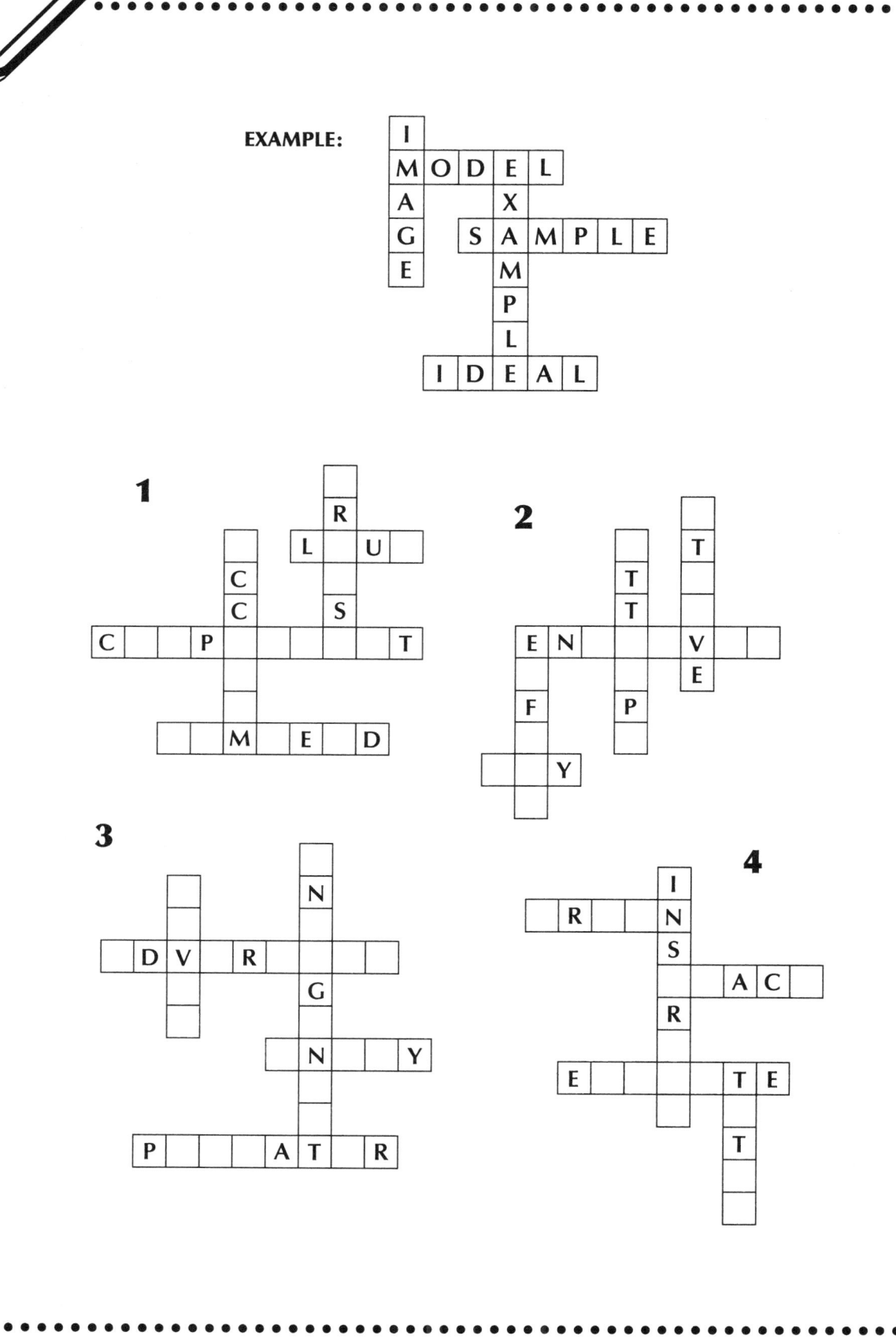

EXAMPLE:

```
    I
    M O D E L
    A     X
    G   S A M P L E
    E   M
        P
        L
      I D E A L
```

1

```
          R
        L U
      C
      C     S
  C   P         T
          M   E   D
```

2

```
            T
        T
        T
    E N       V
            E
      F   P
        Y
```

3

```
        N
      D V   R
          G
        N   Y
  P     A T   R
```

4

```
        I
    R   N S
        R   A C
        R
      E       T E
        T
```

164

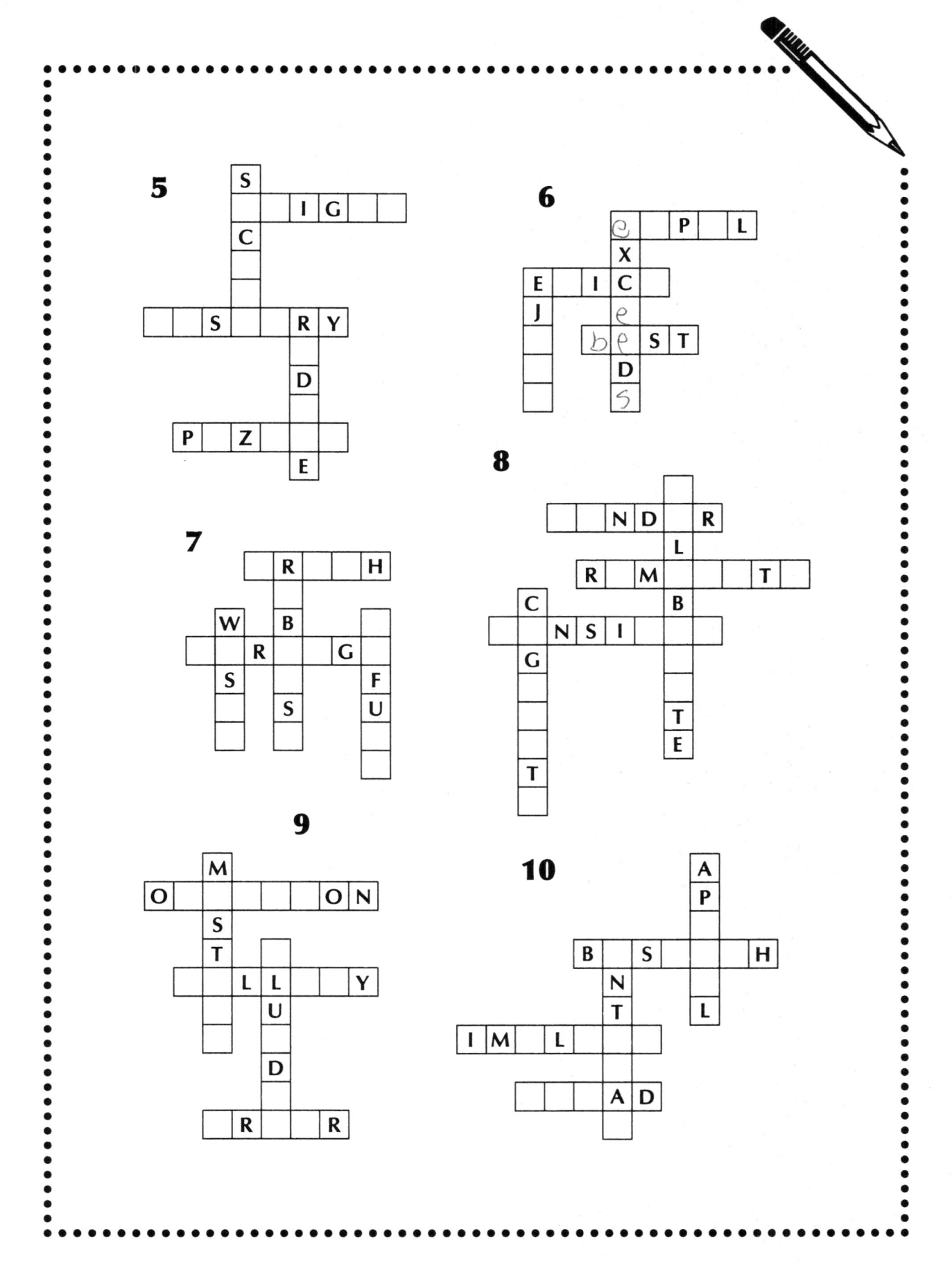

SOLITAIRE BATTLESHIPS: COMMODORE

34

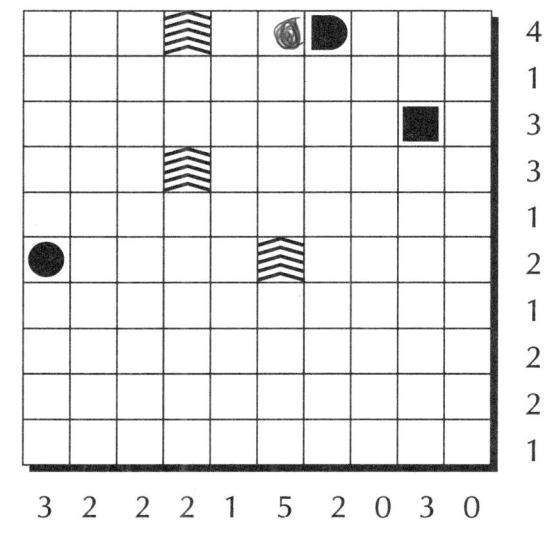

Battleship

Cruisers

Destroyers

Submarines

Solutions—Pages 216-219

35

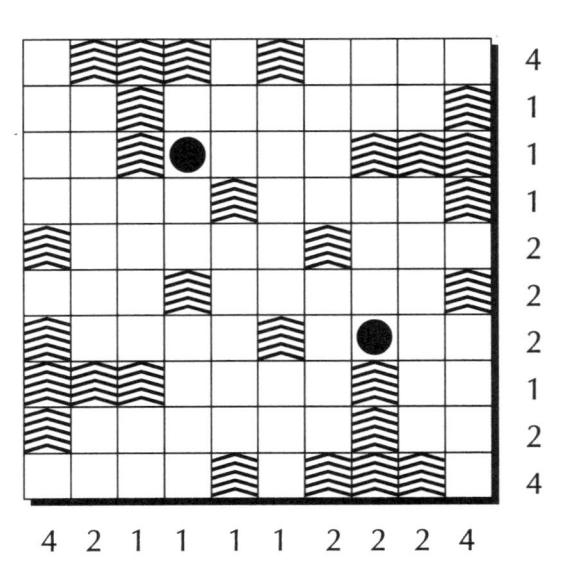

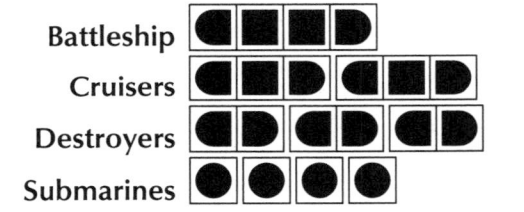

Battleship

Cruisers

Destroyers

Submarines

36

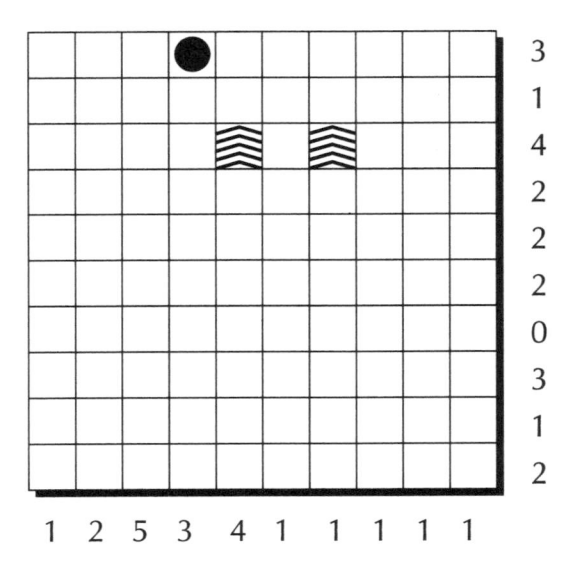

37

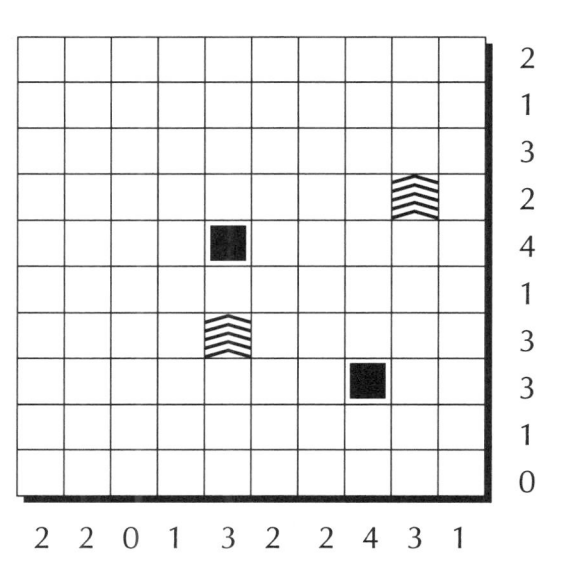

Battleship
Cruisers
Destroyers
Submarines

38

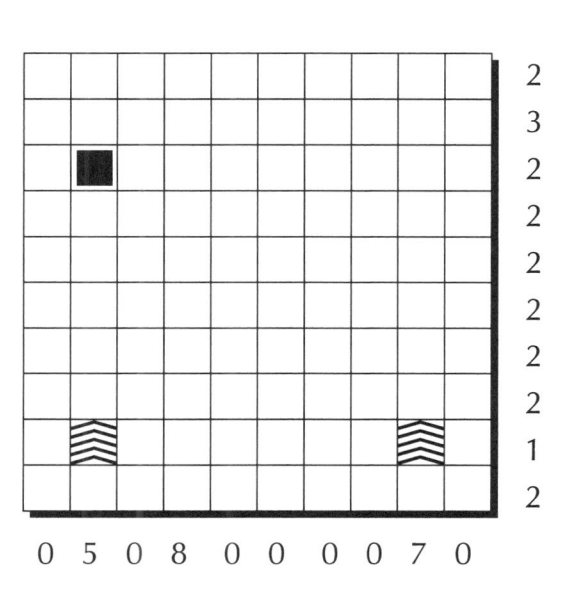

39

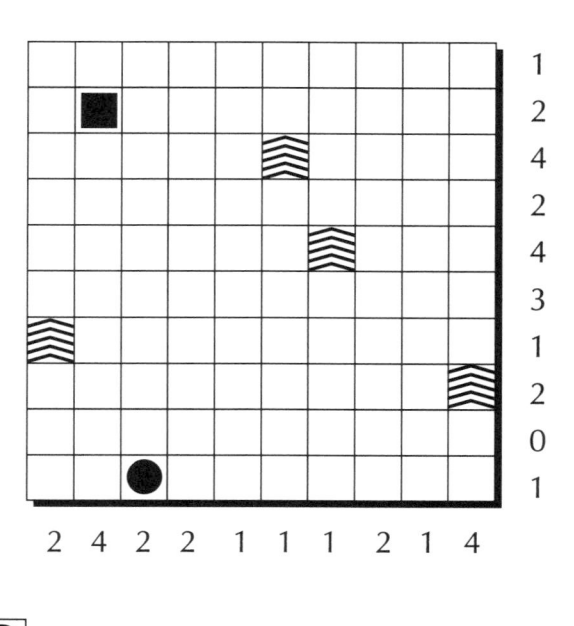

Battleship
Cruisers
Destroyers
Submarines

40

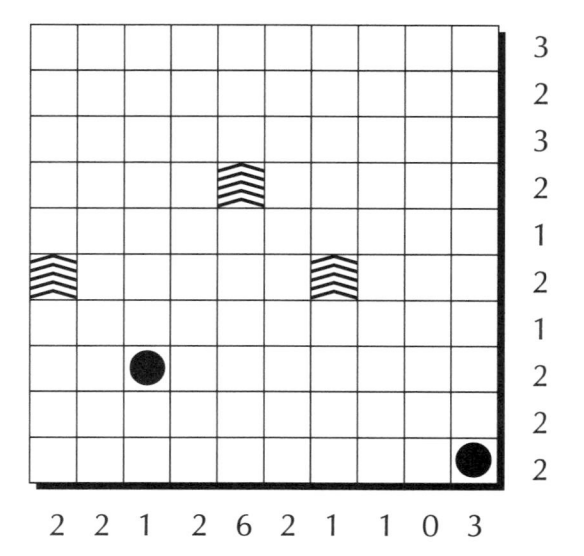

41

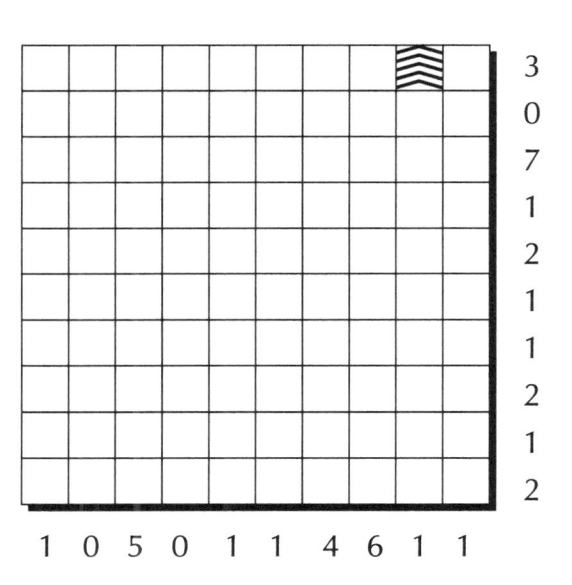

3
0
7
1
2
1
1
2
1
2

1 0 5 0 1 1 4 6 1 1

Battleship
Cruisers
Destroyers
Submarines

42

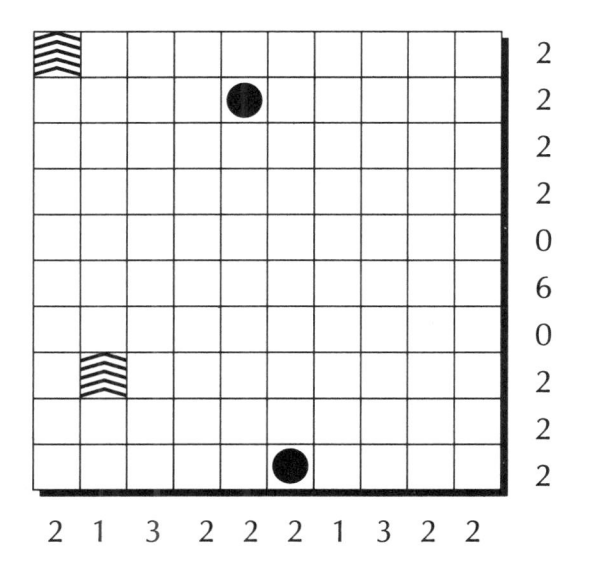

2
2
2
2
0
6
0
2
2
2

2 1 3 2 2 2 1 3 2 2

43

3 0 1 1 2 5 2 2 1 3
1 1 3 2 2 3 3 2 0 3

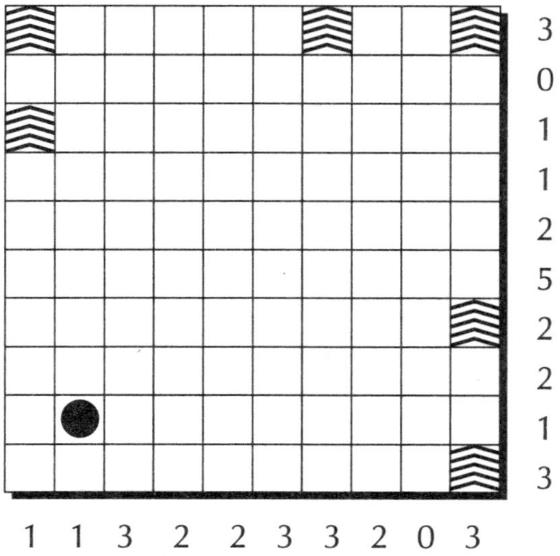

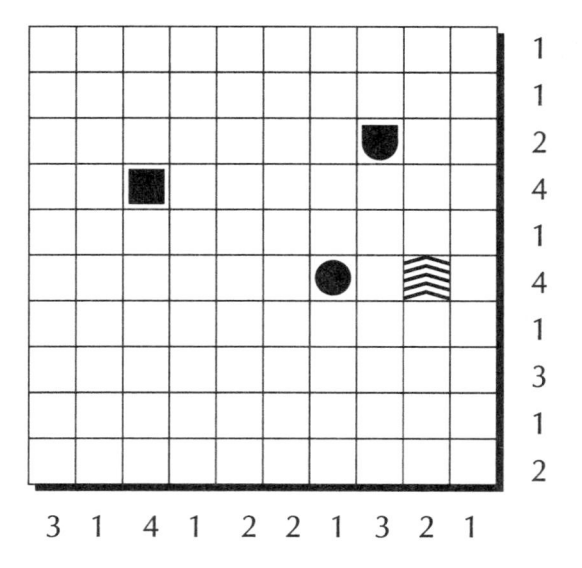

Battleship
Cruisers
Destroyers
Submarines

44

1 1 2 4 1 4 1 3 1 2
3 1 4 1 2 2 1 3 2 1

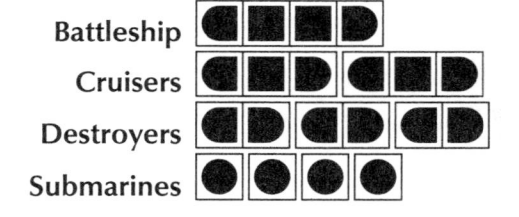

45

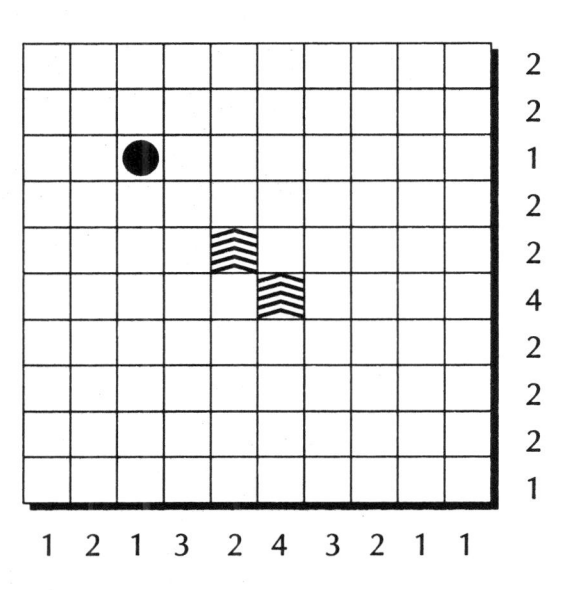

Battleship

Cruisers

Destroyers

Submarines

46

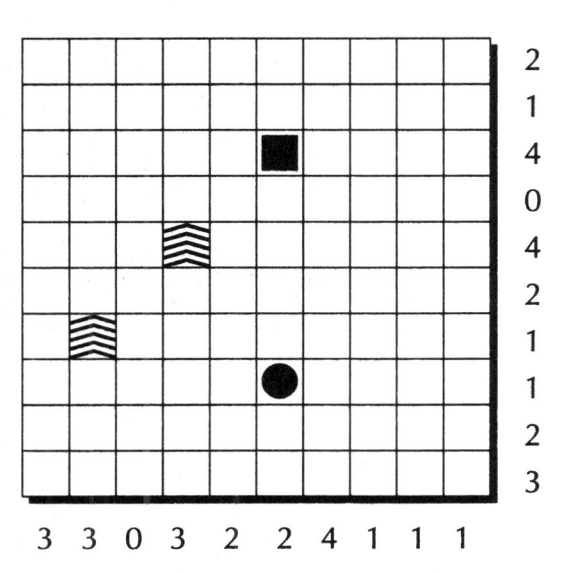

47

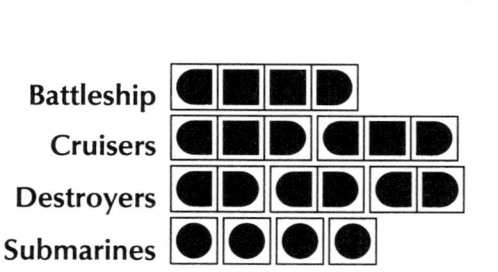

Battleship
Cruisers
Destroyers
Submarines

48

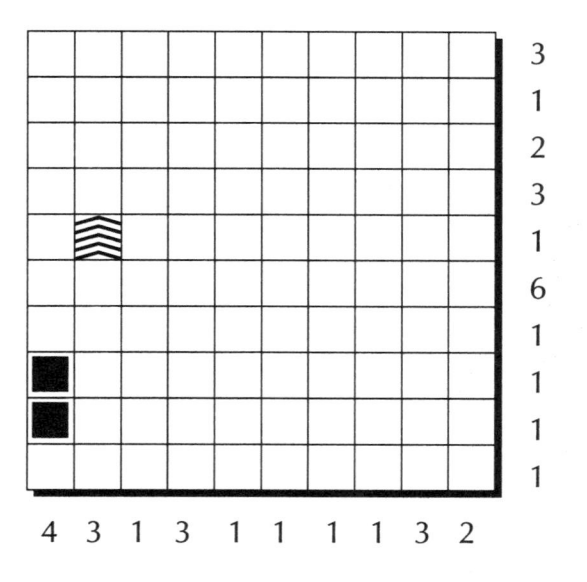

49

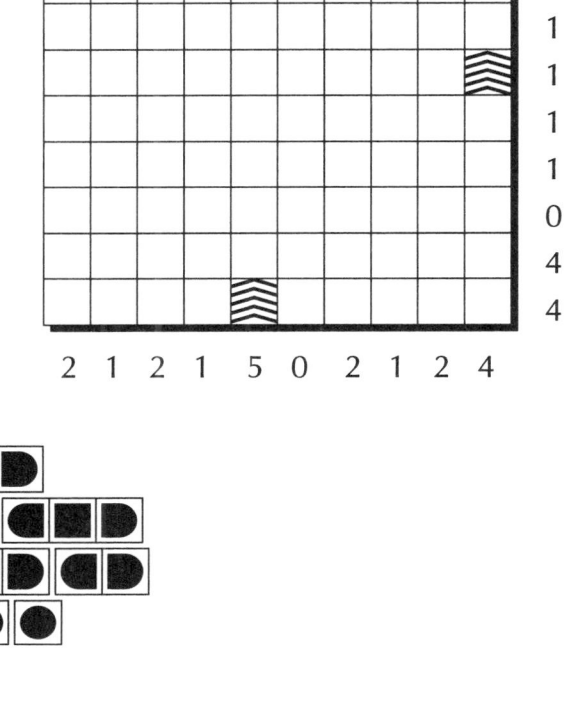

4
4
0
1
1
1
1
0
4
4

2 1 2 1 5 0 2 1 2 4

Battleship
Cruisers
Destroyers
Submarines

50

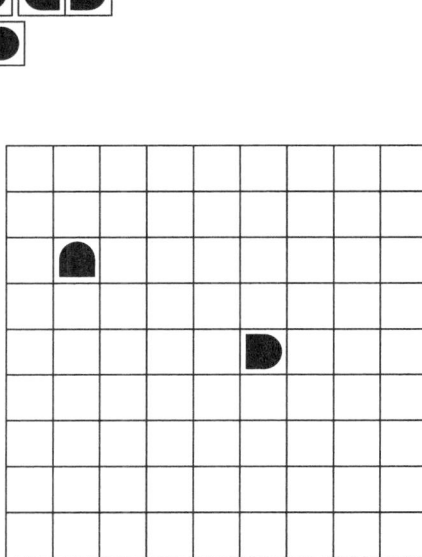

2
6
1
1
4
1
1
2
2
0

1 5 0 2 2 2 3 1 3 1

51

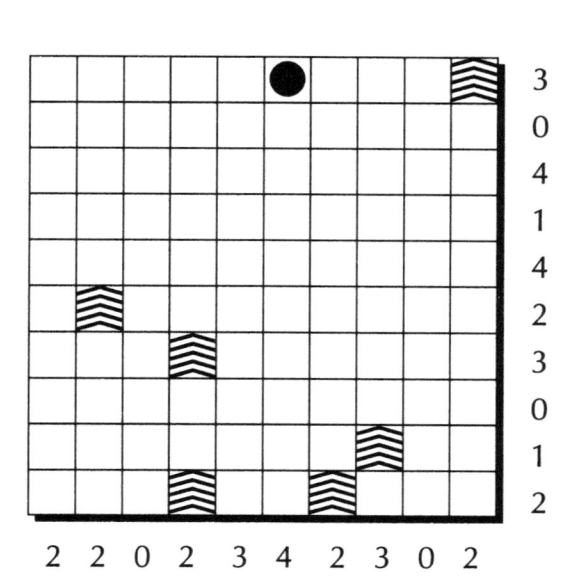

Battleship

Cruisers

Destroyers

Submarines

52

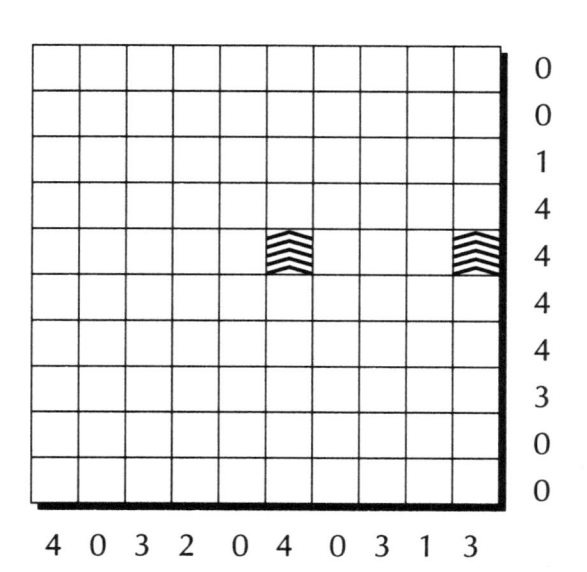

53

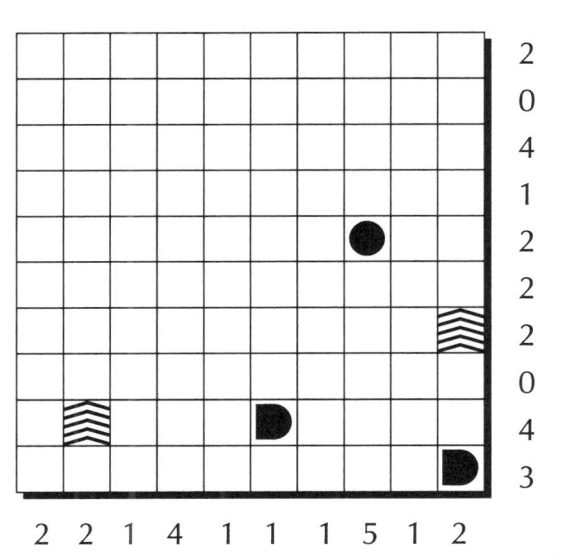

2
0
4
1
2
2
2
0
4
3

2 2 1 4 1 1 1 5 1 2

Battleship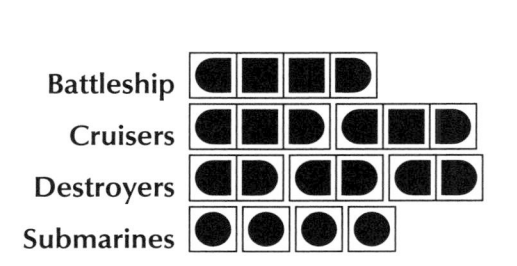

Cruisers

Destroyers

Submarines

54

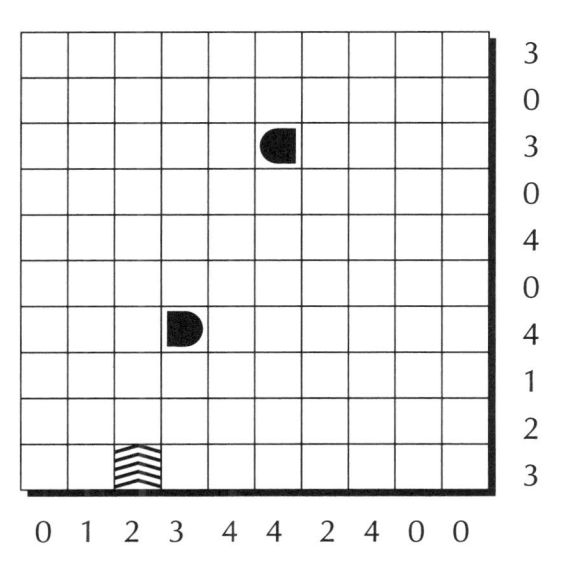

3
0
3
0
4
0
4
1
2
3

0 1 2 3 4 4 2 4 0 0

CLEVER WHODUNITS

Solutions—Page 229

THE REAL McCOY

The men were in the den sipping coffee or root beer. Dr. J. L. Quicksolve had invited several friends for dinner. Since Benjamin Clayborn Blowhard was making his nest on Sergeant Rebekah Shurshot's couch for the week, he was also invited. As usual, Blowhard was doing the talking—this time about his ancestors.

"The men on my father's side were nomadic adventurers like I am," he said. He had spoken of that side of his family before. According to him, his family spread across the globe, meeting and aiding, instructing, or encouraging more famous people than are found in a series of John Jakes novels.

"My mother's side was a little more stable," he went on, "living and prospering in the beautiful state of Virginia. Their name was McCoy. In fact, the expression 'the real McCoy' came from the honesty and integrity of my great-grandfather McCoy, who was once nominated for governor."

Dr. Quicksolve almost choked on his coffee. He sat next to Junior, who smiled and winked knowingly. Captain Reelumin, Lieutenant Rootumont, and Fred Fraudstop listened attentively. Fred was hoping for the chance to talk about his ancestors. His chances were slim. Blowhard seemed to have an endless supply of air and continued talking without the usual necessity of taking a breath.

"Why don't you tell him, Dad?" Junior whispered to Dr. Quicksolve.

What does Junior think Dr. Quicksolve should say?

BEN AGAIN

It was Benjamin Clayborn Blowhard's last night in town. He would be off to "the East" in the morning. For "government reasons" he could not say exactly where he was going. Also "for government reasons" he could not say what he did for the government.

Sergeant Rebekah Shurshot had invited Blowhard and Dr. Quicksolve out to dinner. Dr. Quicksolve reluctantly accepted, to avoid hurting her feelings. As they listened to the end of another of Blowhard's stories, Rebekah said, "You certainly are a man of adventure."

"I come by it honestly," Blowhard replied. Dr. Quicksolve cringed at the thought of hearing more about Blowhard's forefathers. "My ancestors were rugged individuals. My great-great-grandfather was a sheriff back in the late 1800s. One story my father

used to tell about him was when he was almost killed standing over his mother's grave. He was alone at the small cemetery. He took off his hat and held it reverently over his heart. That is what saved him. A bullet, fired by a vengeful desperado my great-great-grandfather had arrested for murder years before, slammed into his wristwatch. His wrist was bruised badly, but the watch saved his life.

"He drew his Colt 45s and shot the gun out of the bad guy's hand. They both mounted their horses, and the chase began. Great-great-grandfather caught up with the killer and dove out of his saddle, bringing the man down off his horse and to the ground. The fistfight lasted 20 minutes before that outlaw gave up because he just could not swing his arms any more. Both his eyes were so swollen from receiving punches that he could not see what he was swinging at!"

Dr. Quicksolve excused himself from the table to avoid laughing out loud.

What was wrong with Ben Blowhard's story this time?

JOKERS WILD

The snowing had just begun, but the bitter winter wind forced Dr. J. L. Quicksolve to grab his hat with one hand and hold his collar closed with the other as he got out of his VW Beetle and walked past the ice-frosted car in the driveway. He walked carefully up the icy steps to the door of the house.

Miss Forkton opened the door when he rang the bell. He introduced himself, and she invited him in. "It sure is cold out there," he said.

"Too cold for burglars, you would think," came her reply.

"Tell me about your robbery, Miss Forkton," Dr. Quicksolve said as he took off his coat. Miss Forkton took his coat and laid it on top of her own fur coat on a chair next to the phone table.

"Well, I just got home a few minutes ago. When I came in the door and saw my safe open," she said, pointing to an open wall safe, "I went straight to the phone and called you. I am glad you could get here so fast."

"Yes, we may have a hot trail for such a cold night," Quicksolve mused.

"I had a fortune in jewels stolen, Dr. Quicksolve. I don't think this is a good time for jokes!" she said.

"I agree with you one hundred percent. So why did you bring me out on such a cold night for this joke of yours, Miss Forkton?" the detective asked.

Why did he mistrust Miss Forkton?

THREAT

It was not the first time Dr. J. L. Quicksolve had received a threatening leter. This one, though, seemed a litle more menacing than the usual prank. It contained a small piece of plastic that was a bit of casing from a cylinder of dynamite.

Dr. Quicksolve had taken steps to protect himself. He left his VW Beetle parked on the street as a temptation for the would-be bomber. He set up a video camera in his upstairs window to watch his car through the night and keep a taped record.

Others were watching too. Sergeant Rebekah Shurshot drove the unmarked police car through the dark neighborhood. Officer Longarm sat beside her. They were going to drive by Dr. Quicksolve's house "just to see if anything looked suspicious." They knew about the threat and were worried about their friend.

As they drove closer to the house, thet saw a large sedan about half a block behind Dr. Quicksolve's VW. The car was dark. They did not realize it was occupied by two men until they were beside it. The small flame of a lighter flickered up to a cigarette on the passenger's side.

"Let's check this out," Sergeant Shurshot said, pulling up in front of the parked car.

She approached the driver's door. Officer Longarm went around to the other side. The driver's window came down. The smiling, mustached driver spoke. "Hi. We're lost, and we stopped to look at our map," he said, holding a map up to prove his point. "Could you help us out?"

Sergeant Shurshot was not smiling when she said, "Please get out of the car slowly with your hands up."

The two men looked at the officers and their drawn guns and did what they were told.

What tipped off the officers?

PLUNGER AND SNAKE

Dr. J. L. Quicksolve got out of his car. He pulled his hat down tighter on his head to avoid losing it to the icy wind on another snowy winter morning. He walked between the two police cars to the front door of Plunger and Snake's Plumbing Supplies. He pulled the front door open and walked in.

Lieutenant Rootumout was talking with a man who played with his mustache nervously as he spoke. Another officer was kneeling over a body on the floor. Lieutenant Rootumout looked up at Dr. Quicksolve and introduced him to Paul Plunger, the mustached man. Indicating the body, Lieutenant Rootumout said, "Stan Snake."

Dr. Quicksolve sat down and listened to Plunger's story. Plunger paused and rolled up his shirt sleeves. "Yes," he said, "I saw Stan's body when I came in this morning, but I did not have time to do anything. Someone had been hiding behind the door and stuck a gun in my back. He made me lie facedown on the floor. Then he left."

"Did he take anything?" Lieutenant Rootumout asked.

"I don't know. We don't keep any money here overnight, if that is what you mean. Maybe that is why he killed Stan—because he could not give him any money. The killer would not know our secretary, Miss Supplewrist, takes the day's earnings to the bank after we close. She brings money for petty cash when she comes to work every morning. She has not come in yet today," Mr. Plunger explained, giving his mustache a final tug.

"We'll talk to her when she arrives," Lieutenant Rootumout said.

"We'll ask if she has any idea why you killed your partner," Dr. Quicksolve added.

Why did Dr. Quicksolve suspect Plunger killed Snake?

SHORTSTOP'S BIKE

Junior got off his bike and knocked on his friend Shortstop's front door. Shortstop was usually sitting on his bike in the driveway when Junior came by, and they would ride to school together each morning. "Where's your bike?" Junior asked when Shortstop came to the door with his backpack in his hand and a sad look on his face.

"Somebody stole it from our garage yesterday afternoon," Shortstop said.

"Did you see anything?" Junior asked.

"No," Shortstop answered, "but my sister did. She heard a noise and looked out the window just in time to see a kid riding off on my bike. She doesn't know who it was, though. She only saw his back. She said he had on a denim jacket. It could have been anyone."

"We can check the bikes at school," Junior said as he pushed his bike down the sidewalk beside Shortstop.

Prissy Powers, the cutest girl on the cheerleading squad, was standing by the long row of bikes behind the school. "Hi, Junior. Hi, Shortstop. How come you're walking?"

"My bike was stolen yesterday," Shortstop said.

"I think we'll find it," Junior said confidently as he walked down the long row of bikes, stroking the crossbar of the first one of many that looked like Shortstop's.

"But there are so many that are just alike, even yours," Prissy said to Junior.

"That's good," Junior said, moving down the row to the next bike like Shortstop's.

Why does Junior think it is good that so many bikes look alike? What is he doing?

CLAUDE VICIOUSLY

"The ringmaster insisted Claude Viciously use that new lion in his act because he was so big and aggressive—a crowd pleaser," Mrs. Viciously told Dr. J. L. Quicksolve as they sat in her trailer discussing her husband's death. "The lion wasn't trained. Claude was afraid of him. Claude hadn't been afraid in years, but this scared him. He sat right there, barely two hours ago at breakfast, and decided he wouldn't go in with the new lion unless he had his gun loaded. He was always proud that he could work with the big cats without even the blank pistol some trainers use. He was scared. Animals sense that, you know."

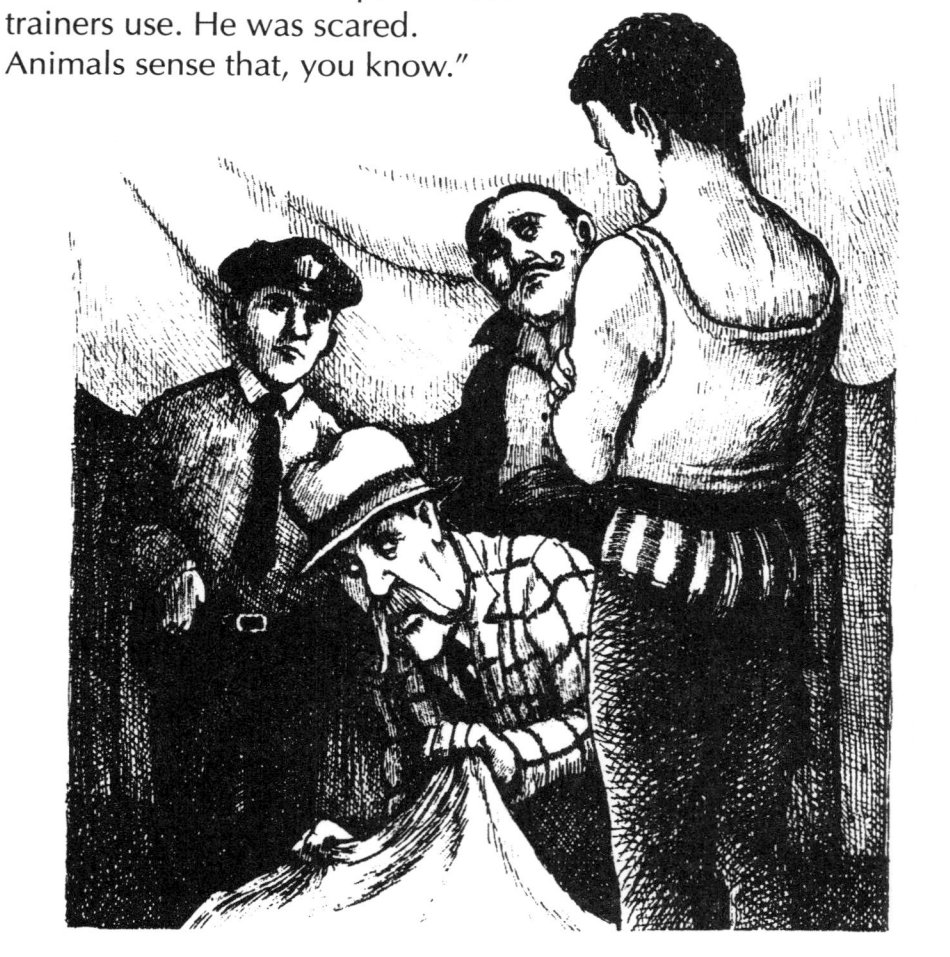

Claude's body lay in the center of the ring covered by a blanket. The lion had been put away, and Lieutenant Rootumout and two other men stood beside the body. One man, obviously the ringmaster, wore a fancy suit with long tails. The other, a performer, wore black tights and a bright red sash.

"I should not have insisted he use that new lion," the ringmaster said, clearly shaken by the death.

Lieutenant Rootumout held up a clear plastic bag as Dr. Quicksolve approached. It contained a large revolver. "It's empty," he said to Dr. Quicksolve.

"I can't believe he forgot the bullets," Stretch Prettitight said. "He was afraid of that lion."

Dr. Quicksolve bent down and lifted the edge of the blanket to look at the body. "Looks like murder," he said.

"Lions can't be charged with murder," Stretch scoffed.

"*You* can," Dr. Quicklove replied.

Why does Dr. Quicksolve suspect Stretch?

STORY BUILDERS

GENERAL INSTRUCTIONS

For these games, add a letter to the underlined letter or letters to complete the blank word that follows. Then, using the same letters, add still another letter to complete the next word, and so on. Letters may or may not appear in the same sequence each time, but each word will always contain the letters from the previous word in addition to the new letter you add.

Solutions—Page 247

1
THE REST IS UP TO YOU

"I T really is a shame to r u n around and feel that life is over because you had to retire," Mona admonished Jack. "In fact, it's the __ __ __ __ ! Why not find a hobby, read a book, or plan some __ __ __ __ __ ? Or maybe you should see our __ __ __ __ __ __ . I'm sure Father O'Malley can offer you some __ __ __ __ __ __ __ from your sorrow over getting too much rest."

2
A LEGEND IN HIS OWN MIND

"I simply D O not understand why you think you're better than everyone else," Ben mused, slowly shaking his head in wonder as he studied Eugene. "Let's face it, you eat, sleep, drink, and walk on the same __ __ __ that a common cur __ __ __ __ , yet you've always __ __ __ __ __ as someone superior. In my opinion, you'd make a perfect __ __ __ __ __ __ , Eugene, and I __ __ __ __ __ __ __ this character flaw the first time we met. The crown you were wearing was a dead giveaway!"

3
WHAT YOU SEE IS WHAT YOU GET

A T what point does a mediocre painting suddenly become a great work of __ __ __ ? Usually it happens when self-appointed critics start to __ __ __ __ and rave about a work's redeeming value, focusing on features that are invisible to most of us. In this way, they __ __ __ __ __ us to doubt our own judgment, and __ __ __ __ __ __ their power to influence our tastes and buying habits.

Obviously it takes a __ __ __ __ __ __ __ amount of self-confidence and strength to say, "My __ __ __ __ __ __ __ __ is as valid as yours, Mr. Critic, and many of those __ __ __ __ __ __ __ __ __ you're calling art aren't on a par with preschool finger painting!"

4
CHARLES DARWIN, PHONE HOME!

"P A , you've known me a long time," grumbled Ma, "and by now it should be obvious that I'm not __ __ __ to pay __ __ __ __ attention to all your foolish notions. You __ __ __ __ __ constantly about science and evolution, neither of which you know very well, and I find it very upsetting when you __ __ __ __ __ __ with theories like the one you mentioned yesterday: that man is the least intelligent __ __ __ __ __ __ __ of all!"

5
WINNER TAKES ALL

"To B E honest, Sam, you've disappointed me," Joey said. "You lost the __ __ __ , but your __ __ __ __ is still outstanding. Now you expect me to stand here with __ __ __ __ __ breath while you __ __ __ __ __ __ the ethics of gambling. Well, you can just forget it, pal, I refuse to be __ __ __ __ __ __ __ for putting the squelch on a welch!"

6
CAREER ORIENTED

"N O individual, not even a very bright _o n e_ , can give you a fool-proof formula for success, Marsha," Mike said patiently, "but even a __ __ __ __ like yours truly can offer some pointers. That company party we attended last night, for instance, makes me __ __ __ __ __ to think you won't get the promotion you're after. It just doesn't look good when you fall asleep on the shoulder of the __ __ __ __ __ __ you're sitting beside at dinner, especially when it's your boss. And I'm sure someone in his position __ __ __ __ __ __ __ the merit of promoting an employee who __ __ __ __ __ __ __ __ , 'I prefer that you call me Marsha,' when he asks if he can call you a cab!"

7
WHO ARE WE TO JUDGE?

"Hi, <u>P A</u>," the young man greeted his father. "I just ran into your old __ __ __ , Judge Mann, and he was so __ __ __ __ I hardly recognized him! I guess he saw me do a double-take, because he smiled and said, 'I'm not sick, my boy, just tired. I've been hearing so many __ __ __ __ __ lately, I sometimes find myself __ __ __ __ __ __ when key witnesses are testifying! I won't be surprised if a higher court __ __ __ __ __ __ __ a lot of my recent rulings.' Then he smiled wearily and added, 'Perhaps we judges should have settled for being __ __ __ __ __ __ __ __ . Then we could just listen to the accused's confession, and leave the judgement to someone much more qualified!"

8
A HARD ONE TO FATHOM

<u>A</u> walk along this lonely beach is __ __ mystifying as the __ __ __ that watches us in cryptic green silence. Here, where countless __ __ __ __ have witnessed the __ __ __ __ __ and laughter of earlier generations, few __ __ __ __ __ __ remain of times that were. It is this great sense of aloneness, I think, that __ __ __ __ __ __ __ the mystique pertaining to oceans, and maintains a certain mysterious appeal __ __ __ __ __ __ __ __ as the sea, herself.

9
FOOD FOR THOUGHT

Some believe that knowledge, <u>P E R</u> se, has no value unless it is shared. Only then, thay maintain, can humankind __ __ __ __ its benefits. Every good seed of thought that is sown and cultivated in the beds of fertile minds then becomes a __ __ __ __ __ of wisdom. Thinkers, in turn, can __ __ __ __ __ __ its benefits with others, expand upon it, and perhaps someday __ __ __ __ __ __ __ it in new, exciting ways. Such is the story of growth.

10
IN DEEP WATER

"Like it <u>O</u> <u>R</u> not, Harold," Hazel said, "I've manned these oars long enough. It's time for you to _ _ _."

Noticing how far they were to shore, he cagily replied, "Okay, but mark my _ _ _ _ , tomorrow you'll regret not getting more exercise."

"More? I'm already so tired that I'd _ _ _ _ _ if I suddenly had to swim," Hazel snapped. "But your concern makes me _ _ _ _ _ _ , Harold, wouldn't you be healthier if you occasionally exercised more than just your prerogative?"

"There you go," Harold hissed. "You always manage to turn our outings into total _ _ _ _ _ _ _ , and now you're doing it again!"

Matters only _ _ _ _ _ _ _ _ from that point, and their canoe trip became just another paddle between the sexes.

TAKE FIVE

GENERAL INSTRUCTIONS

In the grids that follow, fill in each box with an answer beginning with the letter above each of the five columns, and fitting the caregory at the left of each row. Try to list one answer in every box, although some boxes may have more than one correct answer.

Solutions—Pages 248-252

	S	C	O	R	E
AMERICAN INDIANS	Serrano	Chumash	Ohlone		
ICE CREAM FLAVORS	sorbet	cherry	oreo	rasberry	
BIBLICAL FIGURES					
VEGETABLES	salad	carrots	avocados	raddish	eggplant
COLORS	silver	copper	orange	red	

#1

	R	G	P	S	B
CHEESES					
FEMALE SINGERS					
BODIES OF WATER	river	Great lake	pond	sea	
MEN'S FIRST NAMES	Ramnibanth	Garret			
CARD GAMES			Poker	Spoons	

#2

	D	A	B	S	P
STATE CAPITALS	Dover Denver	Augusta		Salem	
CARTOON CHARACTERS	Patsy Donald				
TELEVISION SOAP OPERAS					
PROFESSIONS					
CARY GRANT MOVIES					

#3

	C	H	A	M	P
MOVIE TITLES		Homeward Bound	Aquamarine		
NUTS	Chestnut		Almond	Macadamia	Pistachio
TREES					
7-LETTER NOUNS					
PRO FOOTBALL PLAYERS					

#4

	W	S	C	B	R
PROFESSIONAL GOLFERS	Woods	Stadler	couples crivition	Balvaste-ras	Beid
SEAFOOD	White fish	Sailors Salmon Snmp	Cod	Butter fish	Butter ruffe
TELEVISION NEWSCASTERS	walters	Safer Swayer	Chun	Breaker (KGO)	Butter
BROADWAY MUSICALS		Show boat South Pacific	Cabaret Cats	Bye Bye Birdie	rumple
WORLD CAPITALS	Washington D.C.	Sacramento Singapore sidney	canic	Brussels	Rome

#5

	T	S	M	R	C
TELEVISION SLEUTHS					
FAIRY TALES					Cinderella
CHILD STARS					
DANCES	Tap	Street	Musical Theatre		Character
MODES OF TRAVEL					

#9

	G	**R**	**E**	**A**	**T**
MOVIE STARS					
FLOWERS	Gerbera Daisies				
CAR/TRUCK MODELS				Acura	
FOREIGN COUNTRIES	Greece	Romania	Ethiopia	Astria	Thailand
RIVERS				Amazon	

#7

	C	M	O	G	S
SPORTS-CASTERS					Soccer
MIXED DRINKS					
BIRDS	Cardnals				
MINERALS					
CANDY BRANDS					

#8

	M	A	D	E	N
PAST OR PRESENT WORLD LEADERS	Madison	Adams			
INVENTORS			Edison		
MAMMALS	Mammoth	Ardvark	Dolphin	Elephant	Narwal
ELVIS PRESLEY SONGS					
OPERAS					

#9

	G	E	C	A	S
HERBS	Ginger	Echinea	Cinnamon	Allspice	
U.S. ASTRONAUTS				Armstrong	
MAGAZINES	GL			Astronomy	Sky&Telescope
FRUITS	Grape	euphorbia	Cantaloupe	Apple	Strawberry
POETS					

#10

SOLUTIONS

TRICKY TRIOS

1 "EGR"

A score of 15 is fine; 18, first-rate; 22, fantastic!

begrime, begrudge, biodegradable, degrade, degranulation, degree, degression, disintegrate, egregious, egress, egret, integrand, integrate, integrity, integrodifferential, legroom, megrim, negritude, peregrine, regress, regret, regroup, segregate, telegram, telegraph

2 "OXY"

Find 12, you're batting 1.000; 15, you're an all-star; 17, you're a hall of famer!

boxy, deoxycorticosterone, deoxygenate, deoxyribose, doxy, doxycycline, epoxy, foxy, hydroxyl, oxyacetylene, oxyacid, oxycephaly, oxygen, oxyhemoglobin, oxymoron, oxysulfide, oxytetracycline, oxytocic, oxytone, oxyuriasis, proxy

3 "ADI"

Finding 60 words is dandy; 70, fantastic; 80, phenomenal!

adiabetic, adieu, adios, adipose, adit, amantadine, anadiplosis, arcading, armadillo, badinage, barricading, beading, beheading, besteading, brigadier, brocading, butadiene, cadi, caladium, cannonading, cascading, circadian, contradict, contradistinguish, degrading, eradicate, escalading, evading, extradite, fading, freeloading, gladiator, gladiola, gliadin, goading, gradin, grading, granadilla, haggadist, heading, hexadic, invading, irradiate, irradicable,

jading, kneading, lading, leading, loading, masquerading, monadic, muscadine, nadir, nomadism, paladin, palladium, paradigm, parading, paradise, peccadillo, persuading, pleading, radial, radiant, radiator, radical, radio, radiology, radish, radium, radix, readily, reading, sadiron, sadist, shading, sporadic, spreading, stadium, steadily, threading, toadies, tornadic, trading, tradition, traditor, treading, triadic, wadi, wading

4 "ERT"

Finding 75 words is good; 90, excellent; 100, extraordinary!

advertise, alert, aperture, appertain, ascertain, assert, avert, berth, bertha, certes, certain, certificate, certify, certiorari, chert, concert, concertina, concertino, concertmaster, concerto, controvert, convert, convertible, convertiplane, covert, culvert, desert, desertion, dessert, disconcert, divert, diverticulitis, diverticulosis, diverticulum, divertimento, divertissement, entertain, evert, exert, expert, extrovert, fertile, fertilizer, filbert, gilbert, hypertension, hyperthermia, hyperthyroid, hypertonic, hypertrophy, inadvertent, inert, insert, intertexture, intertribal, intertropical, intertwine, introvert, invertase, libertarian, libertine, liberty, nerts, obvert, offertory, overt, overtake, overtax, overthrow, overtime, overtone, overtop, overtrain, overtrick, overtrump, overture, overturn, pert, pertain, pertinacious, pertinent, perturb, pertussis, pervert, poverty, property, puberty, revert, sertularian, stertor, subvert, summertime, supertanker, supertax, supertonic, tertial, tertian, tertiary, travertine, undertaker, underthings, undertone, undertrained, vert, vertebra, vertebrate, vertex, vertical, verticillate, vertiginous, vertigo, vertu, watertight, wert, wintertime

5 "AZI"

A score of 10 is terrific; 12, great; 15, tops!

amazing, azide, azimuth, azine, blazing, brazier, brazilwood, crazier, dazing, fazing, feazing, gazing, glazier, grazing, hazier, lazier, magazine, razing, triazine

6 "OQU"

A score of 8 is par; 10, a birdie; 14, an eagle!

baroque, coquette, coquille, coquina, coquito, croquet, croquette, croquinole, eloquent, hydroquinone, loquacious, loquat, moquette, roque, roquelaure, toque

7 "ICO"

A score of 65 words is outstanding; 75, magnificent; 82 or better, pure genius!

alnico, anticoagulant, anticonvulsant, apricot, beccafico, bellicose, bicolor, biconcave, biconvex, bicorn, bicorporal, bicostate, calico, chalicosis, chalicothere, chico, chicory, corticoid, corticolous, corticospinal, dicotyledon,

epicotyl, helicoid, helicon, helicopter, icon, iconoclast, iconography, iconoscope, iconostasis, lamellicorn, lexicology, lexicon, licorice, limicoline, longicorn, lumbricoid, machicolate, magnifico, manicotti, manticore, maricolous, medico, medicolegal, minicomputer, multicolored, nicotiana, nicotine, orthicon, particolored, physicochemical, picogram, picoline, picornavirus, picosecond, picot, picotee, politico, portico, ricochet, ricotta, rupicolous, saxicolous, semicolon, semicomatose, semiconductor, semiconscious, silicon, silicone, silicosis, stereopticon, technicolored, terricolous, torticollis, toxicogenic, toxicology, toxicosis, tragicomedy, tricolor, tricorn, tricostate, tricot, tricotine, unicolor, unicorn, unicostate, uricosuric, varicolored, varicose, varicotomy, ventricose, versicolor, vidicon, vorticose, wicopy

8 "LPH"

Locating 6 words is fantastic; 7, stupendous; 8, absolutely colossal!

alpha, alphabet, alphanumeric, alphosis, delphinium, dolphin, phenolphthalein, ralph, sulphur, sylph, telpher

9 "EME"

If you find 40, you're a sharpie; 48, you're brilliant; 55, you're a genius!

bereavement, cemetery, cement, cementite, confinement, deme, demeanor, dementia, demerit, demesne, demeton, emend, emerald, emerge, emergency, emeritus, emersion, emery, emetic, emeu, ephemeral, excrement, heme, hemelytron, hemeralopia, increment, irremeable, irremediable, memento, mincemeat, misdemeanor, nemertean, nemesis, pavement, phoneme, piecemeal, premedicate, premeditate, radioelement, rapprochement, redeemer, refinement, remedial, remedy, remember, retirement, scheme, seducement, seme, sememe, semester, siemens, spireme, statement, supplement, supreme, telemetry, temerity, theme, tremendous, treponeme, trireme, vehement

LETTER PERFECT

1

1. Transparent, 2. Tenement, 3. Turnabout, 4. Treat, 5. Tart, 6. Tenet, 7. Tacit, 8. Triplet, 9. Temperament, 10. Turncoat, 11. Tangent, 12. Transplant, 13. Turret, 14. Transient, 15. Tablet, 16. Truant, 17. Tourist, 18. Threat, 19. Taut, 20. Tent, 21. Trout

2

1. Earthenware, 2. Edifice, 3. Ensemble, 4. Evacuate, 5. Engrave, 6. Earthquake, 7. Eloquence, 8. Embezzle, 9. Enumerate, 10. Evidence, 11. Esplanade,

12. Exorcise, 13. Equate, 14. Eave, 15. Elapse, 16. Escape,17. Excuse, 18. Elegance, 19. Epicure, 20. Encourage, 21. Espadrille, 22. Effervescence, 23. Educate, 24. Editorialize, 25. Elaborate

3

1. Liverpool, 2. Landfill, 3. Laurel, 4. Lysol, 5. Libel, 6. Lateral, 7. Lentil, 8. Logroll, 9. Label, 10. Liberal, 11. Lull, 12. Literal, 13. Lil, 14. Loyal, 15. Lethal, 16. Loll, 17. Lackadaisical, 18. Lapel, 19. Lyrical, 20. Local, 21. Logical

4

1. Nightgown, 2. Noggin, 3. Nonagon, 4. Nylon, 5. Nobleman, 6. Newton, 7. Neon, 8. Nitrogen, 9. Napkin, 10. Newman, 11. Notion, 12. Nubbin, 13. Noon, 14. Nation, 15. Nineteen, 16. Nixon, 17. Napoleon, 18. Nolan, 19. Newborn, 20. Nun, 21. Nelson, 22. Neutron, 23. Nickelodeon, 24. Nucleon

5

1. Haunch, 2. Horseradish, 3. High, 4. Hopscotch, 5. Hooch, 6. Hash, 7. Hogwash, 8. Howdah, 9. Hyacinth, 10. Hallelujah, 11. Hearth, 12. Hairsbreadth, 13. Halvah, 14. Hannah, 15. Hush, 16. Harrah, 17. Homograph, 18. Henceforth, 19. Hunch, 20. Hurrah, 21. Hugh, 22. Homestretch, 23. Health, 24. Hitch, 25. Hashish, 26. Hutch

6

1. Raconteur, 2. Receiver, 3. Rumor, 4. Rooster, 5. Rigor, 6. Rustler, 7. River, 8. Radiator, 9. Reindeer, 10. Rear. 11. Roar, 12. Ranger, 13. Redeemer, 14. Revolver, 15. Renoir, 16. Ruler, 17. Rancor, 18. Rathskeller, 19. Rudder, 20. Rambler, 21. Rather, 22. Rapier, 23. Recur, 24. Recover, 25. Render, 26. Radar, 27. Regular

7

1. Deceased, 2. Dachshund, 3. David, 4. Dilapidated, 5. Diamond, 6. Doodad, 7. Dryad, 8. Distend, 9. Devoid, 10. Dread, 11. Disregard, 12. Dividend, 13. Dagwood, 14. Dashboard, 15. Disneyland, 16. Dud, 17. Dead, 18. Deformed, 19. Dollywood, 20. Dad, 21. Descend, 22. Deed, 23. Discord, 24. Dastard, 25. Druid, 26. Demigod

8

1. Sacrilegious, 2. Spontaneous, 3. Spyglass, 4. Sophocles, 5. Stylus, 6. Suppress, 7. Superfluous, 8. Sans, 9. Sedulous, 10. Stress, 11. Symbiosis, 12. Stradivarius, 13. Sweepstakes, 14. Studious, 15. Sinus, 16. Scandalous, 17. Synopsis, 18. Slanderous, 19. Swiss, 20. Spineless, 21. Surreptitious

BATTLESHIPS

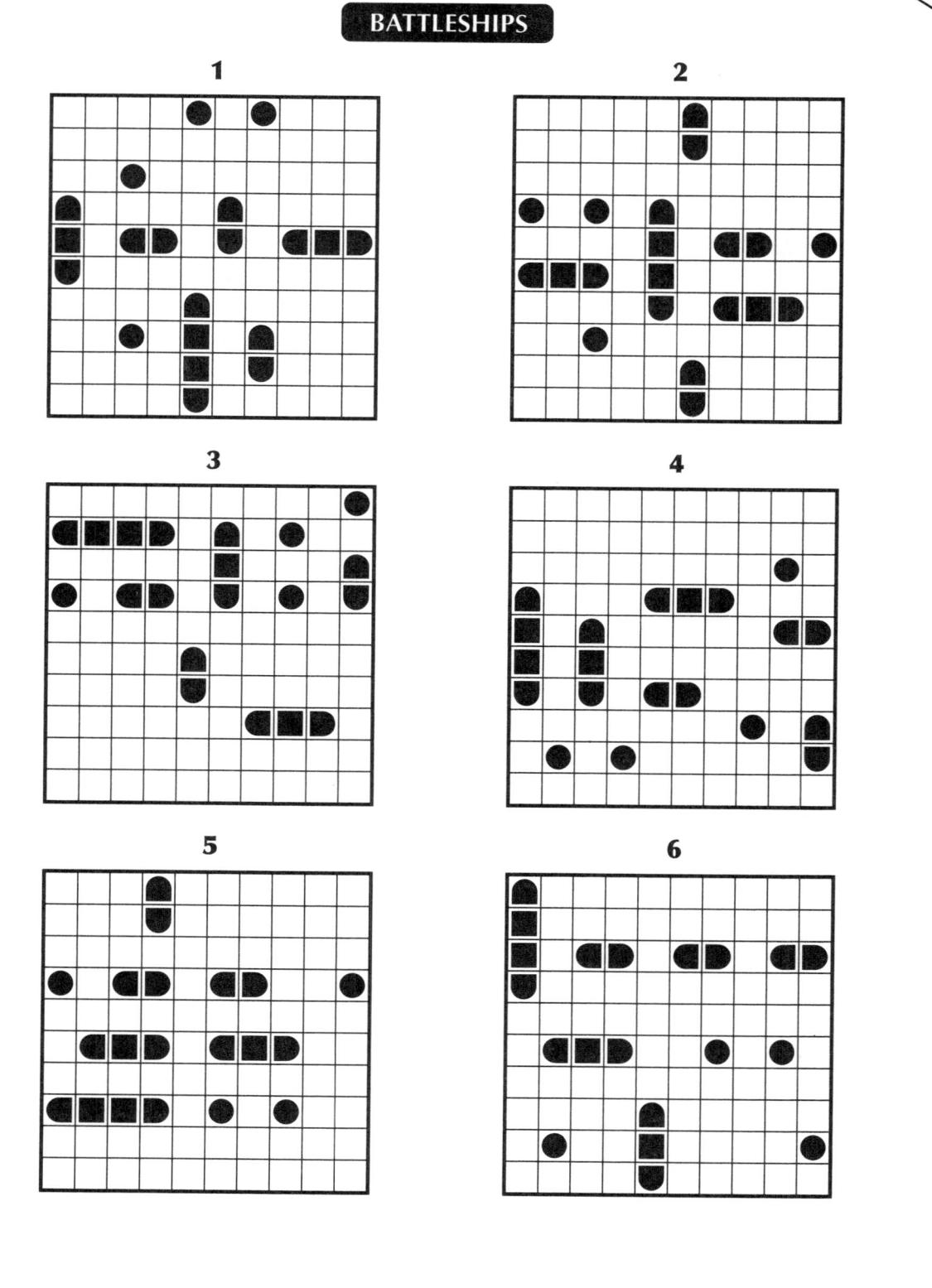

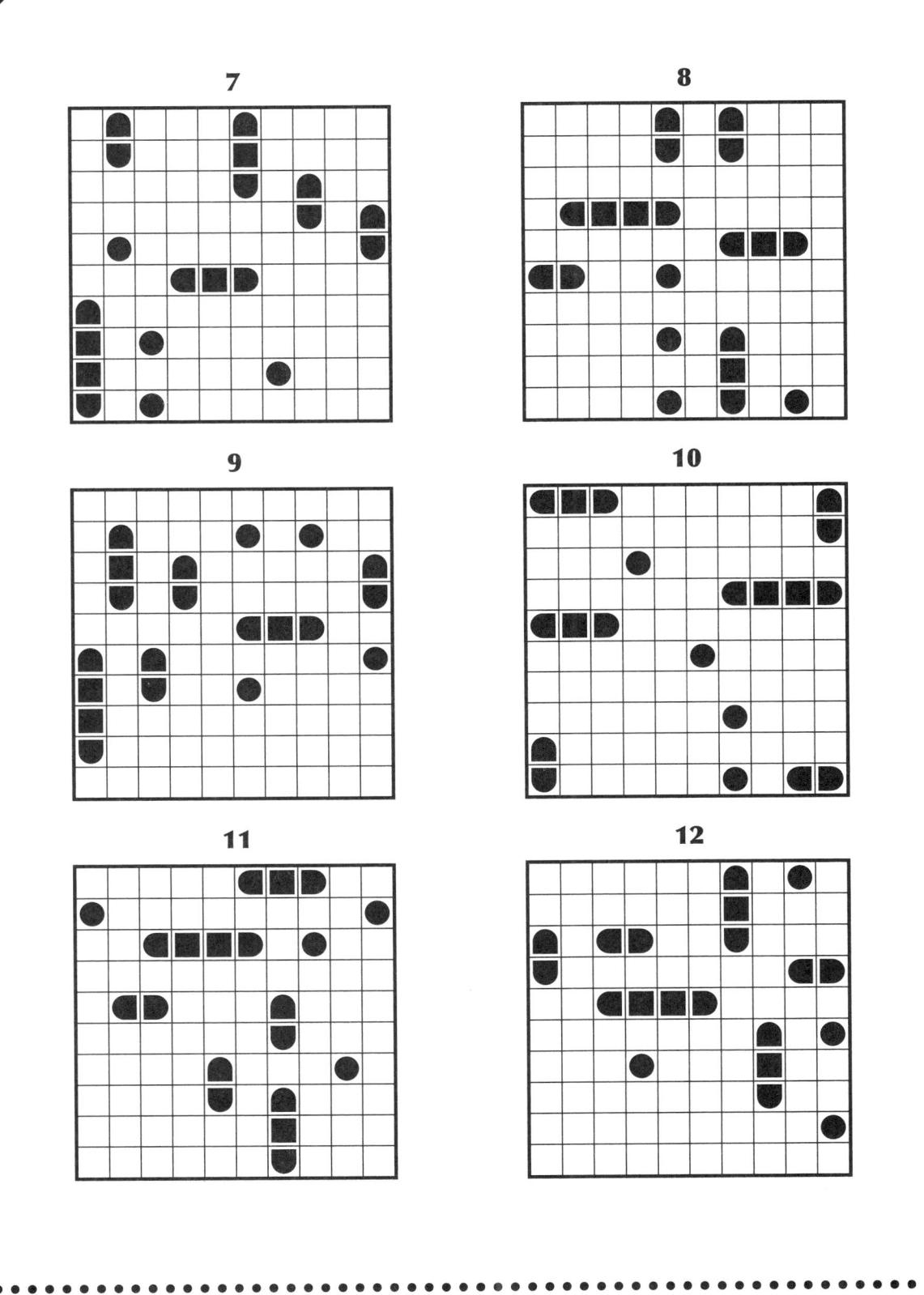

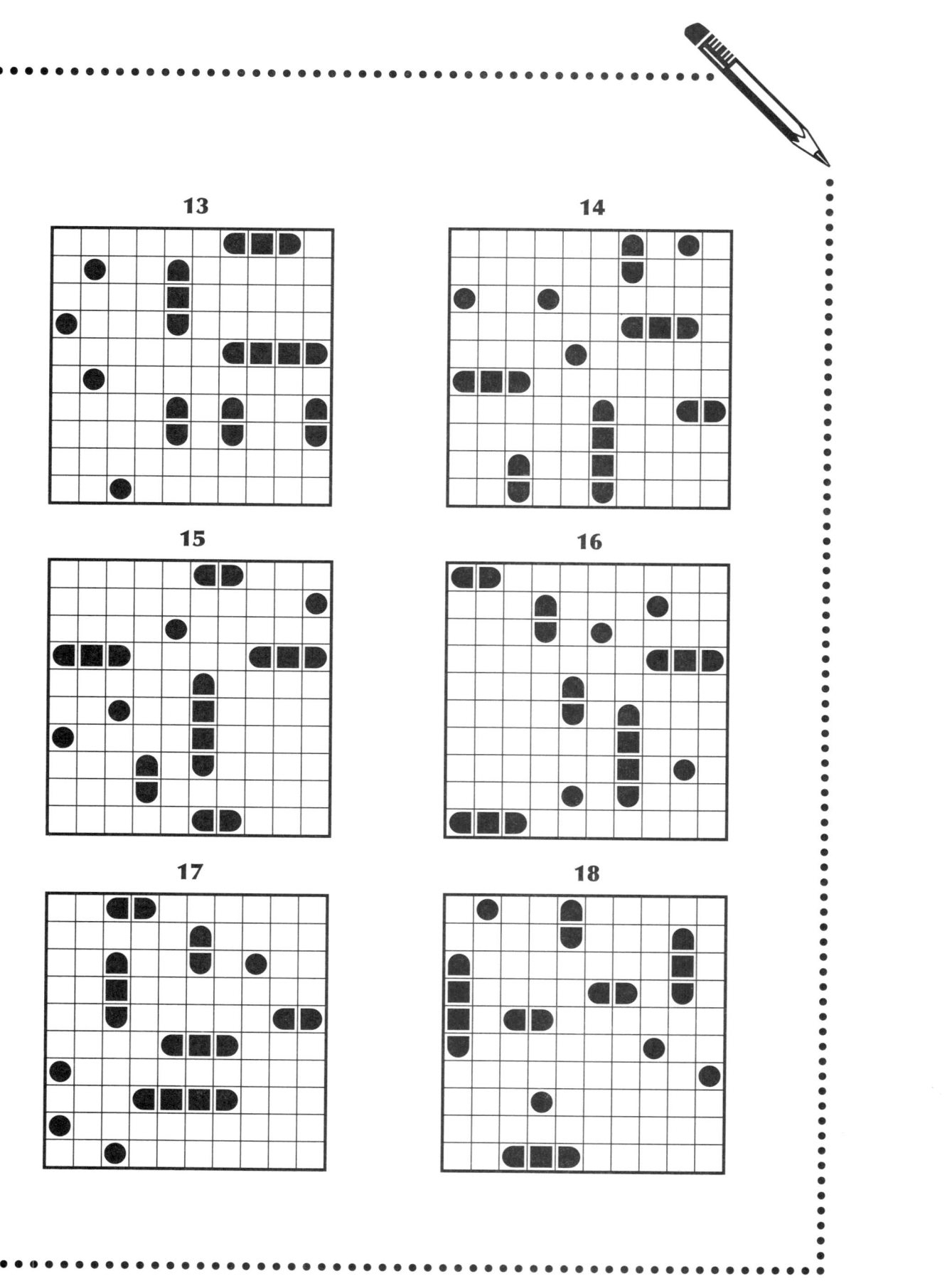

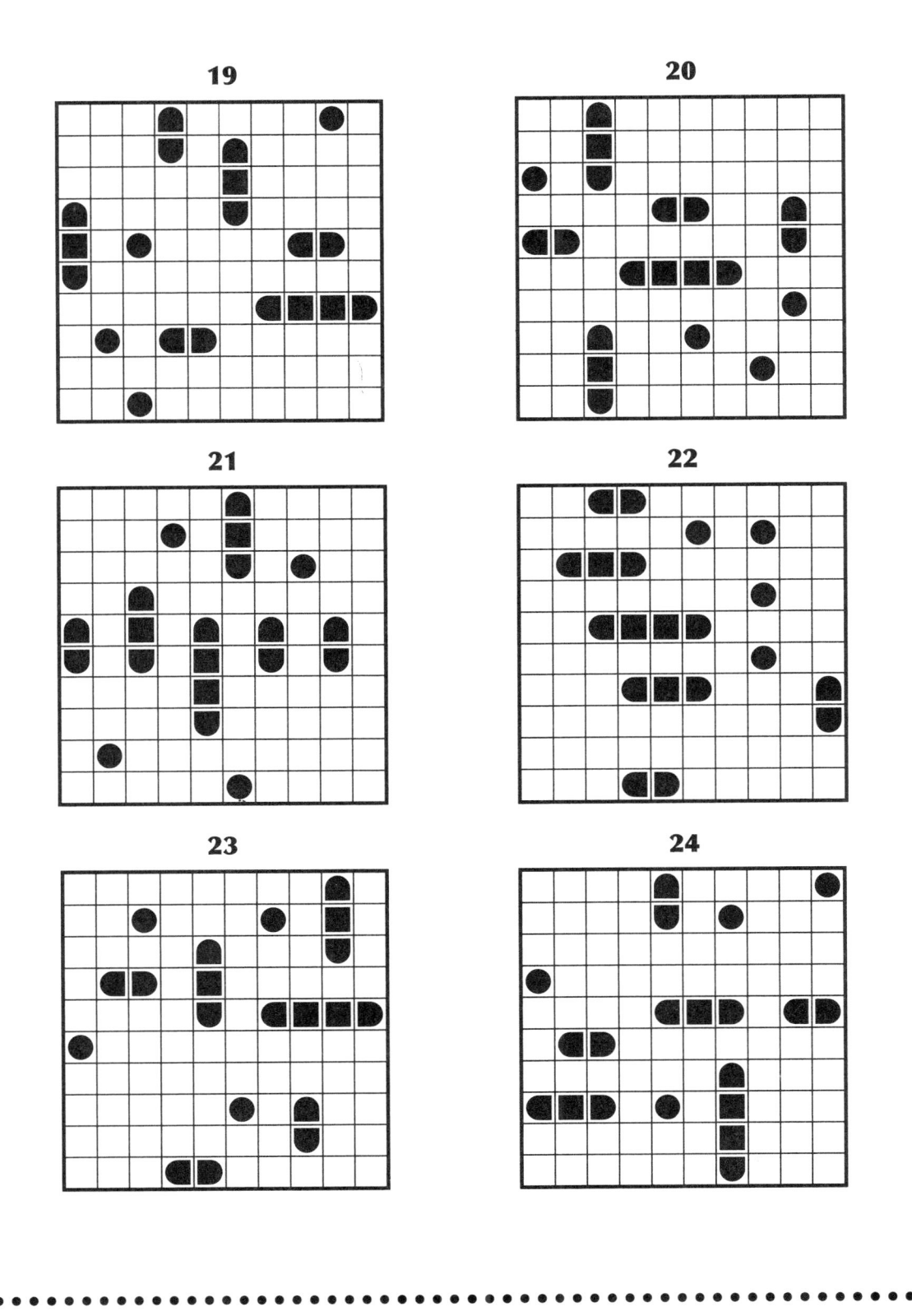

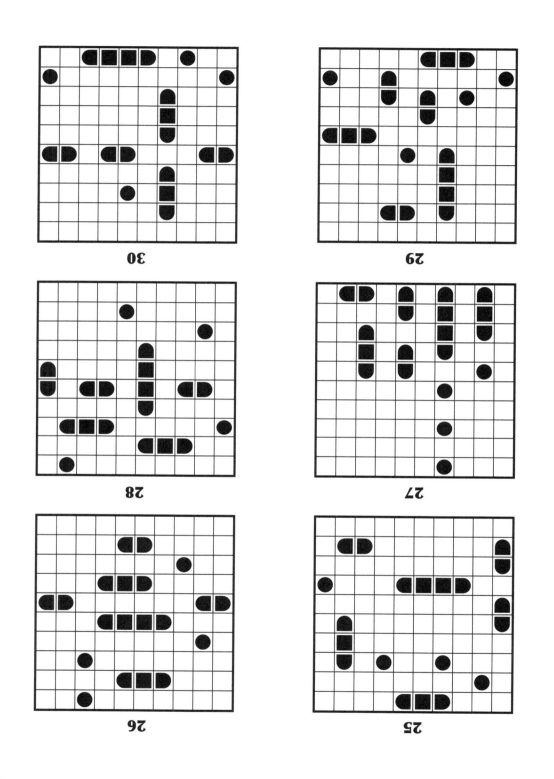

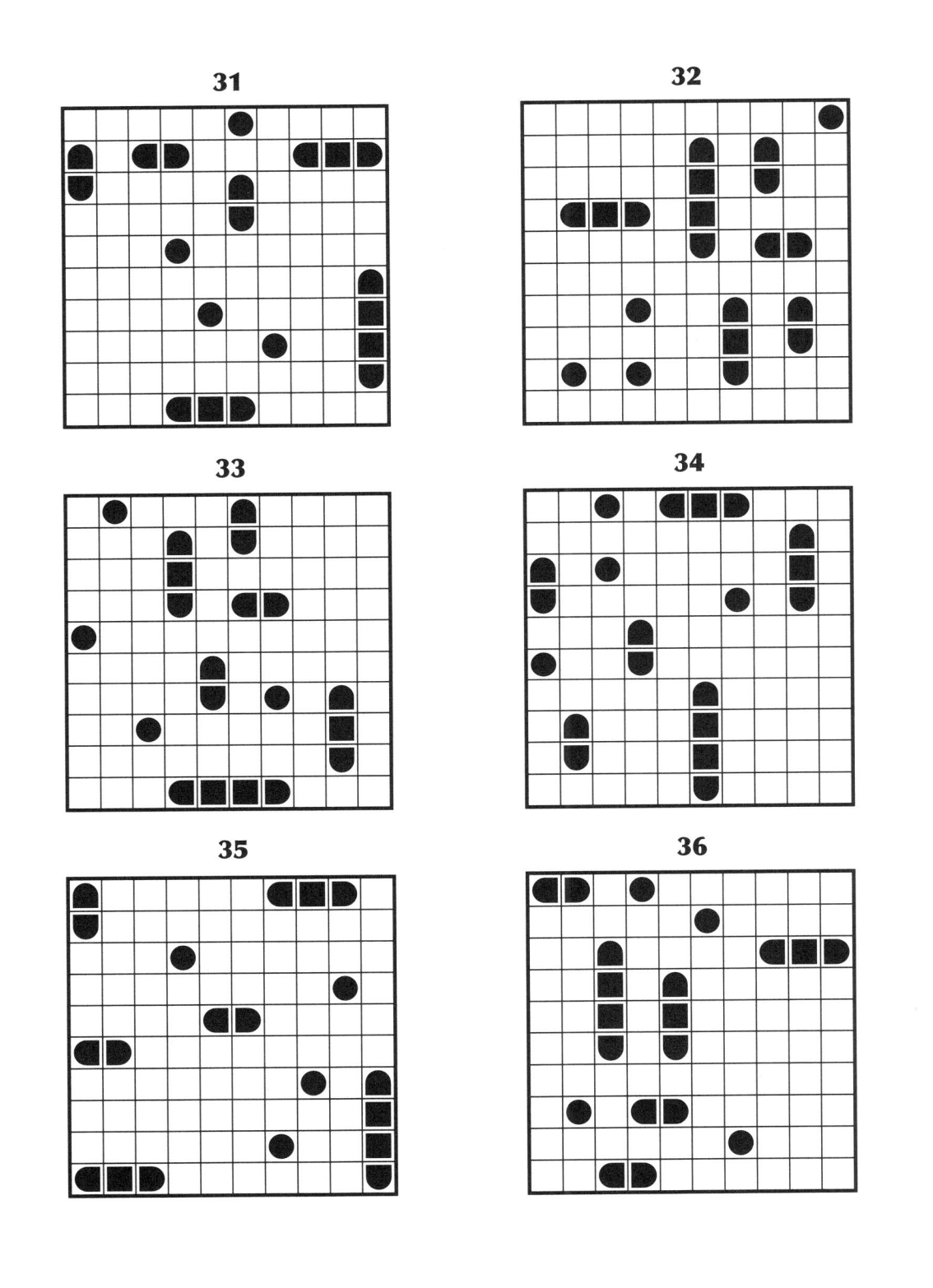

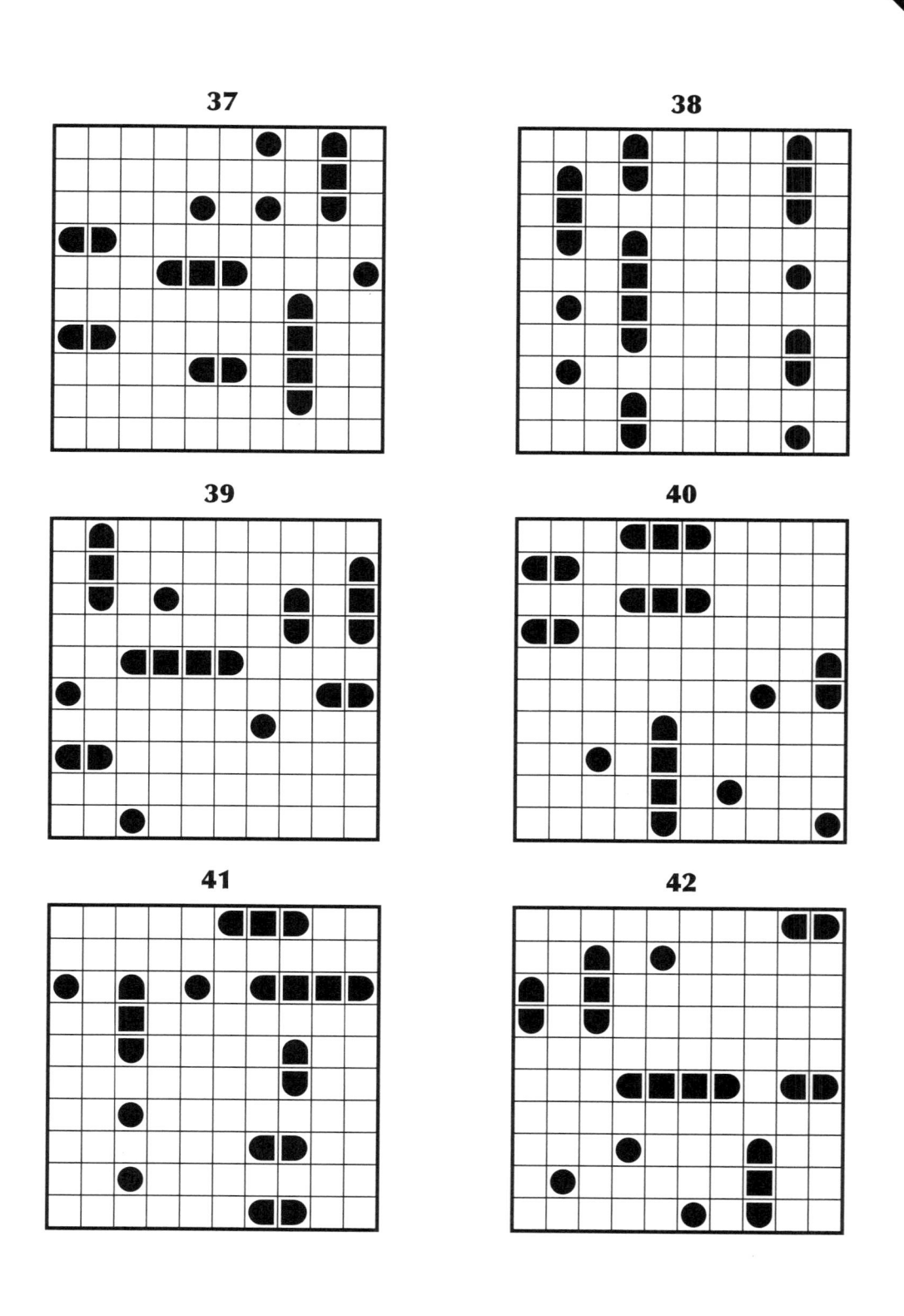

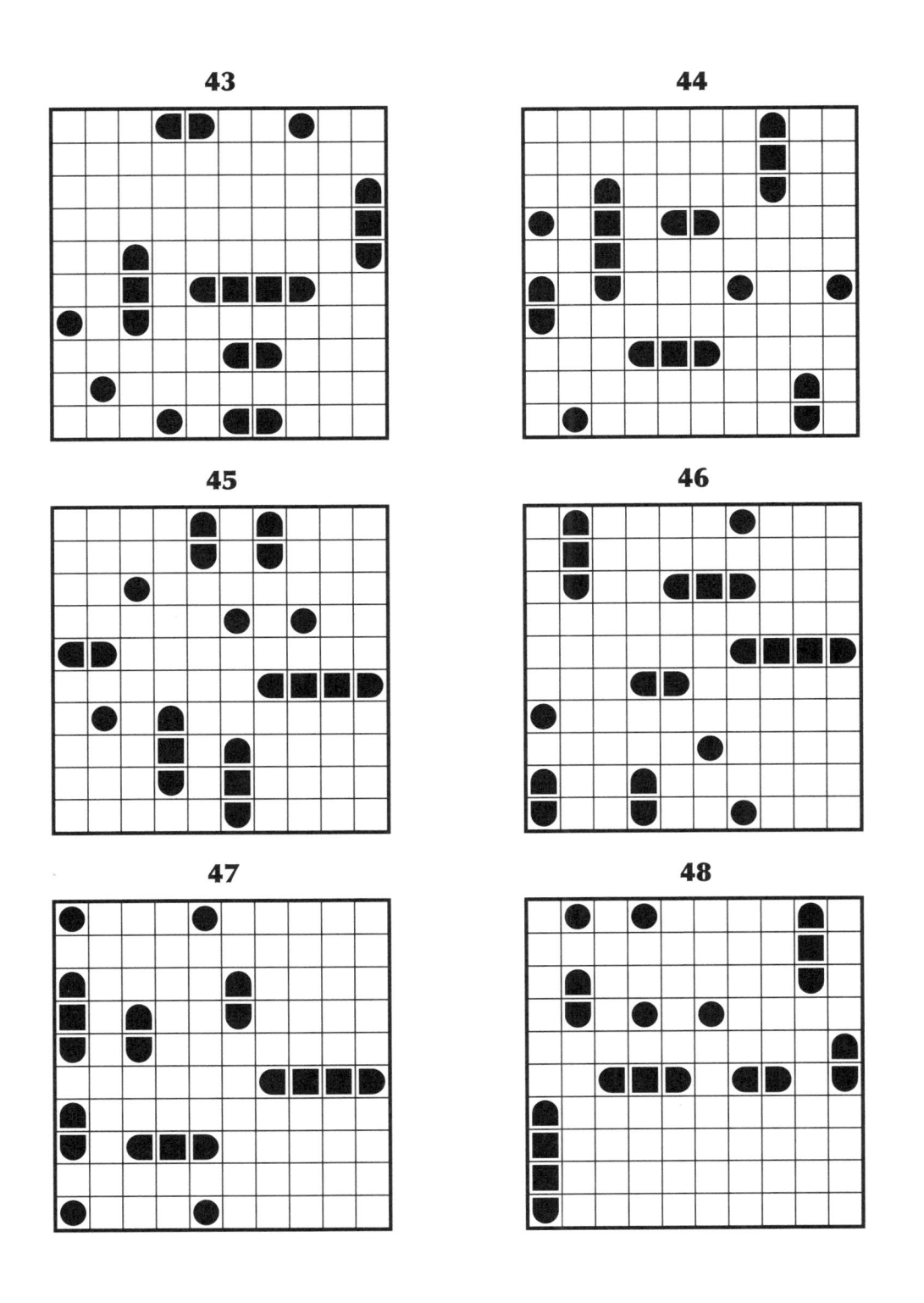

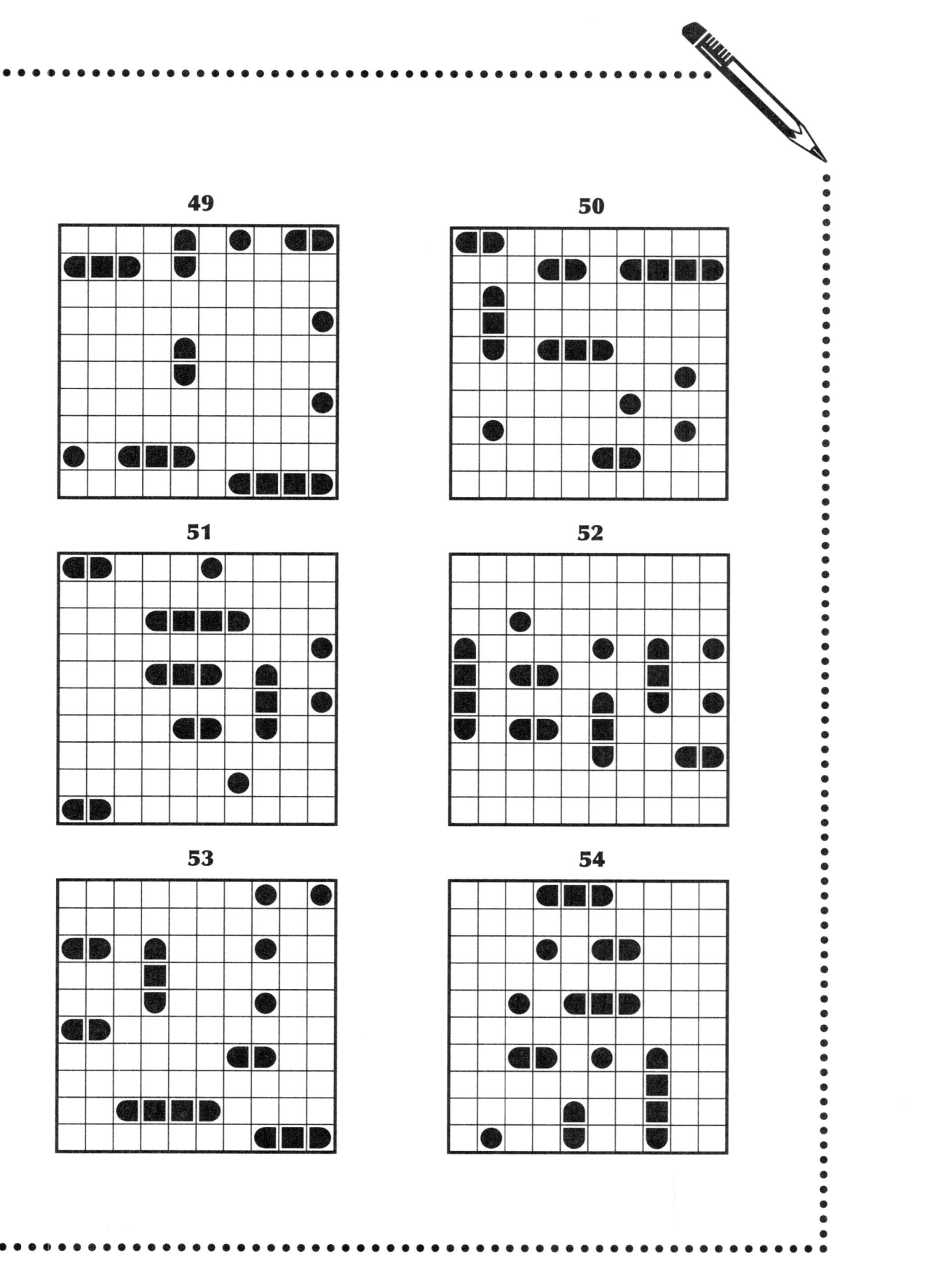

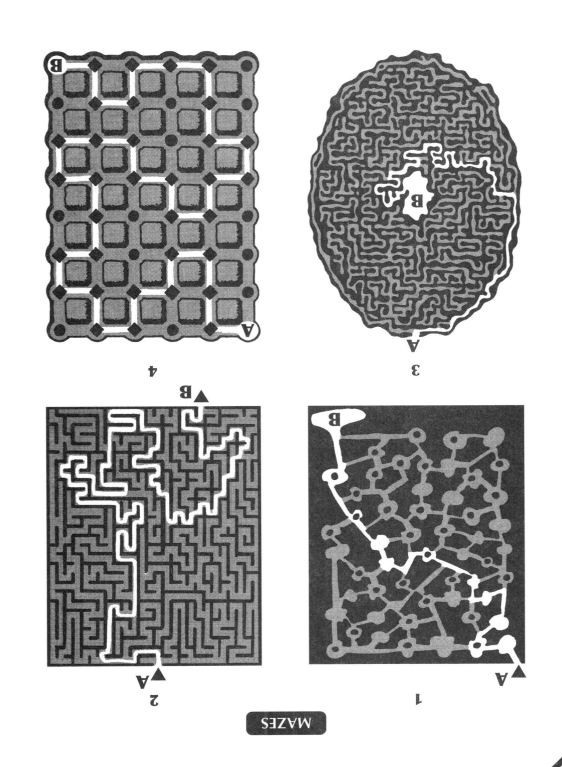

MAZES

4

3

2

1

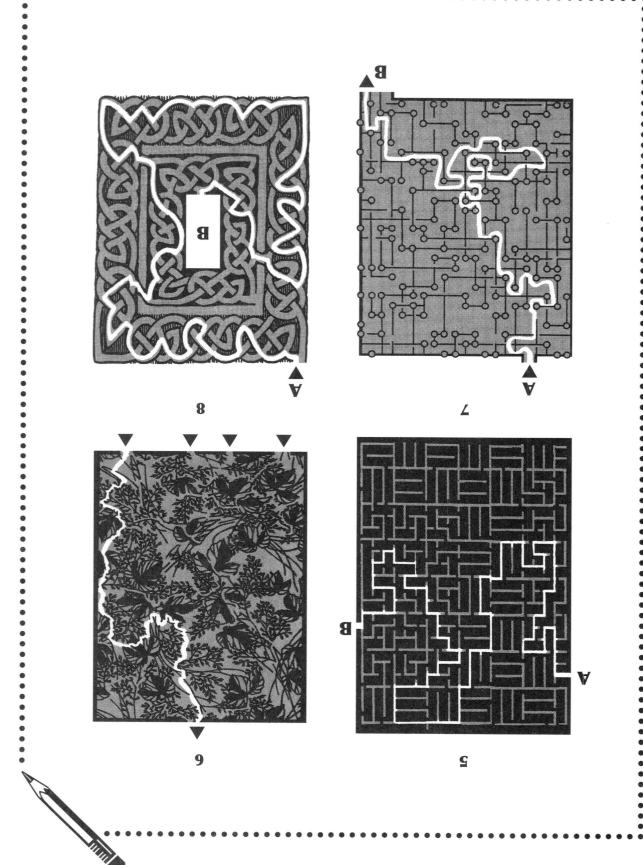

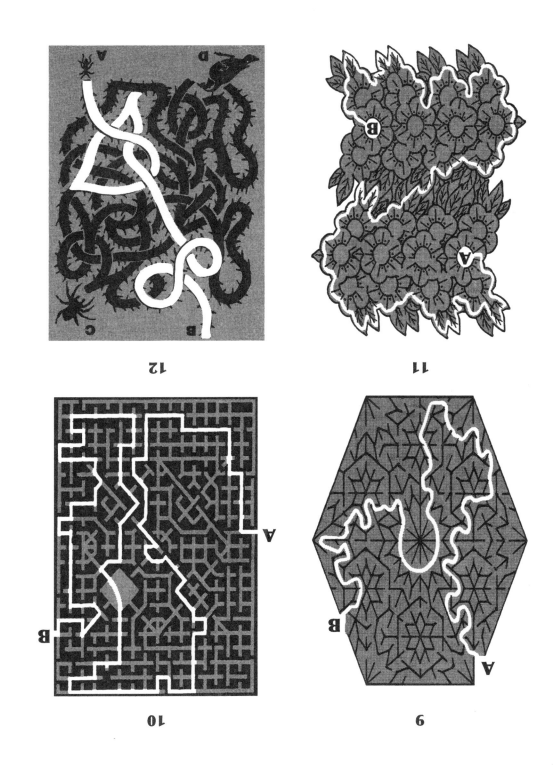

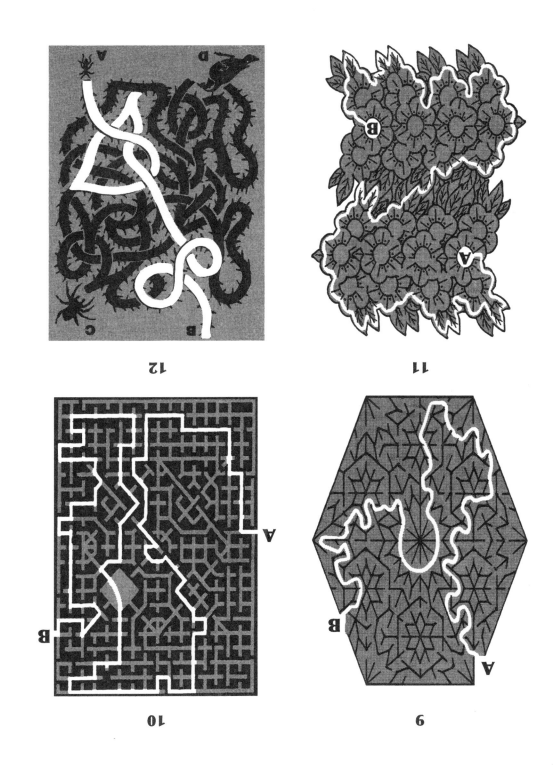

12

11

10

9

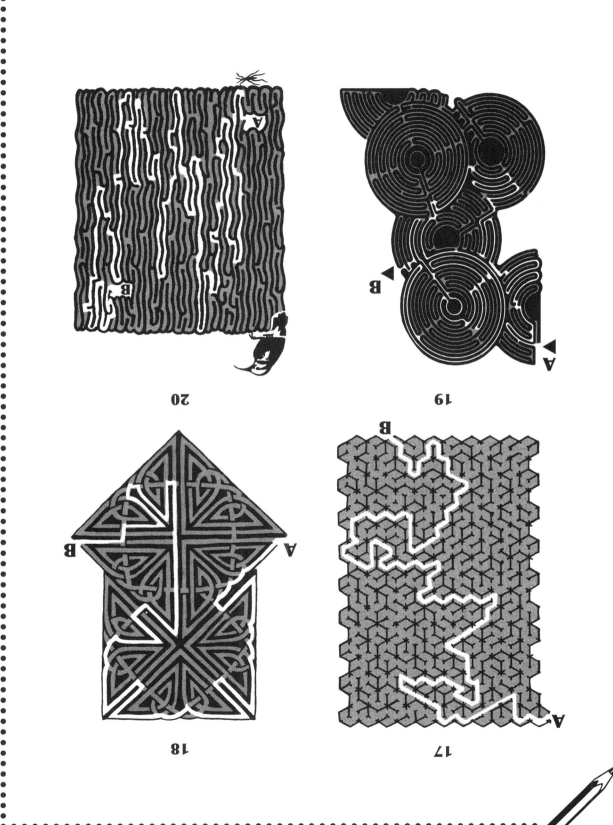

20

19

18

17

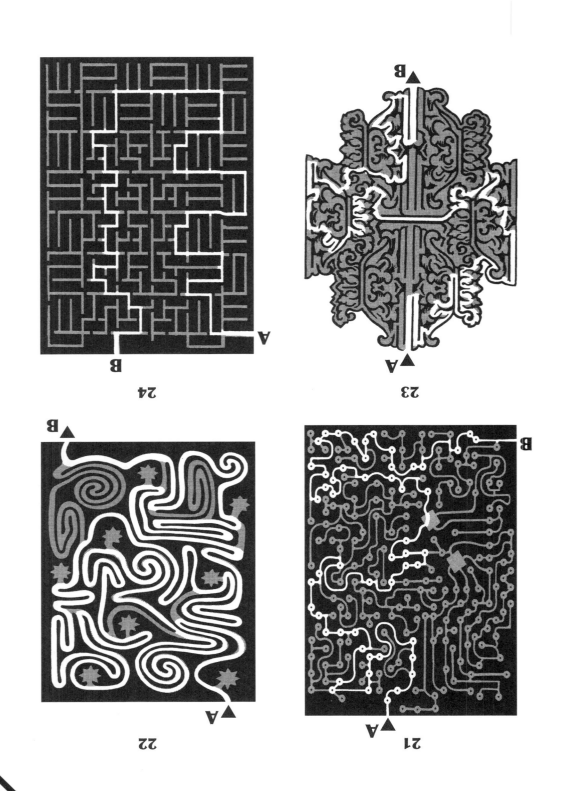

24

23

22

21

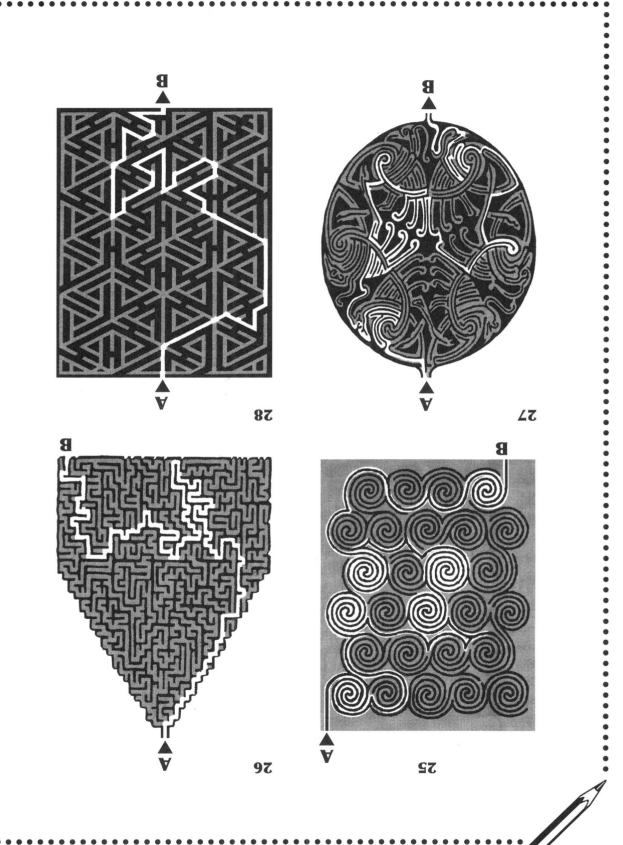

28

27

26

25

29

30

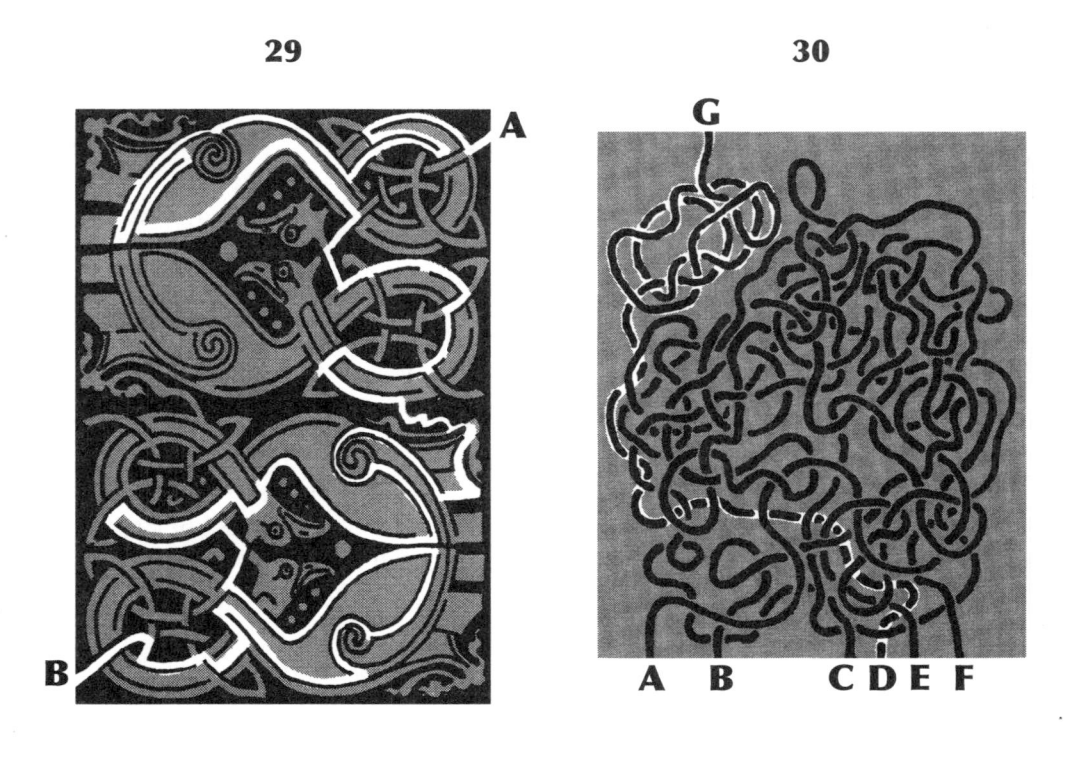

WHODUNITS

MURDER BETWEEN FRIENDS

Dr. Quicksolve suspected Tweeter. Her hearing seemed fine and her music was not loud enough to drown out the sound of gunshots. The hall was quiet and the music did not interfere with their conversation. She may have been angry with Terry for complaining about her music.

Many hearing-impaired people would be able to hear gunshots. Miss Blossom's Labrador was apparently a "hearing ear dog" who brought her to the door when Dr. Quicksolve knocked quietly. There is no reason to suspect Miss Blossom.

INHERITANCE

Dr. Quicksolve wanted to talk to the cousin from North Dakota because he had already eliminated the niece. The deceased, an only child and a bachelor, could not have a niece.

STRIKEOUT

Junior thinks Homer should not be trusted because he sells counterfeit baseball cards. Mickey Mantle played for the Yankees in 1951, so there cannot be a 1953 rookie card.

CODDLED COED

Sergeant Shurshot believes Holly took the money. She thinks Holly made up a quick alibi because no one with a cat in the house would leave unwrapped fish on the counter.

TELEPHONE RING

He expected to see a phone or credit card number on the pad that would match the number belonging to the man in the jacket. Dr. Quicksolve knew that thieves stand around open phones to listen while people say their card numbers into the phone. Then these criminals use the numbers to make calls or charge things. This time, the crook did not get away.

BEN BOINKT

Dr. Quicksolve doubts their story and wonders if Mr. Boinkt was hit at all. How could the robbers find the safe, open it, and be gone so quickly if Mr. and Mrs. Boinkt were both unconscious? He thinks Ben Boinkt and Glenda Cheatenhart killed Mrs. Boinkt.

SOCKS

Bobby said they were playing a team from Jackson. That means his was the home team, which would bat second and wouldn't bat the last inning if they were ahead after the visitors' last bat.

THE REAL MCCOY

Junior knew Blowhard's story about "the real McCoy" was not true. It is generally accepted that the expression is connected to an invention that automatically lubricates moving parts on many kinds of machines. The inventor was an African-American named Elijah McCoy.

BEN AGAIN

The fancy shooting and the long fistfight between the two men is hard to believe. The real problem with the story, though, is the wristwatch. There were wristwatches in the late 1800s, but they were designed only for women! Men used pocket watches at that time.

JOKERS WILD

Miss Forkton said she had just arrived home, yet her car was frosted over.

THREAT

The driver said they were looking at a map, yet he had not turned on the interior light to read it.

PLUNGER AND SNAKE

Plunger said someone hid behind the door. Dr. Quicksolve had just pulled the door open to come in. If the door pulled out to open, no one could have been hiding behind it on the inside.

SHORTSTOP'S BIKE

Because there are so many bikes that look alike, the thief would probably think it was safe to ride it to school, believing Shortstop could not identify his bike.

Junior and Shortstop had wisely etched their names inconspicuously under the crossbars of their bikes where no one would notice, but Junior could feel the engraving with his fingers.

CLAUDE VICIOUSLY

Being a circus performer, Stretch would have known lion tamers use blanks, yet he said "bullets." He only could have known there had been bullets in the gun if he was the one who took them out.

GUESS THE THEME 1 WORD LIST

BAGEL
BELT
BIRDHOUSE
BUTTON
CHEERIOS
DONUT
FLUTE
GOLF GREEN
LIFE SAVERS
NETS

NOSE
NOTEBOOK PAPER
PIERCED EAR
POCKET
SEWING NEEDLE
SOCK
STRAINER
STRAW
SWISS CHEESE
TIRE

GUESS THE THEME 2 WORD LIST

BEACH TOWEL
BEDSHEET
COMIC STRIP
COUPON
DOMINO
DOOR
ENVELOPE
FLAG
MENU
MOVIE SCREEN

PAGE
PLACE MAT
POSTCARD
RECEIPT
RULER
SHELF
STAMP
TENNIS COURT
TWO-BY-FOUR
WINDOWPANE

GUESS THE THEME 3 WORD LIST

AQUAFRESH
BACON
BARBER POLE
BAR CODE
BASS
BILLIARD BALL
BUMBLEBEE
CANDY CANE
CROSSWALK
FLAG

PARFAIT
PLAID
RACCOON
REFEREE
SERGEANT
SKUNK
STRAW
TIES
TIGER
ZEBRA

GETTING STARTED

Driver's advice: Engage mind before putting mouth in gear.

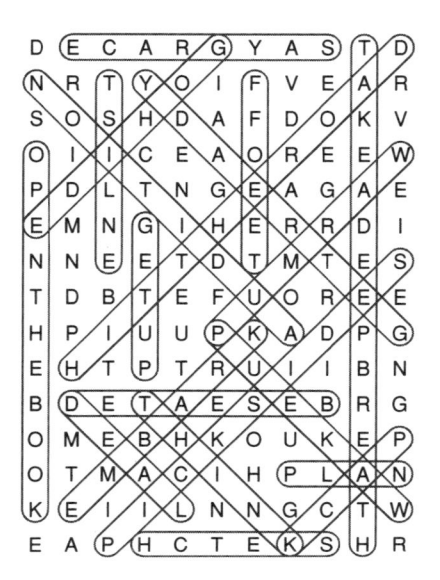

CHECK THIS OUT

If you play chess a lot, are you a chess-nut?

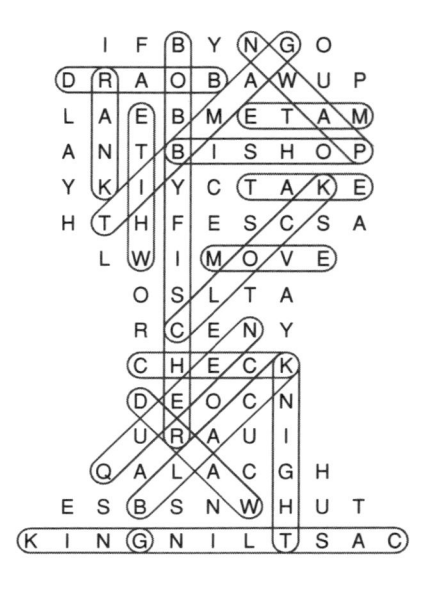

FATHER'S DAY

The best daddy would win a "pop"-ularity contest.

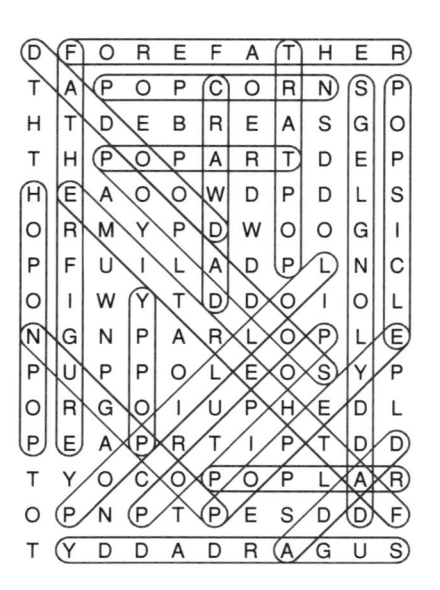

AT THE MALL

Tall Paul saw a scrawl on the wall at that small mall.

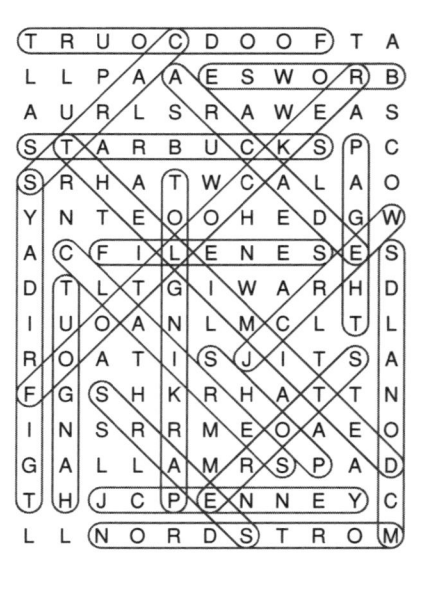

X MARKS THE SPOT

A boxer put the mix of Kix, Trix, and Rice Chex in the icebox.

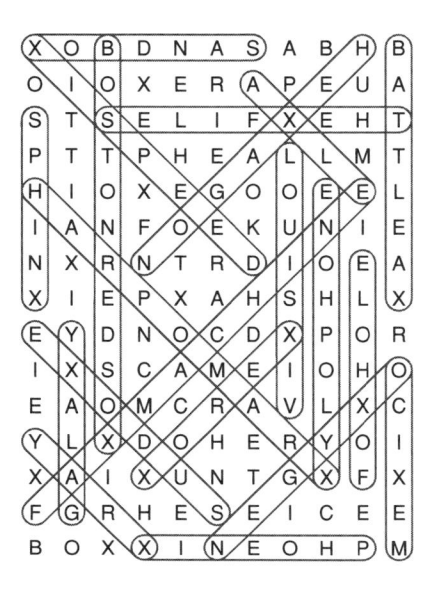

THE SIMPSONS

The space aliens who show up on occasion are Kang and Kodos.

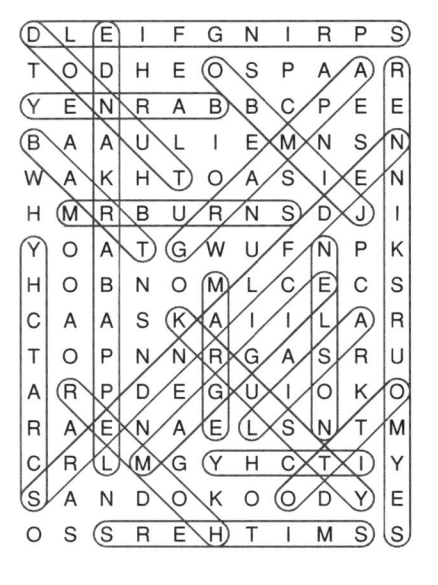

CIRCLING THE BASES

The youngest major leaguer was age fifteen.

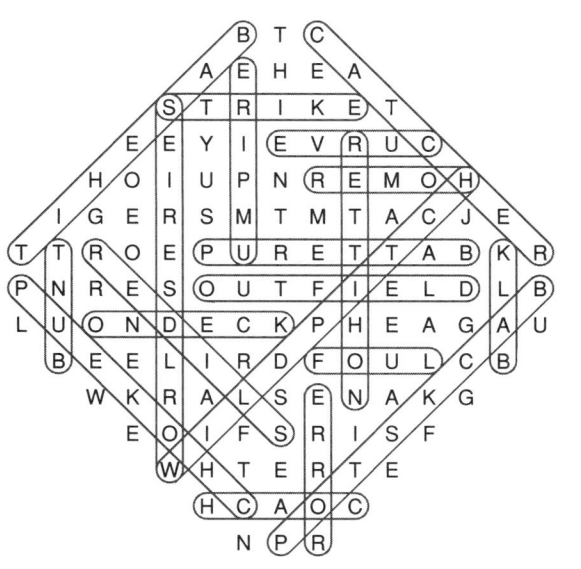

"IT'S ABOUT TIME!"

"Time is the most valuable thing a man can spend."—Theophrastus

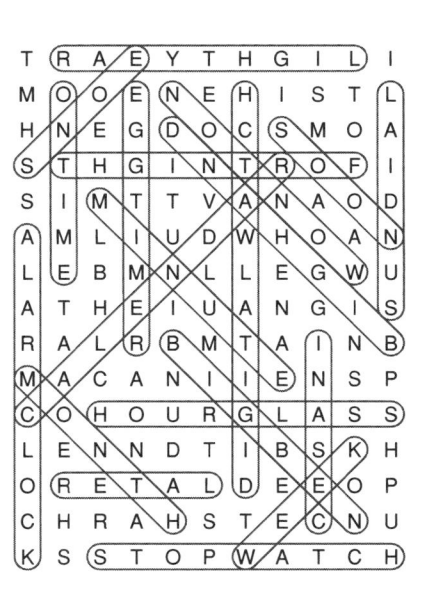

232

AT THE MOVIES

At the movies, you pay to sit in the dark with a lot of strangers.

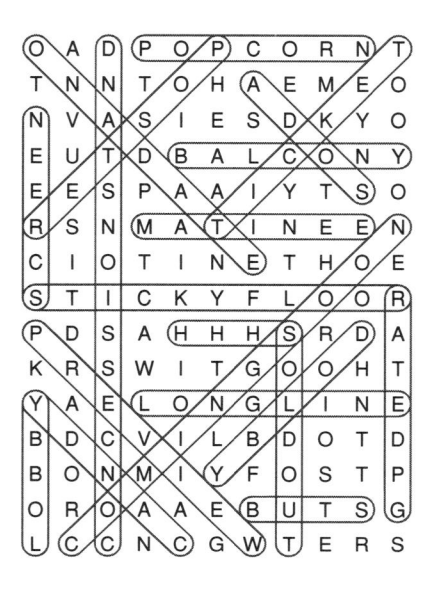

SURFING THE WEB

When a girl sends an electronic message, that's female e-mail.

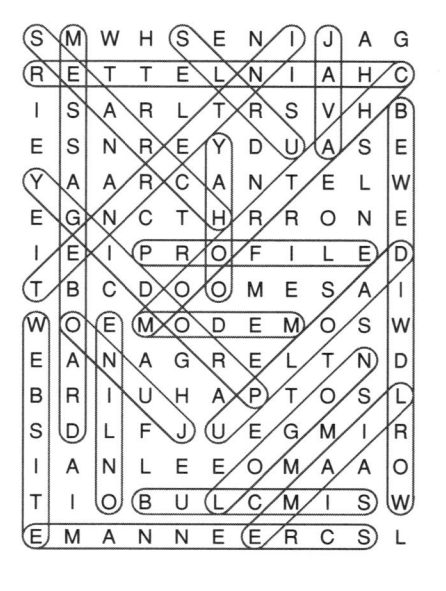

LIFE'S A PICNIC

A picnic means a fun time, a food-filled outing, or easy task.

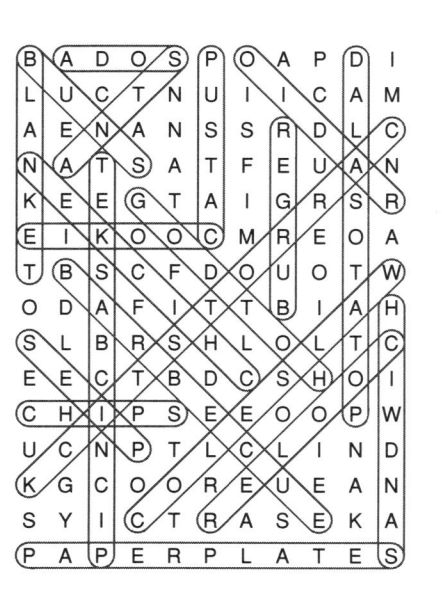

PIECE A PIZZA

No matter how you slice it, you have to admit this was easy as pie.

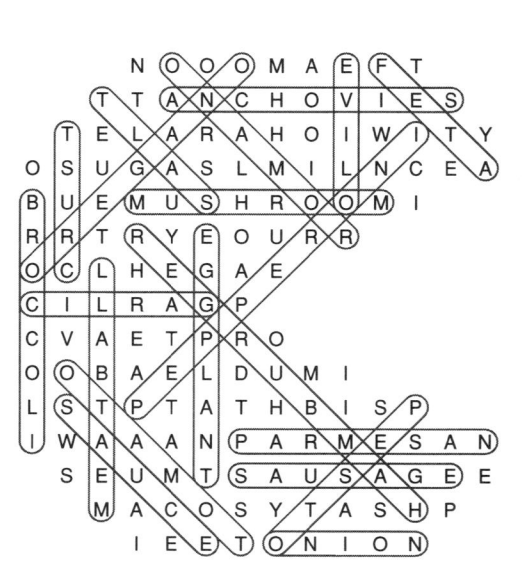

MONOPOLY GAME

Monopoly properties are named after
streets in Atlantic City, NJ.

A BAND WE'D LIKE TO HEAR

"Music is the universal language of
mankind."—Longfellow

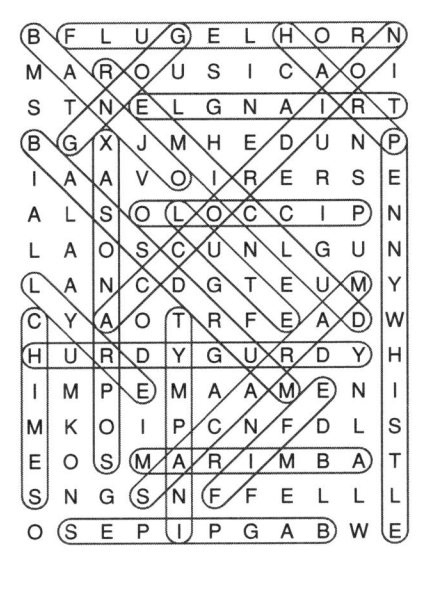

THINGS THAT SPIN

"We are spinning our own fates,
good or evil."—William James

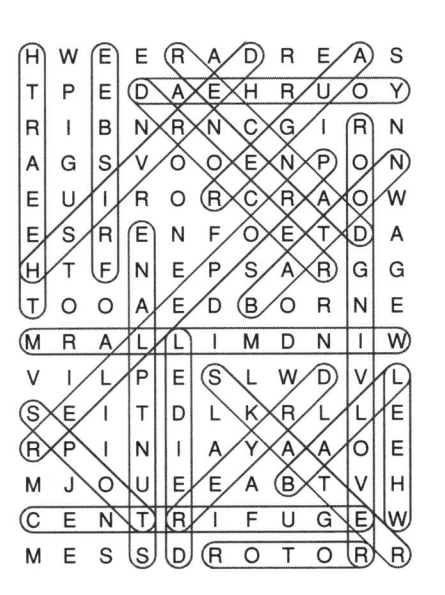

CAMP SIGHTS

Camp songs and scary stories are fun
around the campfire.

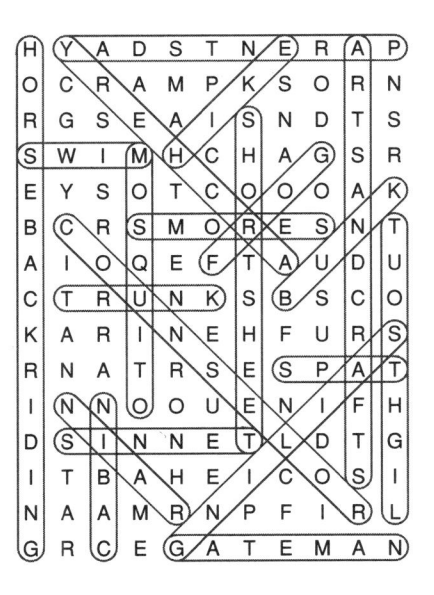

HINKY PINKY

Six hicks froze toes on the Greek peak.

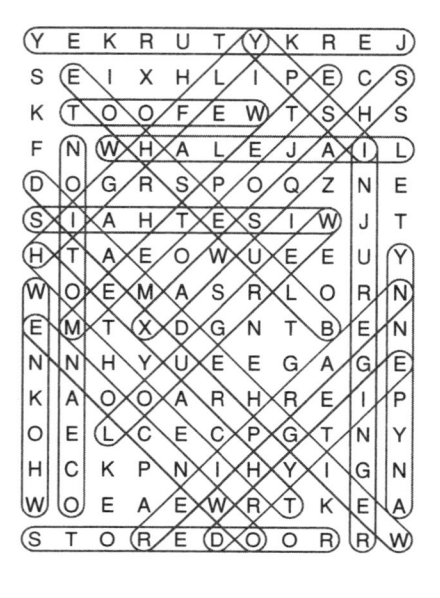

GUESS THE THEME 1

This Swiss cheese grid has things with holes.

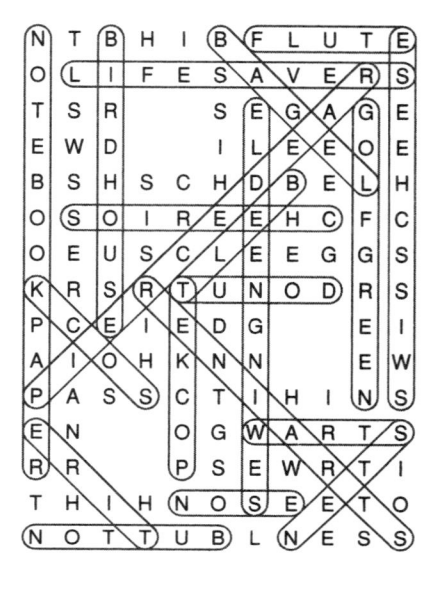

THE LEGEND OF ARTHUR

Arthur alone was able to pull the sword out of the stone.

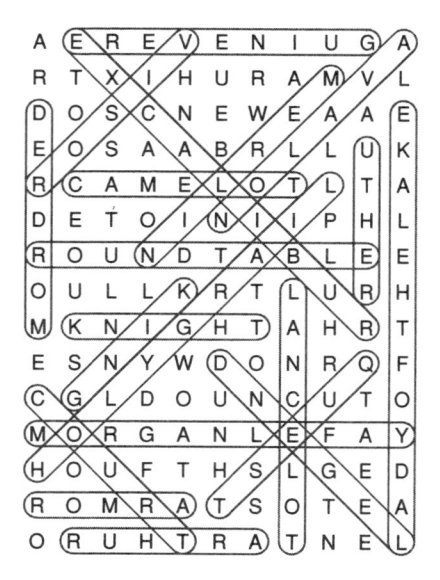

FEELING LUCKY?

Finding a heads-up penny is thought to bring good luck.

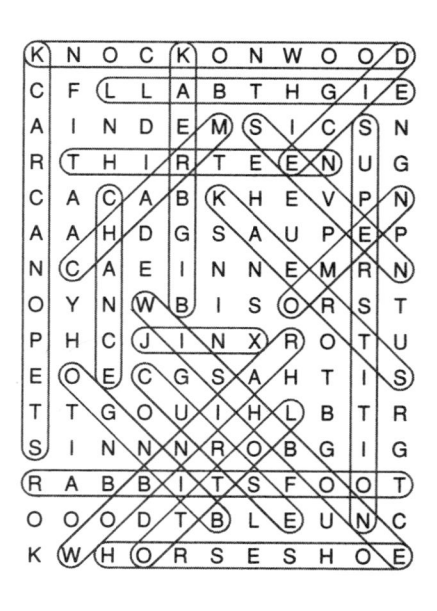

235

IT'S ELEMENTARY

What do you get if you swallow uranium? You get atomic ache.

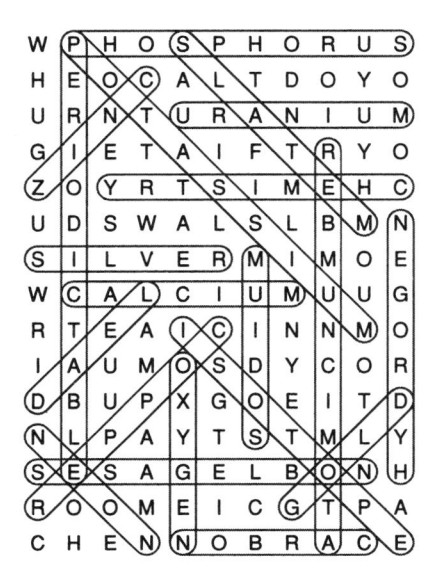

GUESS THE THEME 2

The grid and all the theme entries are usually rectangular.

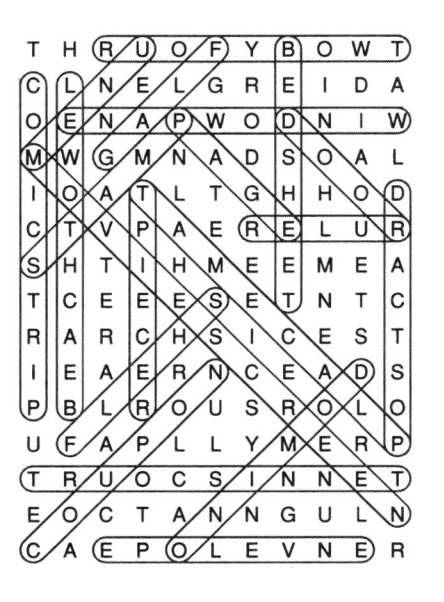

DOG AND CAT SCAN

When it's really pouring, we say it's raining cats and dogs.

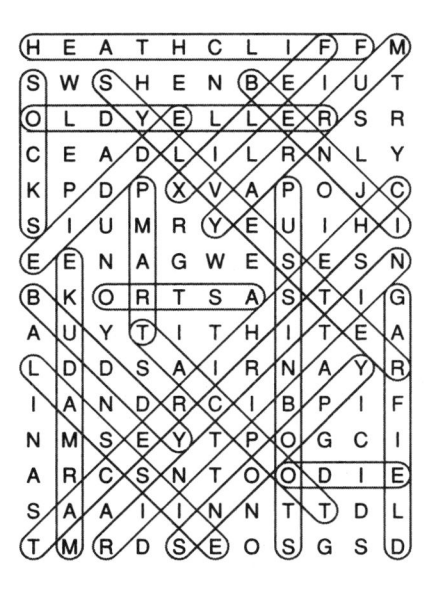

STAR WARS

The film "Spaceballs" was a spoof of "Star Wars."

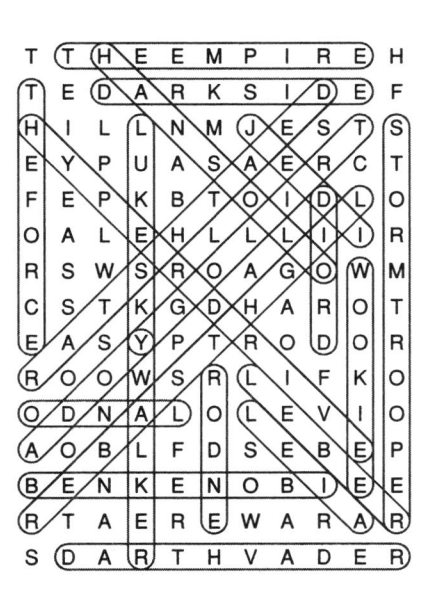

"OH-OH"
Some other double O words are cuckoo, tattoo, Scrooge, and doodad.

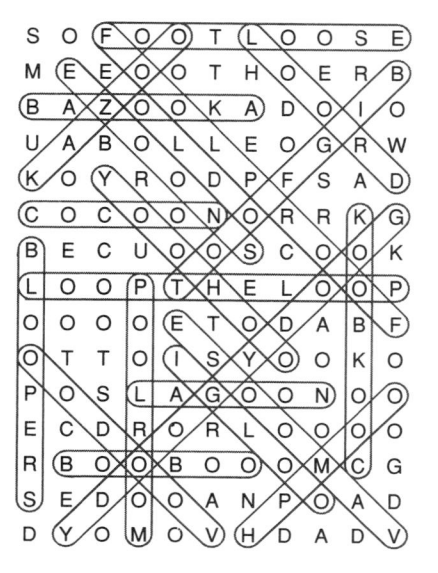

BEACHY-KEEN
Sandcastles require three things: sand, water, and imagination.

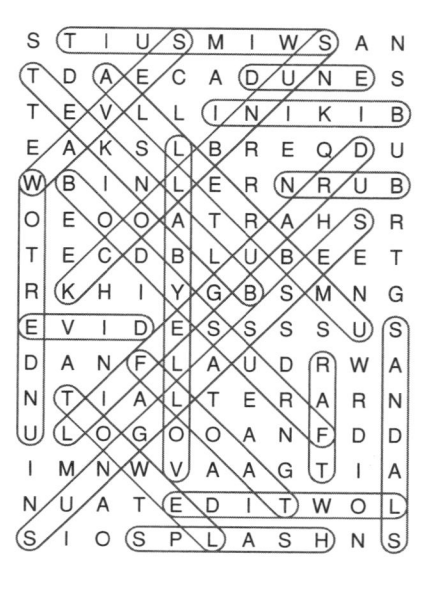

GUESS THE THEME 3
The grid is filled with items that always or often have stripes.

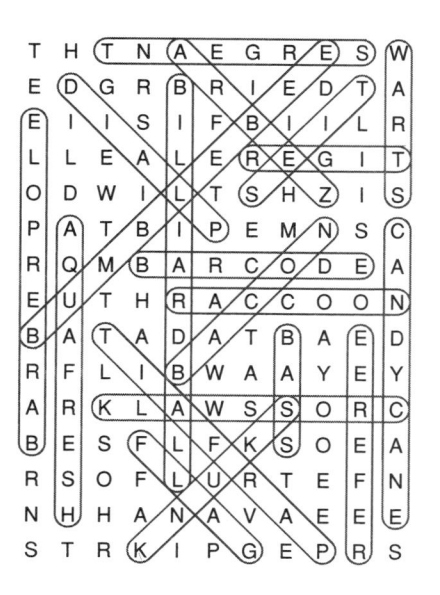

CASUAL DRESS
"Beware. . . all enterprises that require new clothes."—Thoreau

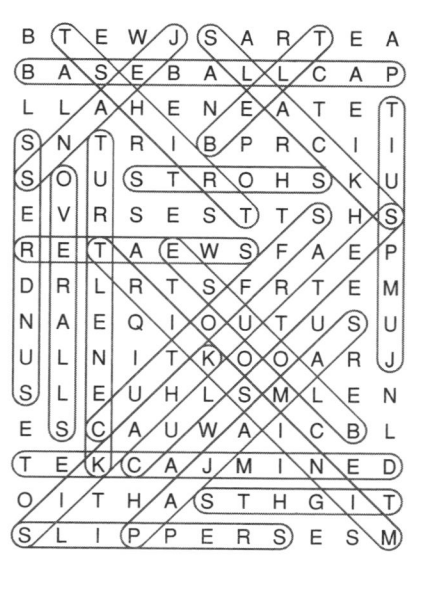

THE LOST WORLD

Not all dinosaurs were huge. Some were the size of a chicken.

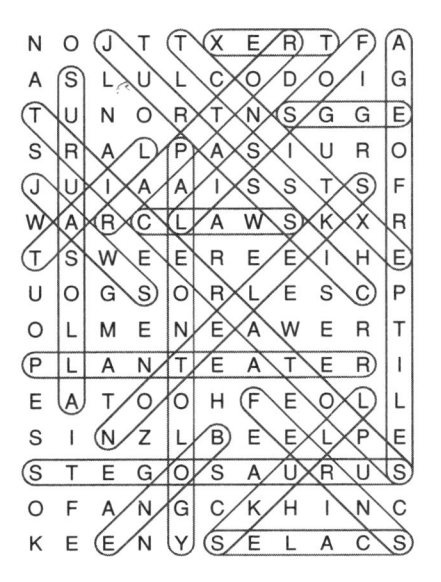

WRITE ON!

During a rite, it is right to write to Orville and Wilbur Wright.

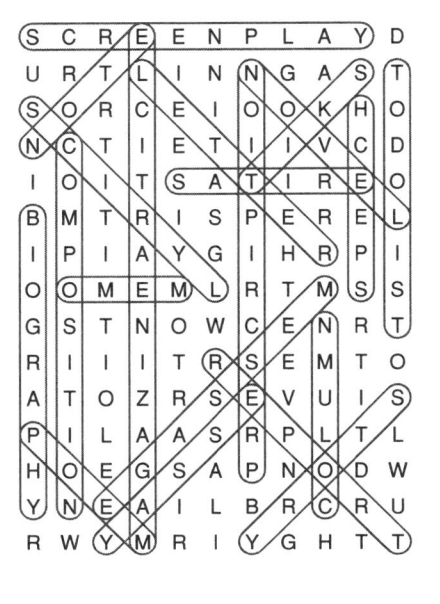

SCHOOL SUPPLIES

Supply costs can add up fast—using a calculator.

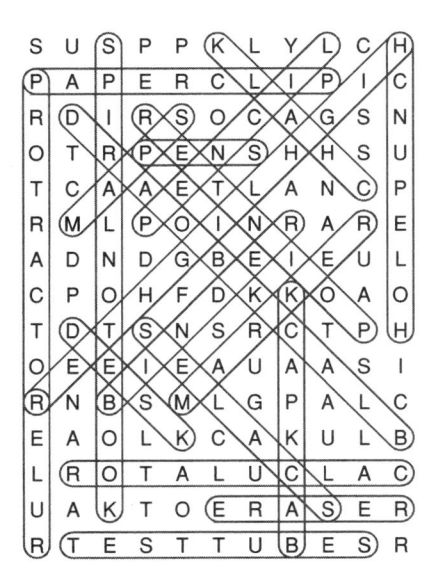

BY THE NUMBERS

The 3 Stooges called 911 to buy 1-way tickets on a Boeing 747.

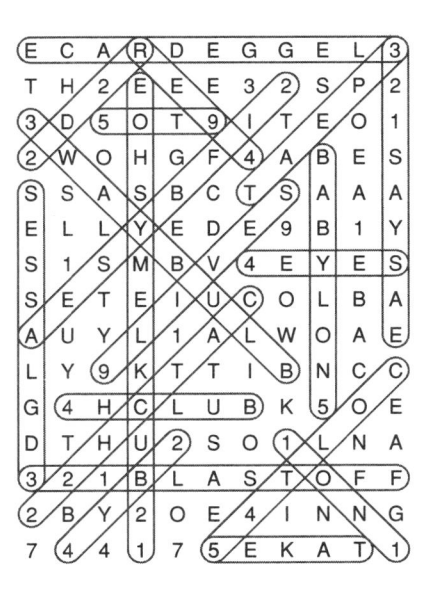

WORDWORKS

1 "GAMESTER"

(4 letters)

ages, arms, ease, east, game, gate, gear, gems, germ, geta, gram, mare, mart, mast, mate, meat, meet, mere, mete, rage, rags, rams, rate, ream, rest, sage, same, sate, seam, sear, seat, seem, seer, sera, sere, seta, stag, star, stem, tame, tare, tear, team, teem, term, tram, tree

(5 letters)

agree, ameer, aster, eager, eater, egest, egret, ester, gamer, grate, great, mater, merge, meter, reset, serge, smart, smear, stage, stare, steam, steer, tamer, tease, terse

(6 letters)

gamest, gamete, grease, master, meager, merest, stream, tamest, teaser

(7 letters)

steamer

2 "FAVORITE"

(4 letters)

aver, fair, fare, fate, fear, feat, feta, fiat, fire, five, fore, fort, frat, iota, over, rate, rave, reft, rife, rift, riot, rite, rive, rota, rote, rove, tare, taro, tear, tier, tire, tiro, tore, trio, vert, veto, vote

(5 letters)

afrit, after, avert, favor, forte, irate, orate, ovate, overt, ratio, rivet, trove, voter

3 "BETROTHAL"

(4 letters)

abet, able, alto, bale, bare, bate, bath, bear, beat, belt, beta, blat, blot, boar, boat, bola, bolt, bone, bore, both, brat, earl, hale, halo, halt, hart, heal, hear, heat, herb, hero, hoar, hoer, hole, hora, late, lath, lobe, lore, oath, oral, rale, rate, real, robe, role, rota, rote, tale, teal, that, tole, tort, tote, tret, trot

(5 letters)

abhor, abort, alert, alter, bathe, berth, betta, blear, bloat, broth, earth, heart, helot, hotel, labor, later, lathe, loath, obeah, orate, other, otter, table, tabor, taler, tarot, throb, throe, torte, total, treat, troth

(6 letters)

bather, batter, battle, bettor, boater, bolter, bother, bottle, breath, halter, hatter, herbal, hotter, lather, loathe, oblate, rattle, rotate, tablet, threat

(7 letters)

battler, betroth, blather, blotter, bottler, brothel

4 "DEVELOPMENT"

(4 letters)

deem, deep, dele, dent, dole, dolt, dome, done, dope, dote, even, lent, lode, lone, lope, love, meet, meld, melt, mend, mete, mode, mold, mole, molt, mope, mote, move, need, node, nope, note, omen, open, oven, peel, peen, pelt, pend, pent, plod, plot, poem, poet, pole, pond, pone, teem, teen, tend, toed, told, tole, tome, tone, tope, veep, vend, vent, veto, volt, vote

(5 letters)

delve, demon, depot, elope, emote, epode, event, lemon, levee, melon, model, motel, novel, olden, opted, peeve, tempo, tepee, veldt

(6 letters)

deepen, delete, demote, devote, needle, omelet, temple

(7 letters)

deplete, develop, devotee, element

(8 letters)

envelope

(9 letters)

elopement

5 "EXEMPLARY"

(4 letters)

aery, apex, army, axle, earl, eery, exam, lame, lamp, leap, leer, lyre, male, mare, meal, mere, pale, pare, peal, pear, peel, peer, perm, play, plea, pram, pray, prey, rale, ramp, rape, real, ream, reap, reel, rely, yare, year, yelp

(5 letters)

ample, amply, early, emery, expel, layer, leery, leper, maple, mealy, merle, payee, payer, pearl, pryer, realm, relax, relay, repel, reply, xylem

(6 letters)

leaper, merely, parley, pearly, player, replay

(7 letters)

example, lamprey

6 "POPULARITY"

(4 letters)

airy, alit, aril, arty, auto, lair, liar, lira, lory, lout, oily, opal, oral, pail, pair, palp, part, pita, pity, plat, play, plop, plot, ploy, port, pour, pray, proa, prop, pulp, pupa, puri, purl, rail, rapt, rial, riot, roil, ropy, rota, roup, rout, tail, tali, taro, tarp, toil, tolu, tori, tour, trap, tray, trio, trip, yaup, your, yurt

(5 letters)

aport, apply, aptly, atrip, laity, lapin, loppy, parol, party, patio, pilot, plait, platy, poilu, polar, polyp, pulpy, pupil, ratio, royal, trail, trial, troup, tulip, ultra

(6 letters)

artily, layout, outlay, papyri, parity, partly, payout, polity, poplar, portal, portly, purity, ripply, uppity

(7 letters)

popular, poultry, topiary

(8 letters)

polarity

7 "HISTORICAL"

(4 letters)

ails, alit, alto, arch, cart, cash, cast, char, chat, chit, clot, coal, coat, coil, cost, hail, hair, halo, hart, hoar, hora, host, iris, itch, laic, lair, lash, last, lath, liar, lira, list, loch, lost, oast, oral, orca, otic, rail, rash, rial, rich, roil, rota, sail, salt, sari, scar, scat, shot, silt, slat, slit, slot, soar, soil, sora, sort, star, stir, taco, tail, taro, this, tiro, toil, tola, tori, trio

(5 letters)

actor, ascot, chart, chili, choir, clash, cloth, coast, coral, crash, hoist, latch, loath, loris, ratio, roach, roast, salic, shirt, shoat, short, sloth, stoic, torch, trail, trash, trial, triol

(6 letters)

aortic, castor, choral, racist, sailor, silica, social, starch, thoria, thoric

(7 letters)

chariot, ostrich, trochal

(8 letters)

historic, holistic

8 "CONCENTRATION"

(4 letters)

acne, ante, cane, cant, care, cart, cent, coat, coin, coin, cone, coot, core, corn, cote, earn, icon, into, iota, iron, near, neat, neon, nine, nice, none, noon, note, oleo, olio, once, onto, oral, race, rain, rant, rate, rein, rent, rice, riot, rite, roan, rote, tact, tare, tarn, taro, tart, tear, tent, tier, tine, tint, tire, tone, torn, tort, tret, trot

(5 letters)

actor, antic, atone, attic, cairn, canoe, canon, canto, cater, caret, crane, crate, crone, croon, enact, inate, inert, inner, irate, nonce, octet, onion, orate, otter, ratio, riant, tacit, taint, tarot, tatoo, tenon, titan, toner, tonic, trace, tract, train, trait, trice, trine

(6 letters)
accent, action, arctic, attire, cancer, cannon, cannot, canter, cantor, carton, cornea, cornet, corona, cotton, crater, intact, nation, nectar, notion, octane, ration, retina, rotate, trance

(7 letters)
cartoon, conceit, concern, concert, connect, connote, contact, contain, content, contort, coronet, entrant, nictate, oration, raccoon

(8 letters)
contract, creation, interact, notation, reaction, rotation, traction

(9 letters)
container

(10 letters)
concertina, connection

(11 letters)
contraction

9 "XYLOPHONE"

(4 letters)
help, hole, holp, holy, hone, hood, hope, hypo, lone, loon, loop, lope, lynx, nope, only, onyx, open, oxen, peon, ploy, pole, polo, pone, pony, pooh, pool

(5 letters)
epoxy, honey, hooey, loony, peony, phlox, phone, phony, pylon

(6 letters)
holpen, openly, phenol, phenyl, phooey

10 "NASTURTIUM"

(4 letters)
amir, anti, aunt, main, mart, mash, mast, mina, mint, mist, mitt, must, mutt, nuts, rain, rani, rant, ruin, runt, rust, sari, sima, smut, snit, star, stir, stun, suit, sura, tain, tarn, taut, tint, tram, trim, tsar, tuna, turn, unau, unit, urus

(5 letters)
astir, manus, matin, minus, ramus, riant, saint, satin, sitar, smart, stain, start, stint, stria, strum, strut, stunt, suint, sutra, taint, taunt, train, trait, trust, unarm

(6 letters)
antrum, artist, autism, instar, mantis, martin, mutant, nutria, strain, strait, struma, tanist, truant

(7 letters)
intrust, stratum, transit, uranium

(8 letters)
transmit

11 "WHISPERING"

(4 letters)

egis, gens, grew, grin, grip, heir, hers, hewn, hire, news, pens, pews, phew, pier, pine, ping, pins, prig, ring, ripe, rise, sewn, shin, ship, sigh, sign, sine, sing, sire, spew, spin, swig, weir, when, whip, whir, wigs, wine, wing, wipe, wire, wise, wish, wisp

(5 letters)

gripe, hinge, pries, prise, reign, resin, rinse, ripen, risen, shine, shire, shrew, sinew, singe, spine, spire, sprig, swine, swing, weigh, whine, wring

(6 letters)

hewing, hiring, perish, resign, sewing, shiner, shrine, signer, singer, siring, spring, whiner, wiping, wiring

(7 letters)

inspire, swinger, wishing

(9 letters)

perishing

12 "POLITICIAN"

(4 letters)

alit, alto, anil, anti, cant, capo, clan, clap, clip, clop, clot, coal, coat, coil, coin, cola, colt, copt, icon, laic, lain, lint, lion, loan, loin, nail, opal, otic, pact, pail, pant, pica, pint, pion, pita, plan, plat, plot, taco, tail, talc, toil, topi

(5 letters)

actin, aloin, antic, canto, capon, coati, iliac, inapt, ionic, licit, nopal, ontic, optic, paint, panic, patio, piano, picot, pilot, piton, plain, plait, plant, plica, point, talon, tonal, tonic, topic

(6 letters)

action, cation, catnip, italic, oilcan, pliant, pontil

(7 letters)

capitol, caption, initial, pinitol, politic, topical

GREET BEGINNINGS

1

1. Incentive, 2. Incognito, 3. Infallible, 4. Inn, 5. Invoice, 6. Intrepid, 7. Interloper, 8. Insomnia, 9. Inherit, 10. Inmate, 11. Infirmity, 12. Inch, 13. Injure, 14. Inert, 15. Interrogate, 16. Infant, 17. Incubate, 18. Inferno, 19. Indigo, 20. Indiana, 21. Infantry, 22. Indict, 23. Ink

2

1. Expel, 2. Exit, 3. Exempt, 4. Excellent, 5. Exaggerate, 6. Extra, 7. Exam, 8. Experiment, 9. Expression, 10, Excuse, 11. Exodus, 12. Expensive, 13. Exile, 14. Exact, 15. Excalibur, 16. Extraterrestrial, 17. Expand, 18. Exhaustion, 19. Expressway, 20. Executioner, 21. Export, 22. Extrovert

3

1. Quagmire, 2. Quartet, 3. Quilt, 4. Quack, 5. Quake, 6. Quiet, 7. Quarrel, 8. Quicksand, 9. Queen, 10. Quandary, 11. Quaker, 12. Quarantine, 13. Quail, 14. Quarry, 15. Quisling, 16. Quaff, 17. Quirk, 18. Query, 19. Queue, 20. Quaint, 21. Quell, 22. Quinine, 23. Quince, 24. Quarterback, 25. Quip

4

1. Wacky, 2. Wafer, 3. Waldorf salad, 4. Waft, 5. Waitress, 6. Wagon, 7. Waif, 8. Walrus, 9. Wallaby, 10. Walnut, 11. Wanton, 12. Wallflower, 13. Wax, 14. Wattle, 15. Wardrobe, 16. Washboard, 17. Warble, 18. Warpath, 19. Washington, 20. Warlock, 21. Wanderlust, 22. Waltz

5

1. Shadow, 2. Sherbet, 3. Shakespeare, 4. Shallot, 5. Shyster, 6. Shard, 7. Shroud, 8. Shirk, 9. Shrapnel, 10. Sham, 11. Shrine, 12. Shilling, 13. Shrug, 14. Sheriff, 15. Shrub, 16. Sheaf, 17. Shoat, 18. Shortening, 19. Shriek, 20. Shrimp, 21. Shrew, 22. Shun

6

1. Poetry, 2. Porcelain, 3. Poltergeist, 4. Polygraph, 5. Poach, 6. Poi, 7. Pontiff, 8. Portfolio, 9. Pollen, 10. Porcupine, 11. Portrait, 12. Posture, 13. Poker, 14. Poppycock, 15. Pompadour, 16. Polka, 17. Posse, 18. Polaris, 19. Politburo, 20. Pony Express

7

1. Mandate, 2. Marmoset, 3. Madrigal, 4. Marble, 5. Martian, 6. Majordomo, 7. Martyr, 8. Macaroni, 9. Mardi Gras, 10. Maneuver, 11. Maze, 12. Malaria, 13. Marsh, 14. Macbeth, 15. Marathon, 16. Manicure, 17. Mambo, 18. Martini, 19. Magenta

8

1. Foal, 2. Folly, 3. Forte, 4. Fondue, 5. Forgery, 6. Football, 7. Foe, 8. Footnote, 9. Forever, 10. Font, 11. Foliage, 12. Forest, 13. Forceps, 14. Foible, 15. Fodder, 16. Fob, 17. Forage, 18. Foundling, 19. Fortnight, 20. Fossil, 21. Forget-me-not, 22. Forbid

9

1. Noodle, 2. Nostalgia, 3. November, 4. Notch, 5. Noah, 6. Nominee, 7. Noxious, 8. Nonchalant, 9. Noise, 10. Novena, 11. Noel, 12. Nobel (Alfred), 13. Noose, 14. Nozzle, 15. Nom de plume, 16. Notary, 17. Nougat, 18. Note, 19. Nomad, 20. Nocturnal, 21. Novice, 22. North pole, 23. Nodule

SAY IT AGAIN, SAM

1

compliment, acclaim, praise, laud, commend

2

effort, endeavor, attempt, strive, try

3

adversary, rival, antagonist, enemy, predator

4

instruct, train, teach, educate, tutor

5

secret, enigma, mystery, riddle, puzzle

6

eject, evict, exclude, expel, oust

7

garbage, waste, trash, rubbish, refuse

8

consider, cogitate, deliberate, ruminate, ponder

9

mistake, omission, fallacy, blunder, error

10

implore, entreat, beseech, appeal, plead

STORY BUILDERS

1 THE REST IS UP TO YOU

it, sit, pits, trips, priest, respite

2 A LEGEND IN HIS OWN MIND

do, sod, does, posed, despot, spotted

3 WHAT YOU SEE IS WHAT YOU GET

at, art, rant, train, retain, certain, reaction, creations

4 CHARLES DARWIN, PHONE HOME!

pa, apt, rapt, prate, tamper, primate

5 WINNER TAKES ALL

be, bet, debt, bated, debate, berated

6 CAREER ORIENTED

no, one, peon, prone, person, ponders, responds

7 WHO ARE WE TO JUDGE?

pa, pal, pale, pleas, asleep, repeals, prelates

8 A HARD ONE TO FATHOM

a, as, sea, eras, tears, traces, creates, as secret

9 FOOD FOR THOUGHT

per, reap, pearl, parley, reapply

10 IN DEEP WATER

or, row, word, drown, wonder, downers, worsened

TAKE FIVE

1	S	C	O	R	E
AMERICAN INDIANS	Seneca Shoshone Sioux	Cherokee Comanche Crow	Ojibway Osage	Ree Rikari	Erie
ICE CREAM FLAVORS	Strawberry	Chocolate	Orange	Raspberry Rocky Road	Eggnog
BIBLICAL FIGURES	Salome Saul Solomon	Cain Christ	Obadiah Ozymandius	Rachel Raphael Ruth	Esther Ezekiel
VEGETABLES	Spinach Squash	Cabbage Cauliflower Corn	Okra Onion	Radish Rutabaga	Eggplant Endive
COLORS	Scarlet Sienna	Cerulean Coral Crimson	Ochre Olive	Red Russet	Ebony Ecru

2	R	G	P	S	B
CHEESES	Romano Roquefort	Gorgonzola Gouda	Parmesan Provolone	Saanen Swiss	Boursin Brie
FEMALE SINGERS	Helen Reddy Linda Ronstadt Diana Ross	Crystal Gayle Lesley Gore	Patti Page Dolly Parton	Carly Simon Grace Slick Barbra Streisand	Joan Baez Anita Baker Pat Benatar
BODIES OF WATER	Red Lake Red Sea Gulf of Mexico	Guanabara Bay	Pacific Ocean Persian Gulf	Salton Sea Sea of Cortez Strait of Magellan	Baltic Sea Bering Sea Black Sea
MEN'S FIRST NAMES	Ralph Richard Robert Roger	George Gilbert Grant	Paul Perry Peter Philip	Sal Simon Steve Stuart	Bill Bruce Bryan
CARD GAMES	Red Dog Rummy Russian Bank	Garbage Gin Go Fish	Parliament Pinochle Poker	Sixty-Six Skat Solitare	Baccarat Blackjack Bridge

3	**D**	**A**	**B**	**S**	**P**
STATE CAPITALS	Denver Des Moines Dover	Albany Austin Atlanta	Baton Rouge Bismarck Boise	Sacramento Salem Salt Lake City	Phoenix Pierre Providence
CARTOON CHARACTERS	Daffy Duck Donald Duck Dudley Doright	Archie Atom Ant	Betty Boop Bugs Bunny Bullwinkle	Scooby Doo Spiderman Superman	Pepe Le Pew Popeye Porky Pig

TELEVISION SOAP OPERAS	Dallas
	Days of Our
	  Lives
	Dynasty
		All My
		  Children
		As The World
		  Turns
			(The) Bold
			  and The
			  Beautiful
				Santa Barbara
				Search For
				  Tomorrow
					Peyton
					  Place

PROFESSIONS	Dancer Dentist Doctor Draftsman	Actor Astronaut Auctioneer Author	Baker Barber Bartender Butler	Salesclerk Scribe Shepherd Surgeon	Policeman Potter Preacher

CARY GRANT MOVIES	Destination
	  Tokyo
	Dream Wife
		(The) Awful
		  Truth
		An Affair to
		  Remember
			(The) Bishop's
			  Wife
			Bringing Up
			  Baby
				Suspicion
				Sylvia
				Scarlett
					Penny
					  Serenade
					Philadelphia
					  Story

4	**C**	**H**	**A**	**M**	**P**

MOVIE TITLES	Casablanca
	(The) Color
	  Purple
	Cool Hand
	
	  Luke
		Harold and
		  Maude
		High Noon
		(The) Hustler
			Adam's Rib
			All About Eve
			Annie Hall
				Marnie
				Married to
				  the Mob
				Marty
				Moonstruck
					Parenthood
					Pinocchio
					The
					  Producers

NUTS	Cashew Castana Chestnut	Hazel Head Hickory	Acorn Almond Applenut	Macadamia Maranon Mast	Peanut Pecan Pistachio
TREES	Carob Cedar Chinaberry	Hardtack Haw Hickory	Alder Ash Aspen	Maple Mimosa Mulberry	Pecan Pine Poplar
7-LETTER NOUNS	Clothes Coaster Command Culvert	Handful Heathen History Hygiene	Admiral Alimony Ammonia Avarice	Mammoth Mineral Mongrel Monster	Pattern Playpen Poultry Primary

PRO FOOTBALL PLAYERS	Earl
	  Campbell
	Dwight
	  Clark
		Drew Hill
		Tony Hill
		Paul
		  Hornung
			Tony Aikman
			Marcus Allen
			Lyle Alzado
				Dan Marino
				Joe Montana
				Jim McMahon
					Drew
					  Pearson
					Dan
					  Pastorini

5	W	S	C	B	R
PROFESSIONAL GOLFERS	Tom Watson Tom Weiskopf	Gene Sarazen Sam Snead Curtis Strange	Billy Casper Bruce Crampton	Seve Ballesteros Julius Boros	Mike Reid Chi Chi Rodriguez
SEAFOOD	Walleye Whitefish	Salmon Scrod Sole	Catfish Cod Crayfish	Bass Bluefish Butterfish	Red Snapper Roughy
TELEVISION NEWSCASTERS	Mike Wallace Barbara Walters	Morley Safer Diane Sawyer Bernard Shaw	Connie Chung Walter Cronkite	Ed Bradley David Brinkley Tom Brokaw	Dan Rather Harry Reasoner
BROADWAY MUSICALS	West Side Story Wildcat	Show Boat South Pacific	Cabaret Cats (A) Chorus Line	Band Wagon Brigadoon Bye Bye Birdie	Rhapsody Rumple
WORLD CAPITALS	Warsaw Washington, D.C.	San Salvador Santiago Sydney Singapore	Cairo Caracas Copenhagen	Brasilia Brussels Bucharest Budapest	Reykjavik Rome

6	T	S	M	R	C
TELEVISION SLEUTHS	Dan Tannna Vinnie Terranova Harry S. Truman	Maxwell Smart Remington Steele B.L. Stryker	Thomas Magnum Mannix McCloud	Rockford	Cannon Columbo Dale Cooper
FAIRY TALES	Three Little Pigs	Snow White and the Seven Dwarfs	Mother Goose	Rapunzel	Cinderella
CHILD STARS	Elizabeth Taylor Shirley Temple	Fred Savage Ricky Schroeder Brooke Shields	Jerry Mathers Hayley Mills Kurt Russell	Mickey Rooney	Kirk Cameron Jackie Coogan
DANCES	Tango Twist	Samba Square Dance Swim	Mambo Mashed Potato Monkey	Reel Rumba	Cancan Cha-Cha Charleston Conga
MODES OF TRAVEL	Taxi Train Tricycle Trolley Car	Skateboard Space Shuttle Subway	Moped Motorcycle	Raft Rickshaw Rocket ship Rowboat	Canoe Car Caravan Carriage

7	G	R	E	A	T
MOVIE STARS	Clark Gable Greta Garbo Cary Grant	Robert Redford Christopher Reeve	Emilio Estevez Dame Edith Evans Tom Ewell	Alan Alda Julie Andrews Dan Aykroyd	Rip Torn Spencer Tracy Kathleen Turner
FLOWERS	Gardenia Geranium Gladiolus	Rhodora Rose	Edelweiss Elite Essence	Amaryllis Aster Azalea	Truss Tulip Tutty
CAR/TRUCK MODELS	Grand Prix Gremlin Grenada	Ram Ranchero Regal	Eagle Edsel Excel	Accord Ambassador Aries	Taurus Torino Toronado
FOREIGN COUNTRIES	Germany Great Britain Greenland	Romania Russia Rwanda	Egypt El Salvador Ethiopia	Albania Algeria Argentina	Taiwan Tunisia Turkey
RIVERS	Ganges Gila Green	Rhine Rhone Rio Grande	Ebola Elbe Euphrates	Allegheny Arkansas Avon	Thames Tiber Truckee

8	C	M	O	G	S
SPORTS-CASTERS	Harry Carey Bob Costas	John Madden Jim McKay Al Michaels Brent Musberger	Pat O'Brien	Joe Garagiola Frank Gifford Greg Gumbel	Dick Stockton Pat Summerall
MIXED DRINKS	Cape Cod Cuba libra	Mai Tai Manhattan Martini Mimosa	Orange Fizz	Gimlet Gin & Tonic	Sloe Gin Fizz Screwdriver
BIRDS	Canary Cardinal Chickadee Crow	Meadowlark Mockingbird Mynah	Oriole Osprey Ostrich Owl	Goldfinch Goose Grebe Grouse	Sandpiper Sparrow Starling Swallow
MINERALS	Cinnabar Copper Corundum Cryolite	Malachite Mica Microline	Oroide Orthoclase	Gold Graphite Gypsum	Silica Sulfur
CANDY BRANDS	Cadbury's Caramello Charleston Chew Cherry Mash	Mars Bar Milk Duds Mr. Goodbar	O Henry	Good & Plenty Goo Goo Cluster	Snickers Sugar Babies

9	M	A	D	E	N
PAST OR PRESENT WORLD LEARDERS	Meir Mubarak Mulroney Mussolini	Adenauer Attlee	De Gaulle De Valera	Eben Eisenhower	Nehru Nixon Noriega
INVENTORS	Samuel Morse Guglielmo Marconi	Nicholas Appert Howard Aiken	John Deere Leonardo Da Vinci	George Eastman Thomas Edison	Alfred Nobel Thomas Newcomen
MAMMALS	Marmoset Mongoose Monkey	Aardvark Anteater Antelope	Deer Dik Dik Dog	Eland Elephant Elk	Narwhal Numbat
ELVIS PRESLEY SONGS	Make Me Know It	Are You Lonesome Tonight All Shook Up	Don't Be Cruel Devil in Disguise Don't	Easy Come, Easy Go End of the Road	Night Rider
OPERAS	Madam Butterfly (The) Marriage of Figaro	Aida Alcina Andrea Chenier	Don Carlos Don Giovanni	Elektra Eugene Onegin	Nabucco Norma (The) Nose

10	G	E	C	A	S
HERBS	Garlic Gentian	Elder Eryngium	Chervil Chicory Cumin	Alecost Angelica	Saffron Sage
U.S. ASTRONAUTS	John Glenn Virgil Grissom	Don Eisele Anthony England	Scott Carpenter Michael Collins	Buzz Aldrin Neil Armstrong	Walter Schirra Alan Shepard
MAGAZINES	GQ Glamour Gourmet	Ebony Elle Esquire	Cook's Country Living Car & Driver	Advertising Age Architectural Digest Auto Age	Southern Living Sports Illustrated
FRUITS	Grape Grapefruit Guava	Elderberry	Cherry Coconut Cranberry Currant	Apple Apricot	Strawberry
POETS	Kahlil Gibran Thomas Gray Robert Graves	T S Eliot Ralph Waldo Emerson	Samuel Coleridge e.e. cummings	Conrad Aiken W H Auden	Carl Sandburg Sir Walter Scott

INDEX

Page references to solutions are in italics.